D0574580

AMERICANS in AGRICULTURE

portraits of diversity

1990 YEARBOOK OF AGRICULTURE

Foreword

by Clayton Yeutter
Secretary of Agriculture

The United States is blessed with abundant resources and excellent technology to help us lead the world in agriculture. But the richest resource of American agriculture is its people–over 20 million men and women whose talent and effort drive the abounding productivity of our food and agriculture industry.

They seek out the best wheat varieties, select the healthiest livestock, and find the best packaging for cut flowers. They develop a system to grow food in space. They look for ways to cure–or prevent–diseases in plants, animals, and humans. They find exciting new ways to teach young people.

The initiative, creativity, and plain hard work of these millions of people are the key to our efficiency and our ability to compete in the world marketplace.

This book will introduce its readers to dozens of the dedicated people involved in America's greatest industry–food and agriculture. But readers must remember that these few are only representative of the millions more who work in our food and fiber sector. In our complex society many people today still hold a simple and limited view of agriculture–perhaps a barn and silo along the road, or planting and harvesting a crop, or getting up early to milk the cows.

The American food and agriculture industry today is this and much more. It encompasses thousands of agribusiness firms and millions of people who process, deliver, and sell food and other products for domestic and global customers. It involves institutions and people who provide credit, machinery, and information; scientists contributing to greater bounty with less environmental impact; people who teach agriculture and people who study agriculture. Our industry supports an economic system that is truly the envy of the world.

If American agriculture is anything, it is diverse, and it is this diversity we celebrate in **Americans in Agriculture**.

American farmers produce hundreds of different crops and dozens of breeds of livestock on a countryside that ranges from lush pasture lands to deserts, huge plains to high mountains, and vast rural areas to suburbia. Our farm families spring from differing ethnic backgrounds, work successfully in every imaginable kind of farming structure, and have a unique combination of entrepreneurial genius and managerial skill.

I salute **all** Americans in agriculture–farmers, processors, marketers, scientists, educators, our own government officials, and consumers.

Special congratulations go to everyone associated with the 1890 Institutions (the historically black land-grant colleges). The 1990 Yearbook helps to celebrate the centennial of these institutions, which for 100 years have served agriculture through teaching, research, and extension. They are doing ever more important work today, and several "portraits of diversity" in this Yearbook are written by the faculty of these fine institutions.

To the young people reading this book–and to others who enjoy a challenge–I invite you to join the food and agriculture industry. It's a great place to work!

Agriculture abounds with good opportunities: Exciting careers to help sustain our international competitiveness; marketing opportunities in a global trading environment; efforts to ensure an abundant and healthy food supply; finding industrial uses for farm products; producing food and fiber in an environmentally sensitive way while still providing a fair return for farmers and others in the food chain. The profiles of workers in this book will provide ideas on how you can participate in this country's largest industry.

It is critical to understand the diversity of American agriculture and how it influences our daily lives–whether or not we work in agriculture or live on a farm. Agriculture needs and merits the support and understanding of all Americans, and the diverse portraits in this Yearbook are designed to show the American public just what agriculture is all about in 1990.

Preface

by Deborah Takiff Smith
Yearbook Editor

The 1990 Yearbook is about the people of American agriculture—their jobs, their lives, their goals, and their families.

Abraham Lincoln called the U.S. Department of Agriculture "the people's department," and it still is.

The 1990 Yearbook of Agriculture introduces several dozen interesting people who work in U.S. agriculture. They are only a few, but they represent more than 20 million Americans who work in the U.S. food and fiber system—a system that provides the food, fabric, forests, and other goods that we need every day. It also introduces a few representatives of the many Americans who teach and study agriculture.

Americans in agriculture are a diverse group. They pursue farming, business, science, education, and government service. They include the farmers who grow wheat and wood, broccoli and beef, hay and horses, carnations and Christmas trees. They also include the rural banker, the food safety researcher, the high school agriculture teacher, and the Extension worker helping farmers raise livestock or vegetables.

People are the essence of any enterprise. These stories and portraits of real working people, representing the essence of U.S. agriculture, make agriculture immediate to the reader as they describe their current jobs, how they got where they are, and their aspirations, problems, and satisfactions. Their stories should help farm and nonfarm readers come face-to-face with the realities of U.S. agriculture today.

Part I, Facts and Figures, provides an overview of who works in the U.S. food and fiber sector, and key facts about American farmers, farms, and farmworkers.

Part II, Farming, introduces farmers from dozens of States from New England to the West Coast, and from the Deep South to the Midwest. These men and women raise all sorts of crops and livestock, farming full time and part time. They have small farms and large farms. They work alone, or with big staffs, or with a spouse or other family members. They live near town or far away. They own their land or rent it or work as employees for others. They are young and old, and come from varied ethnic backgrounds. They have different kinds of families and different approaches to farming. Some participate in Government farm programs; many do not.

Part II introduces—

- An ex-city dweller who raises goats in Candor, NY
- A farm family who grow vegetables organically in California
- The operator of a huge agricultural enterprise in California's Imperial Valley
- A black farm family in Arkansas that grows and markets fruits and vegetables
- Grain farmers from Kansas, Illinois, and Ohio
- A couple from Mexico who left the migrant stream to prune apple trees over the winter

Their stories reveal something of what farmers are up against—the insects, the weather, the markets, the plain hard work involved in producing food and other agricultural products—as well as the satisfactions that some farmers get from their livelihood and lifestyles.

Beyond production agriculture, the business of agriculture employs about 16 million Americans who provide the inputs, processing, wholesaling, retailing, banking, and other business functions of agriculture.

Part III, The Business of Agriculture, introduces–

- A small-town banker in Kansas
- A 25-year-old pilot who, with her husband, dusts rice and other crops in Texas
- A family of wholesale produce marketers from Minnesota
- A food technologist who is developing new products in Florida

Science and education are crucial to American agriculture if it is to retain its cutting edge in technology and competitiveness. ***Part IV, The Science of Agriculture,*** tells the stories of several scientists delving into the mysteries of how nature works, including–

- Forest Service researchers who are studying wildlife and their habitats
- The inventor of "fluffy cellulose," which improves the fiber content of food while using a farm byproduct
- A veterinarian who is helping to conquer brucellosis
- A team of microbiologists who are working to ensure food safety

Education in agriculture is a never-ending process from elementary school to adult education. ***Part V, Education: The Future of Agriculture,*** presents a few of the millions of Americans studying in such programs as Ag in the Classroom, 4-H, FFA, high school agriculture classes, colleges and universities, the Cooperative Extension System, and Walt Disney World in Florida.

Government workers—local, State, and Federal—play an important role in supporting agriculture, and many of them depend on the active support of volunteers to be effective.

A few of the portraits included in ***Part VI, Government Serving Agriculture,*** include—

- A supervisor from USDA's Meat and Poultry Hotline
- The South Dakota State entomologist
- Forest Service volunteers
- Extension workers in Mississippi, South Carolina, and Washington

The 1990 Yearbook offers a special salute to the 1890 Institutions (the historically black land-grant universities), which are celebrating their centennial this year. One chapter traces the history of these institutions, and other chapters in each part of the Yearbook help celebrate the centennial by featuring teachers, researchers, Extension workers, students, and graduates of the 1890 Institutions.

A special note to young people reading this book, and to those who want a new challenge: Agriculture is a good place to work. Even though the number of farming jobs is declining, career opportunities beckon in other areas of agriculture, such as science and engineering, finance, marketing, and exporting. I hope that this look at the diverse careers in agriculture will inspire people to consider the opportunities for men and women, rural and urban. They may find their niche while helping to meet some challenges agriculture faces: how to provide an abundant and healthy food supply while protecting the environment for future generations, how to safely harness the power of biotechnology, and how to make U.S. agriculture more efficient and competitive in the global marketplace.

Agriculture needs the support of the general public. I hope that these portraits of Americans in agriculture will help to improve your understanding of agriculture.

The 1990 Yearbook has a different format from that of previous books. I hope that the new square page will make the book more appealing and readable, by providing adequate space for photographs and charts.

The photographs for this yearbook merit special attention. USDA photographers Perry Rech and Bob Nichols traveled throughout the United States to take original portraits of most of the book's farflung subjects, to bring you face to face with the people featured here.

The members of the 1990 Yearbook Committee, who helped plan the content and recruit authors, are—

Calvin Beale and **Tom Carlin,** Economic Research Service, USDA

Ben Blankenship, Economics Management Staff, USDA

Judith Bowers, Patricia Calvert, and **Fred Woods,** Extension Service, USDA

Ruth Coy and **Bob Norton,** Agricultural Research Service, USDA

Patrick Casula, Jane Coulter, Howard (Bud) Kerr, and **McKinley Mayes,** Cooperative State Research Service, USDA

John Crowley and **Sally Katt,** Office of Public Affairs, USDA and

Samuel Donald, Alcorn State University, Lorman, MS

In addition, **John Lee** of the Economic Research Service offered initial suggestions for a book on the diversity of U.S. agriculture, and **Tom Willis** of Extension Service helped prepare the chapters in Part III.

The 1990 Yearbook Production Team members, all with USDA's Office of Public Affairs, are—

Vincent Hughes, Design Coordinator

Joseph Stanton, Composition Coordinator

Perry Rech and **Bob Nichols,** Photography Coordinators

Victor Newman, Cover Designer

Warren Bell and **Jim Cecil,** Printing Coordinators

Contents

PART I
facts and figures

Agriculture: A Critical U.S. Industry

Contrary to what you may have heard, "farming" and "agriculture" do not mean exactly the same thing. Growing crops and raising livestock are part of agriculture. But agriculture also includes the manufacture of farm supplies and the processing and distribution of farm commodities and products made from them. U.S. farming and agriculture sometimes appear to be headed in separate economic directions, but both are critical to the well-being of domestic and foreign consumers.

Because of increased mechanization, fewer and fewer people work on farms in the United States. But agriculture in the broad sense is and will continue to be an important sector of the U.S. economy and a major source of job opportunities. Agriculture encompasses the entire U.S. food and fiber system and 20 million workers—including farm laborers, food processors, transporters, grocery checkout clerks, and food preparers. Ironically, someone seeking a job or a career in agriculture today is more likely to be successful in cities, towns, and suburbs than in the countryside.

Although the tasks of U.S. agricultural workers are enormously varied and often complex, their goal is simple: to feed and help clothe all of us and many others abroad and to continue to do so, profitably and efficiently, for coming generations.

In much of the rural United States there is great concern over the declining number of farming jobs, but declining employment on farms is not necessarily ominous for the whole food and fiber system. Technological advances in farming have increased production, and they continue to do so. That's good for the Nation's economic health, because commercial exports of agricultural products are the Nation's largest single source of earnings from abroad.

by T. Alexander Majchrowicz, Agricultural Economist, and Mindy Petrulis, Economist, Agriculture and Rural Economy Division, Economic Research Service, USDA, Washington, DC

Agriculture Today

Farming today is a complex business, very different from what it was a few decades ago. Adoption of modern technology has brought great change. Increased mechanization has allowed farms to become larger and more specialized. As farms and farming methods have changed, the production, marketing, and financing of agriculture have become more interdependent. The modern farm family buys most of its food at the grocery store. Furthermore, farmers rely on agribusiness firms for production needs such as chemicals, fuels, and farm machinery; on farm lenders for needed capital; and on a centralized food system that requires more processing, wholesaling, and retailing of farm products.

The food and fiber system is today's counterpart of yesterday's farm-centered and farm-dominated economy. The system includes employment in farming and all businesses that support the production and delivery of food, clothing, shoes, tobacco, and other agricultural products to domestic and foreign consumers.

The 20 million jobs in the U.S. food and fiber system account for 18 percent

Gordon Baer/USDA 0878X1014-4

of all the Nation's jobs. Food and fiber wholesaling and retailing account for about half (52 percent) of the jobs in the system. About 3.8 million jobs (19 percent) are in farm production—farmers, hired farmworkers, and workers in forestry, fisheries, and agricultural services. About 15 percent of agricultural jobs are in agricultural marketing and processing industries; other related agribusinesses account for 12 percent, and industries providing farm supplies account for 2 percent. The agricultural processing and trade industries provide the link between farmers and consumers, where wheat becomes a loaf of bread or cotton becomes a shirt to be sold in stores. In this sense, agricultural processors and retailers determine what is made available for consumers to eat and wear.

Jobs in the food and fiber system

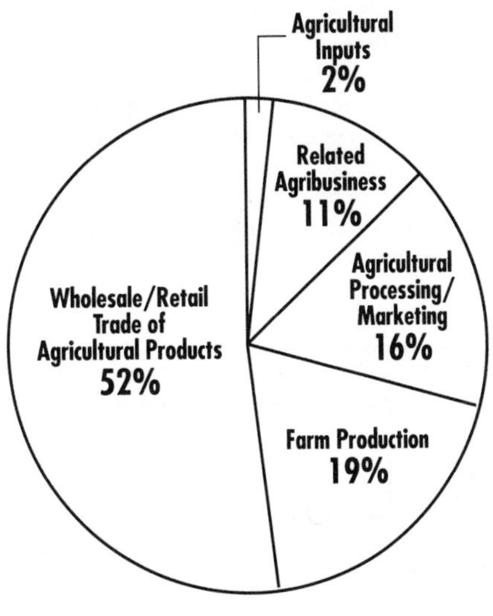

Urban and Rural Jobs

About 20.1 million jobs of all kinds were located in nonmetropolitan areas—beyond city and suburb—in 1986. Nearly 30 percent of these nonmetro jobs involved agricultural businesses. Farm production accounted for 2.4 million nonmetro jobs, but more jobs were in nonfarming agribusinesses than on farms. About 3.5 million nonmetro agricultural jobs were in farm supply (input) industries, processing and marketing industries, and wholesale and retail trade of agricultural products.

Because of the growing market orientation of food and fiber processors, wholesalers, and retailers, many agricultural jobs are now located in metropolitan areas. As the cost of transporting raw agricultural products has declined, many agriculture-related industries have been drawn to metropolitan areas, where consumer markets continue to expand. Food and fiber industries provide 16 percent of all metro jobs. More than three-fourths of all jobs in farm-related processing and marketing and wholesale and retail trade agribusinesses were in metro areas.

Rural Economies Vary by Region

The food and fiber system is an important source of rural jobs in every farm production region in the United States. The farm sector and agriculture-related industries account for more than 35 percent of local nonmetro employment in the Northern Plains, 32 percent in the Lake States, and 23 percent in the Northeast.

Regions also differ in the kinds of food and fiber jobs offered. Farm production provides 19 percent of the nonmetro jobs in the Northern Plains but less than 6 percent in the Northeast. Processing and marketing industries, primarily textiles and apparel, account for a large share of nonmetro jobs in the Southeast and Appalachia. In contrast, the Pacific region has the largest share of nonmetro jobs in wholesale and retail agricultural trade industries.

Metro and nonmetro food and fiber system jobs, 1986

Industry	Jobs (millions) Metro	Nonmetro
Total employment	86.6	20.1
Agricultural employment	14.1	5.9
Farm production	1.4	2.4
Input industries	.2	.2
Processing and marketing	1.9	1.1
Food and kindred products manufacturing	1.0	.4
Apparel and textiles manufacturing	.8	.5
Other processing and marketing	.2	.2
Wholesale and retail trade	8.6	1.8
Other indirect agribusiness	1.9	.4

Detail may not sum to total because of rounding.

Future Jobs

The increase in demand for basic agricultural goods, plus changing consumer tastes that lead to the introduction of new products, will ensure that the food and fiber system continues to be a vital component of the U.S. economy. Employment opportunities will be best in agriculture-related wholesale and retail firms, which will benefit from population growth and increases in consumer purchasing power. The growing participation of women in the labor force is also an important factor, as it increases family incomes while shifting some food and meal preparation to the food and fiber retail sector, making that sector one of the fastest growing industries in the U.S. economy.

In rural areas, however, where only 17 percent of all agricultural wholesale and retail jobs are located and population growth is slow, the prospects for rapid job gains are limited. Although growth in rural jobs may be unspectacular, such jobs offer long-term employment because of the relative stability of domestic food and clothing demands.

The food and fiber system

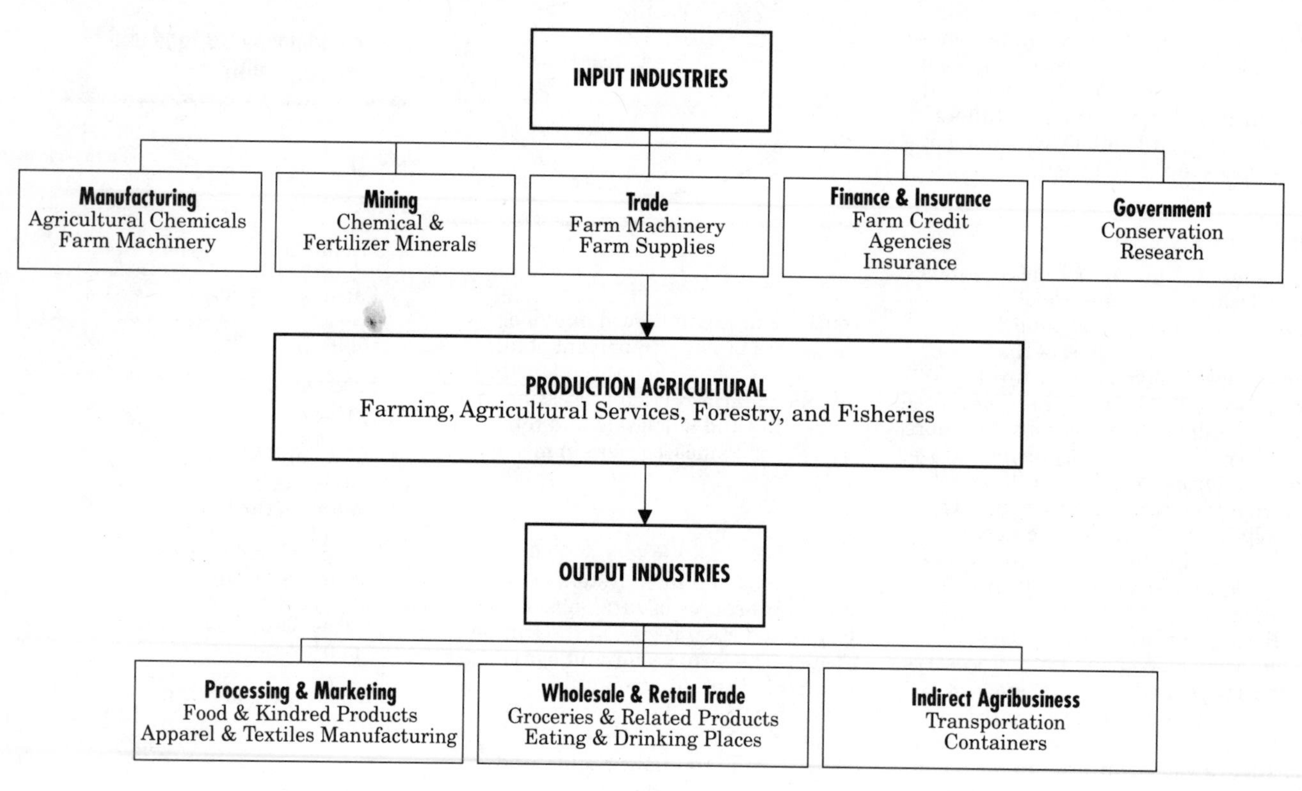

Nonmetro food and fiber employment: Important in all regions

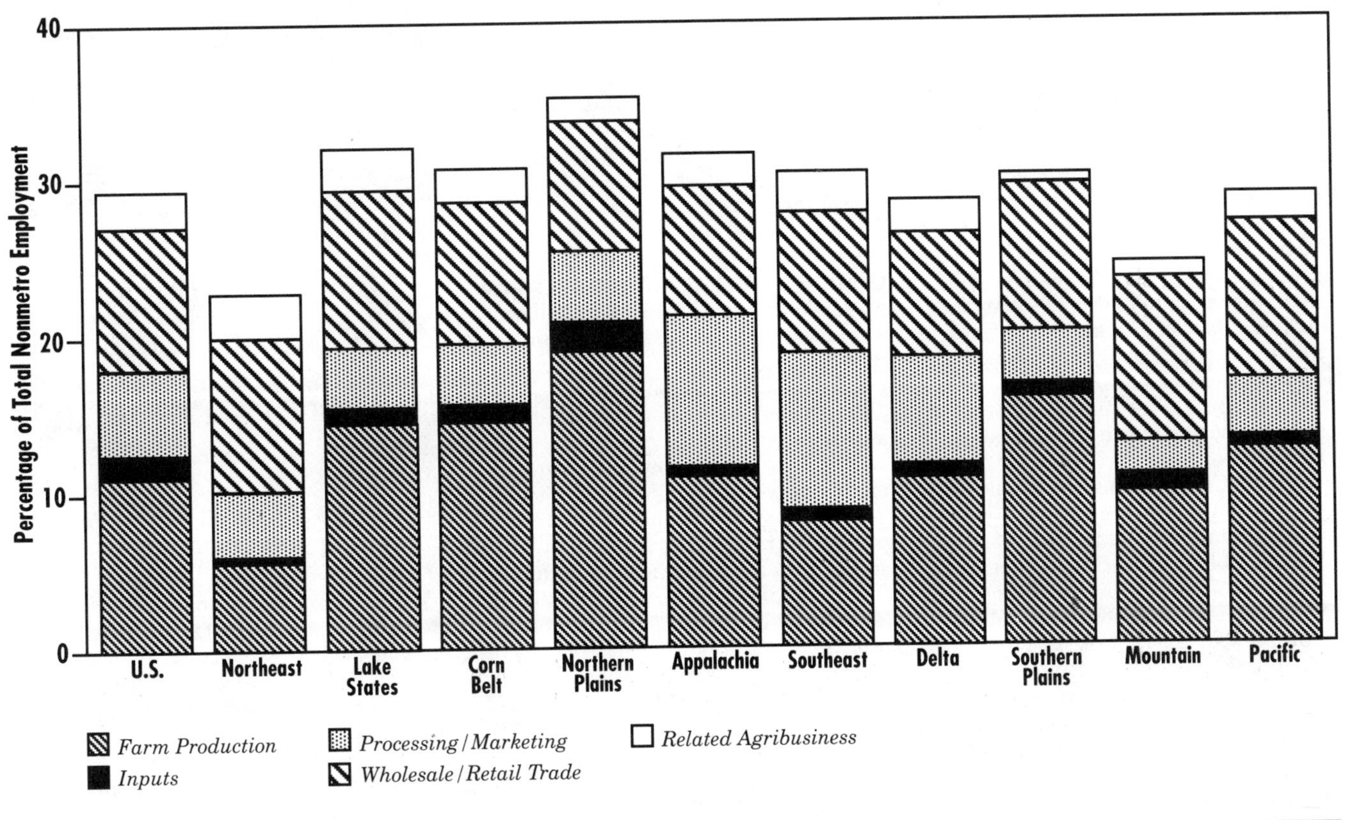

Who Are America's Farmers?

In pioneer days, and as late as the 1870's, most people in the United States lived on farms (and ranches) and worked in agriculture. Although the number of farmers kept growing, they were soon a minority because urban industrialization increased even more rapidly.

In 1916 the U.S. farm population peaked at 32.5 million. Then, with no more new land to settle and with fewer people needed in agriculture as mechanization and other labor-saving procedures came along, the farm population started to decrease. At first, the decrease was gradual; there were still 30 million U.S. farm residents in 1940. After 1940, however, the modernization of farming and the exodus of people to the cities became very rapid.

By 1989, only 4.8 million people of all ages remained on farms. In addition, a growing minority of farmers are choosing to live off the farm, often in town. And some people who live on farms are not farm operators. But if we count all people in households that report having either a farm operator or income from farm self-employment, the total population of such households comes to just 5.3 million, or 2 percent of the total U.S. population. Despite the decline, and thanks to advances in technology, U.S. farms today produce much more than they ever did in the past.

Farms and farming regions have changed. As late as 1950, half of all farm people were in the South, and one-third were in the Midwest. Southern farming was dominated by cotton and, to a lesser extent, tobacco. Both of these crops supported a dense farm population because they required so many hours of work per acre. In the decades after 1950, however, when cotton and tobacco farming were both modernized and reduced, hundreds of thousands of southern farmers were displaced. The soybean and livestock farms that are emphasized in the South today use much less labor, and some poorer land has been taken out of farming altogether.

by Calvin L. Beale, Senior Demographer, Economic Research Service, USDA, Washington, DC

In the Midwest, the number of typical Corn Belt and Wheat Belt farms also has declined, mainly through consolidation, but not as fast as in the South. Today the positions of the two major farm regions are reversed: half of all farm people are now in the Midwest, and only three-tenths are in the South.

The farm population has declined more slowly in the highly irrigated West, giving that region a rising proportion of the total, now about one-seventh. In the Northeast, our smallest farming region, the farm population has fallen rapidly throughout most of this century, especially as large areas have been overrun by urbanization.

Ethnic Diversity

Many immigrants came to America seeking land, and many national origins are represented in the U.S. farming population. In much of the South, farmers are largely descendants of the early colonial settlers—English, Scotch Irish, and Scots. In 1920 there were also more than 900,000 black farmers in the South, a majority of them tenants working for white landowners. In an extraordinary exodus thereafter, black families poured out of farming. They were enticed by the prospect of a better life in the cities and pushed by the near demise of cotton and tobacco tenant farming. Many black farm owners joined the exodus because they suffered from the lack of capital or adequately sized units to compete in modern agriculture.

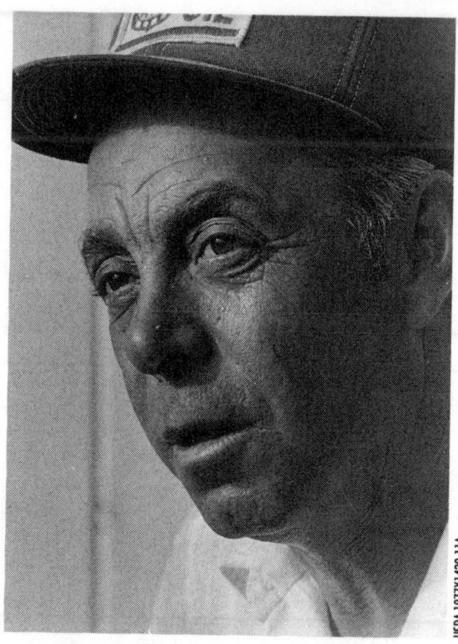

USDA 1077X1430-11A

The most recent farm census (1987) found only 23,000 black farm operators in the United States, a 97.5-percent decline from 1920. Nearly half of the farms operated by black farmers have less than 50 acres of land, and the average age of the black operators has risen to 58 years, because few young people are entering farming.

In the Midwest, the early American-born settlers soon were joined by immigrants from Europe, who came to be the dominant ethnic strains in most parts of the region. German farmers and their descendants were by far the most numerous and were so persistent in farming from one generation to the next that people of sole or partial German ancestry today account for three-fifths of the entire midwestern farm population. Nationally, the numbers of German-descended and British-descended farm people are about equal.

The next largest 19th-century immigrant farm group was the Norwegians, who located primarily in the Upper Midwest. Although they were not nearly as numerous as the Germans, they were more likely to settle in farming areas and avoid the big cities. Today, the percentage of people who work as farmers is higher among persons of Norwegian background than among any other U.S. ethnic group (8 percent for men and 2 percent for women in 1980). Other groups disproportionately represented among farmers are the Danes, Dutch, Czechs, and Swedes, most of whom are in the Midwest.

In the Southwest, there are Hispanic farmers of Mexican-American background from central California to the Lower Rio Grande Valley. Some families have been on the land for generations; others are relative newcomers. Although Hispanics have not been able to defy the downward trend in number of farmers and ranchers, their overall rate of loss since 1950 has been less than that of other farmers. Many hired farmworkers in the Southwest are Mexican-Americans, and in recent decades some have managed to become farm operators, especially in California, where they focus on fruits and vegetables.

American Indian farmers are scattered throughout the United States, but except in North Carolina they are largely in current or former reservation areas. More than any other class of farmers, Indians have specialized in cattle operations, in part because so much of their land is ill-suited or too dry for crop farming. In 1987 crops were harvested from only 1 percent of Indian-operated farmland and ranchland. Reservation farms and ranches may be individually or tribally owned, depending on the history of the reservation. In Oklahoma, which has the most Indian-operated farms, the units tend to be very modest in size and output. Some tribally owned operations elsewhere are very large.

People of Asian origin engage in farming mostly in California and Hawaii. A majority are of Japanese descent. They have been inclined toward intensively worked, small-acreage, irrigated farms. Four-fifths of them focus on vegetables, fruits, nuts, and horticulture. Farms are often exceptionally small, with two-fifths having less than 10 acres of land. In spite of such small acreage, Asian farmers are much more likely than others to have farming as their principal occupation rather than as a sideline.

Following in the Footsteps

A national survey in the early 1970's showed that 81 percent of all male farmers under 65 years old were the sons of farmers. No other occupation came close to having such a high percentage of men who had chosen their fathers' occupations. Most farm youth have gone into nonfarm pursuits—after all, the number of farms has dropped and farm families were rather large. However, farm-reared people remain dominant in farming because of its complexity, the financial advantages of inheritance in a business with high capital costs, and the lack of attractiveness of a declining occupation to outsiders.

Women in Farming

The traditional image of the farmer has been masculine, but women always have played a major, if silent and overlooked, role.

In the past, most women on farms were not viewed as being in the labor force, regardless of the farmwork they may have performed. A minority were counted as unpaid family workers. Only a farm widow was likely to be viewed as a farm operator. Over the years, more women have entered farming on their own, and farm women spouses have more frequently come to view themselves as co-operators with their husbands. At the same time, though, so many farm women have taken off-farm jobs that nearly three-fourths of those who now work do so solely or primarily in a nonfarm industry.

Gordon Baer/USDA 0878X1010-25A

The 1987 Census of Agriculture identified 132,000 farms whose operators or senior partners were women. This represented 6 percent of all farms, and was an increase of 10,000 in 5 years, at a time when the overall number of farms was falling. A large minority of these women were widows, for nearly one-fourth of them were 70 years old or over, twice the percentage found among male farmers. Nevertheless, there are many young women farming.

Women are involved in all types of agriculture. Their most common enterprise is beef cattle, in which more than one-third of them specialize. Their greatest relative presence, though, is in animal specialty farming, where they have one-sixth of the farms. By far the greater part of these are horse-breeding operations. Poultry, horticultural products, fruits, and nuts are other types of farming favored by women.

From Strong Backs to Strong Minds

Just a generation or two in the past, most farm people had limited formal education. High schools were either absent from many rural school districts or not conveniently available. Furthermore, many farm people did not think higher education was necessary for a life in farming and did not enroll their children any longer than required. In 1950 only one-fifth of farm adults 25 years old or over had graduated from high school (the urban figure was two-fifths).

Since then, it has become obvious that farmers need a good education, and farm children also have been integrated into larger school systems. In nonfarm areas, the pace of higher educational achievement has slowed, partly because of the influx of large numbers of poorly trained immigrants. The result of these two trends has been an impressive reversal of traditional rankings with respect to high school attainment. In 1988, 81 percent of adults in farmers' households had completed high school, compared with 76 percent in all other households. Nonfarm people are still somewhat more likely to have completed 1 or more years of college, but the days of wide inferiority in schooling among farmers and their families are over.

Older Farmers and Fewer Heirs

With fewer farms and a decline in the birth rate of farm people over the last 30 years, the average age of the farm population has risen. Farm people used to be younger, on average, than urban and other nonfarm residents, but today they are much older, on average. In 1988, half of the farm population was 38 years old or over, compared with a nonfarm median of 32.2 years. There is a relative shortage of people 20 to 39 years old on farms compared with those 45 to 69 years old. Between 1960 and 1988, the number of farm children under age 15 per every 100 farm adults 20 to 54 years old fell from 85 to 46. Unless the proportion of farm children who decide to go into farming increases substantially, there will be a rise in the proportion of farm families who lack an heir to take over the enterprise.

Joe Valbuena/USDA 0377B260-22

Dynamic Demographics

The United States has drawn a variety of ethnic strains into farming and ranching. The demography of farm operator families has been very much in flux in recent decades, and it remains so. Trends of the post-World War II era have greatly affected the numbers, location, and ethnic background of farmers, with notable losses among southern and black farmers.

Rapidly advancing education and increased participation by women in the nonfarm workforce are two major societal changes that are shared by the farm population. All of these events have influenced the average age and family size of farm people. The situation is dynamic, with many questions yet to be answered about the ultimate number, location, characteristics, and intergenerational continuity of our farm operators and their families.

The Hired Farm Workforce: Portrait of Diversity

A popular image of hired farmworkers is that of people harvesting fruits and vegetables for part of the year in California and other West Coast States. In fact, hired farmwork comprises a wide range of activities performed all over the United States, for example:

- Cutting sugarcane in Florida,
- Stripping and baling tobacco in Kentucky,
- Herding sheep in Idaho,
- Operating a combine in Kansas,
- Milking cows in Vermont, and
- Shearing Christmas trees in Michigan.

Hired farmworkers not only perform widely different activities, but they themselves are a diverse group who work for a variety of reasons. Farmworkers include:

- Heads of households who do hired farmwork year-round and whose families depend on their farm earnings for economic support,
- People employed primarily at nonfarm jobs who do seasonal farmwork to supplement their nonfarm earnings, and
- Students who do farmwork for only a few days during the year to earn extra spending money.

Hired Farmworkers in U.S. Agriculture

Agriculture provides employment to many people, including farm operators, members of the operators' families who work without pay, and hired farmworkers who do farmwork for cash wages or salary. Although farm operators and their families account for most agricultural employment, hired farmworkers are a vital resource. Of the almost 7.7 million people who worked on U.S. farms at some time during 1987, about 2.5 million did hired farmwork, and they accounted for about one-third of the total hours of farmwork (fig. 1).

The relative importance of hired farmworkers in agricultural production has increased over the past 4 decades. Mechanization and other technological innovations, along with increased off-farm employment opportunities, have reduced the number of people working on farms. However, the decline in operators and family members has been greater than the decline in hired farmworkers, and the hired farmworkers' share of total farm employment has increased from less than one-fourth in 1950 to about one-third in the 1980's.

The trend toward fewer but larger farms has reduced the number of family workers, but it has increased the average farm's hired labor requirements. In the past decade, as the trend toward fewer farms has slowed, hired workers' share of total farm employment has stabilized.

The amount of hired labor used on farms is related to the size of the farm operation and the commodity that it produces. Larger farms are more likely to have labor needs in excess of the capacities of the families who farm them. Some commodities whose production has been largely mechanized (such as many grains and cotton), as well as most livestock operations, do not require large amounts of labor per farm.

However, there are crops that require hand harvesting or labor-intensive cultivation—such as many fresh fruits and vegetables, tree nuts, and horticultural specialties—that continue to use large amounts of hired labor. Because these crops are perishable, much labor is needed for short periods, especially during harvesting seasons, to prevent reduction in quality (and thus value) of the commodities.

Figure 1. Hours worked on farms by farm operators, unpaid farmworkers, and hired farmworkers, 1987

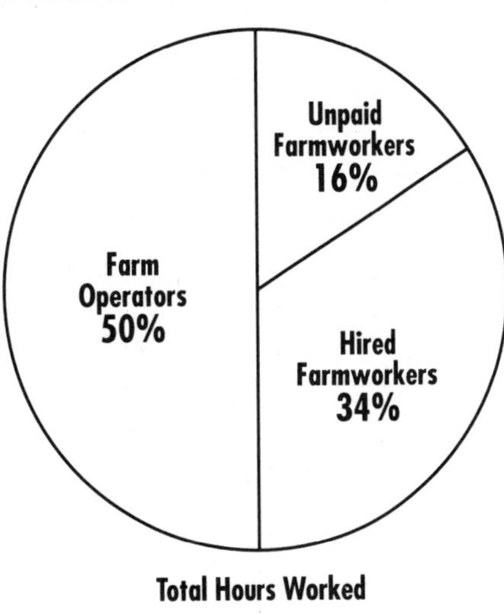

Characteristics of the Hired Farm Workforce

A look at the demographic and economic characteristics of the 2.5 million people aged 14 years and older who did hired farmwork during 1987

by Victor J. Oliveira, Agricultural Economist, Economic Research Service, USDA, Washington, DC illustrates the diversity of the hired farm workforce.

Demographics. In 1987, almost 80 percent of all hired farmworkers were male. About 78 percent were white, 14 percent were Hispanic, and 8 percent were black or members of other racial or ethnic groups. The racial and ethnic characteristics of hired farmworkers varied significantly across geographic areas. For example, Hispanics made up 44 percent of all workers in the Pacific region, while blacks and other minority groups accounted for 36 percent of the workers in the Southeast.

About 70 percent of all hired farmworkers were less than 35 years old, and half were 26 or younger. The large proportion of youths among hired farmworkers reflects the fact that much of hired farmwork, unlike some occupations, requires little previous work experience.

Hired farmworkers had lower education levels than most occupational groups. Half of all hired farmworkers had not completed high school, and only 17 percent had some college education. Many workers were still in school, but even among workers aged 25 and older (when most schooling has been completed), 40 percent had not completed high school.

Employment. Agricultural employment is extremely seasonal (fig. 2). Farmwork has periods of peak labor use, for example during the harvesting of perishable fruits and vegetables. In most States, labor use peaks during the summer and few workers are employed during the winter. In Florida, however, summer is the slack season for farm employment. Only 36 percent of all hired farmworkers in 1987 worked in

Figure 2. Hired farmworkers employed by month, 1987

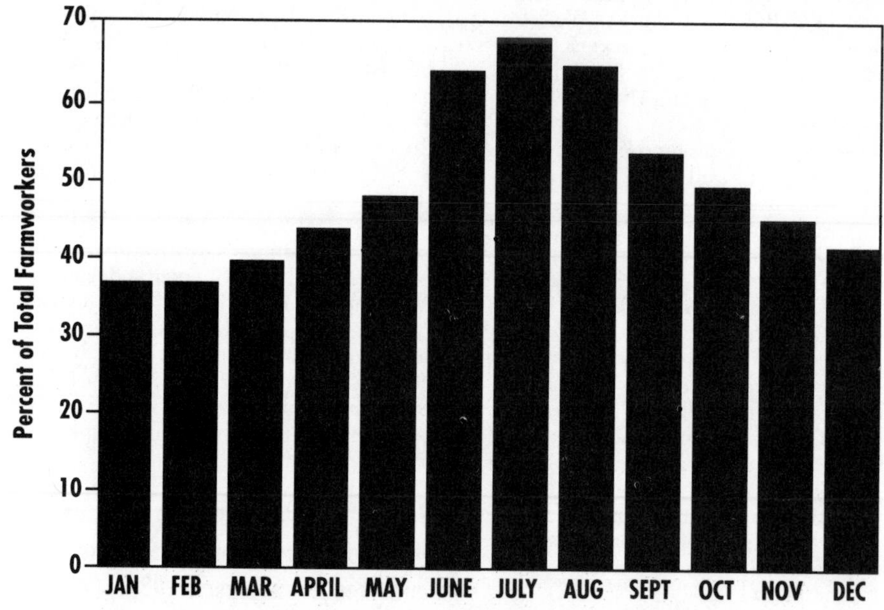

January or February. The proportion increased to more than 60 percent in June, July, and August and then steadily declined through December.

Because of the seasonal nature of agriculture, much hired farmwork is unstable and short-term. In 1987 the average hired farmworker spent 112 days doing farmwork. However, there was extreme variation. More than half of hired farmworkers (55 percent) worked fewer than 75 days during the year, and about one-third worked fewer than 25 days (fig. 3). Only about one-fifth were year-round workers (working 250 or more days at farmwork). Even some of these year-round workers had to piece together a series of farm jobs to work most of the year.

Hired farmworkers were paid an average of $4.87 per hour for farmwork in 1987. This low wage and the seasonal employment combined to make hired farmworker earnings among the lowest of all occupational groups in the United States. Hired farmworkers earned an average of only $6,663 in 1987, of which $3,368 was from hired farmwork. However, total earnings were highly

Figure 3. Days worked by hired farmworkers, 1987

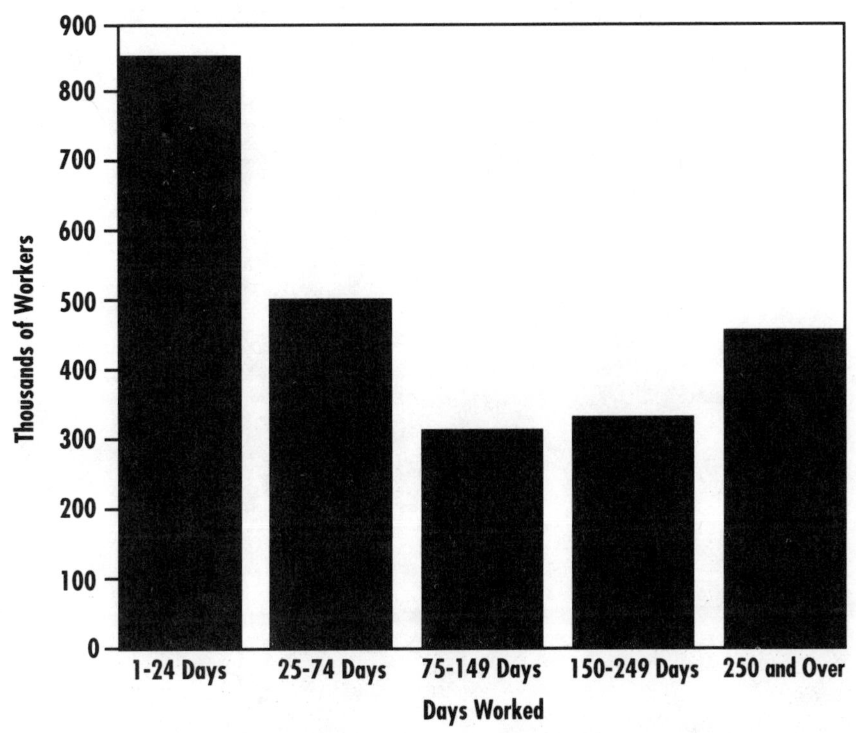

variable: About one-quarter of all hired farmworkers earned less than $2,500, and one-quarter made more than $10,000.

Because of the low earnings associated with much hired farmwork, many farmworkers work at nonfarm jobs to increase their incomes. In 1987, almost half of all hired farmworkers did some nonfarm work. About $3,295, or 49 percent, of the average hired worker's total earnings was from nonfarm work. Workers who did nonfarm work in addition to hired farmwork generally worked fewer days at hired farmwork and had significantly greater annual earnings than workers who did farmwork only. However, many hired workers with few labor market skills and little education had limited opportunities to find better paying nonfarm employment.

The majority of hired farmworkers in 1987 had only a weak attachment to farmwork and did not consider it to be their major labor activity. About 40 percent of all hired workers, most of them students, were not in the labor force during most of the year. Another 22 percent of hired farmworkers were chiefly nonfarm workers who did farmwork for brief periods. Only 29 percent considered themselves to be primarily hired farmworkers, and they were the most likely to be employed in agriculture year-round.

Foreign Workers

Foreign as well as domestic workers do hired farmwork in the United States. The short duration of employment, the relatively low wages, the strenuous nature of the work, and the lack of job security associated with much seasonal farmwork make these jobs unattractive to many domestic workers. Foreign workers leave their home countries to work in U.S. agriculture because there are more jobs and higher wages here. Lack of education, work experience, or language fluency does not hinder foreign workers as much in agriculture as in many other types of jobs. As a result, many U.S. farm employers have come to rely on foreign workers as a ready source of labor.

Legal Foreign Workers. Some foreign nationals are legally admitted to the United States to do hired farmwork under the H-2A temporary foreign worker program. The H-2A program, administered by the U.S. Department of Labor, permits their entry into the United States to do temporary farmwork when there are not enough available qualified domestic workers to do the work, and when the foreign workers will not adversely affect the wages or working conditions of similarly employed U.S. farmworkers. About 26,000 farms jobs were certified for foreign workers under the H-2A program in 1989. Due to their small numbers, H-2A workers have little effect on the national farm labor market. However, they provide an important share of the farm labor used in harvesting apples in the East and sugarcane in Florida.

Illegal Aliens. Because many foreign workers, including farmworkers, worked in the United States illegally, Congress passed the Immigration Reform and Control Act of 1986 to control this illegal immigration. There are no good estimates of the number of illegal aliens, or undocumented workers, who worked in agriculture before 1986. However, they apparently comprised a significant part of the farm workforce. Many of them worked in seasonal agricultural jobs and returned home each year after completing their work in the United States. Their labor was crucial to the many fruit and vegetable farms that hire large numbers of workers for short periods during planting and harvesting seasons.

For further reading, see *The Agricultural Work Force of 1987: A Statistical Profile,* Economic Research Service, USDA, AER–609, May 1989, and *Trends in the Hired Farm Work Force, 1945–87,* Economic Research Service, USDA, AIB–561, April 1989.

Harvester with bucket of bell peppers. Many U.S. farm employers rely on hired farmworkers as a ready source of labor.

USDA 0581X490-5

Hundreds of Commodities Produced on U.S. Farms

Beef cattle, hogs, milk, corn, wheat, and cotton come readily to mind when we think about what U.S. farmers produce. However, farmers also produce a bewildering variety of other commodities for domestic and export markets. The 1987 Census of Agriculture lists more than 200, but the actual number is even greater, because some minor specialty commodities are grouped together for statistical purposes.

The diversity of the farm sector reflects not only the climatic and resource variations across the United States, but also the many occupational and lifestyle choices of farm operators, as well as the local and regional markets and opportunities for profits. In addition to providing a cornucopia of food and fiber for the American consumer, U.S. farms provide for many of our industrial, recreational, and aesthetic needs.

Livestock

In 1987, nearly 1.5 million farms, representing about three-quarters of the 2.1 million farms counted in the 1987 Census of Agriculture, produced livestock and poultry (fig. 1). The graph is not all-inclusive (data are deficient on ostrich output, for example). Although more farms produce beef cattle than any other kind of livestock, roughly one-third of these farms keep 10 or fewer beef cows. These are frequently part-time or rural residence farms. Because of its low labor requirement, the raising of beef cattle is well suited to small operations where farming is a sideline to the farm operator's primary occupation.

Although most farmers focus on raising livestock and poultry that produce the major meat, milk, and poultry items, some produce specialty livestock commodities that not only add variety to our food and fiber supply but also serve other needs. Nearly 90,000 farmers raise horses and ponies for sale to fill recreational demands. Other recreational demands are filled by farmers who raise game birds, such as pheasant and quail.

Nearly 40,000 honeybee keepers not only provide our tables with a delicious sweetener but also provide a vital pollination service to many crop farmers. Beekeepers rent hives of bees to farmers to pollinate crops and ensure high yields. Without bees, the production of most fruits, legume seeds, and many vegetables would be sharply reduced. For many beekeepers, the production of honey is secondary to the pollination services they provide for other farmers.

Crops

Crops were produced on more than 1.6 million U.S. farms in 1987. The most widely produced crop in the United States is not corn, soybeans, or wheat (the major grain and oilseed crops). It is hay, which is grown on about 995,000 farms. Some farms are specialized hay farms, which produce hay as their principal cash crop, but

by Donn A. Reimund, Agricultural Economist, Agriculture and Rural Economy Division, Economic Research Service, USDA, Washington, DC

Gene Alexander/USDA NE-2253

Nearly half of all U.S. farms produce hay. This popularity places hay as the most widely produced crop in the United States.

Figure 1. Producers of Livestock

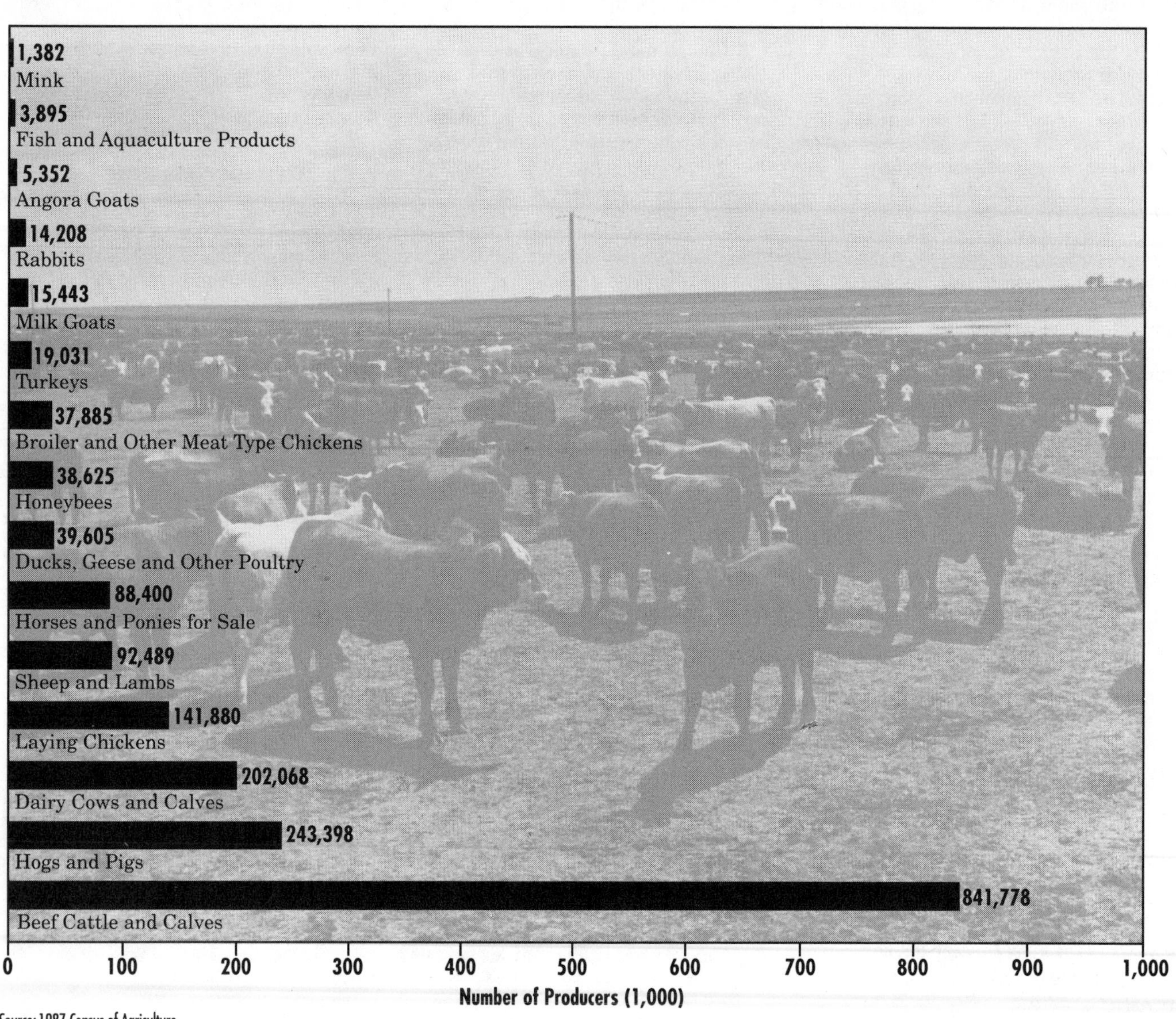

Source: 1987 Census of Agriculture

most hay is produced on other farms. Nearly half of all hay-producing farms are beef cattle and dairy farms, where hay is grown for livestock feed. Beef cattle and dairy farms accounted for 58 percent of the acreage in hay crops and 53 percent of hay tonnage produced in the United States in 1987. Hay crops accounted for about one-fifth of the harvested cropland in 1987.

Hay is also commonly produced on other types of crop farms—such as grain, vegetable, potato, cotton, and tobacco farms—as a rotation crop. Hay crops grown in rotation with other crops serve as soil builders, reduce soil erosion, and help farmers control insects and other pests. Legume hay crops, such alfalfa and clover, also add nitrogen, a vital crop nutrient, to the soil.

In addition to hay, grains, and oilseeds, U.S. farmers produce a wide range of food, ornamental, and industrial crops (fig. 2). The nursery and greenhouse group, for example, encompasses more than 37,000 farmers and includes such commodities as cut flowers, potted plants, ornamental shrubs and bushes, fruit and nut trees, mushrooms, greenhouse-grown vegetables, and lawn sod. Although some farmers producing these crops specialize in growing only one or two specific crops, others (probably most) produce a wide range of nursery or greenhouse crops.

The fruit and vegetable categories also include a large number of commodities. In addition to apples and oranges, fruits include such products as raspberries, olives, kiwis, and mangoes. The 1987 Census of Agriculture lists nearly 50 different major fruits, berries, and nuts produced in the United States.

Doug Wilson/USDA 0983X1267-3

According to the 1987 Census of Agriculture, more than 1.6 million U.S. farms produce commercial crops. Wheat growers accounted for 352,237 of the farms surveyed.

The vegetable category, in addition to such widely known crops as tomatoes, lettuce, and green beans, includes many less well-known commodities, such as artichokes, daikons, and hot peppers. Over 50 different major vegetable and melon crops are listed in the 1987 Census count. Many fruits and vegetables are distributed nationally, whereas others are produced by a few farmers to meet local or ethnic demands.

Farm Types

Most farmers produce more than one commodity. For example, it is common for corn and soybeans to be raised on the same farm. Many livestock producers grow feedgrain and forage crops, such as hay or silage, to feed to their animals. Also, sound agricultural practices often call for several crops to be grown in rotation for soil building, disease control, and insect control. Even so, most farms in the United States are highly specialized in the production of a specific commodity.

One method of classifying a farm is by type, based on the commodity that accounts for the largest proportion of the farm's gross sales. A farm is classified as a cotton farm, for example, if 50 percent or more of the value of its commodity sales comes from cotton. A farm on which no one commodity (or commodity group) accounts for at least

Figure 2. Producers of crops

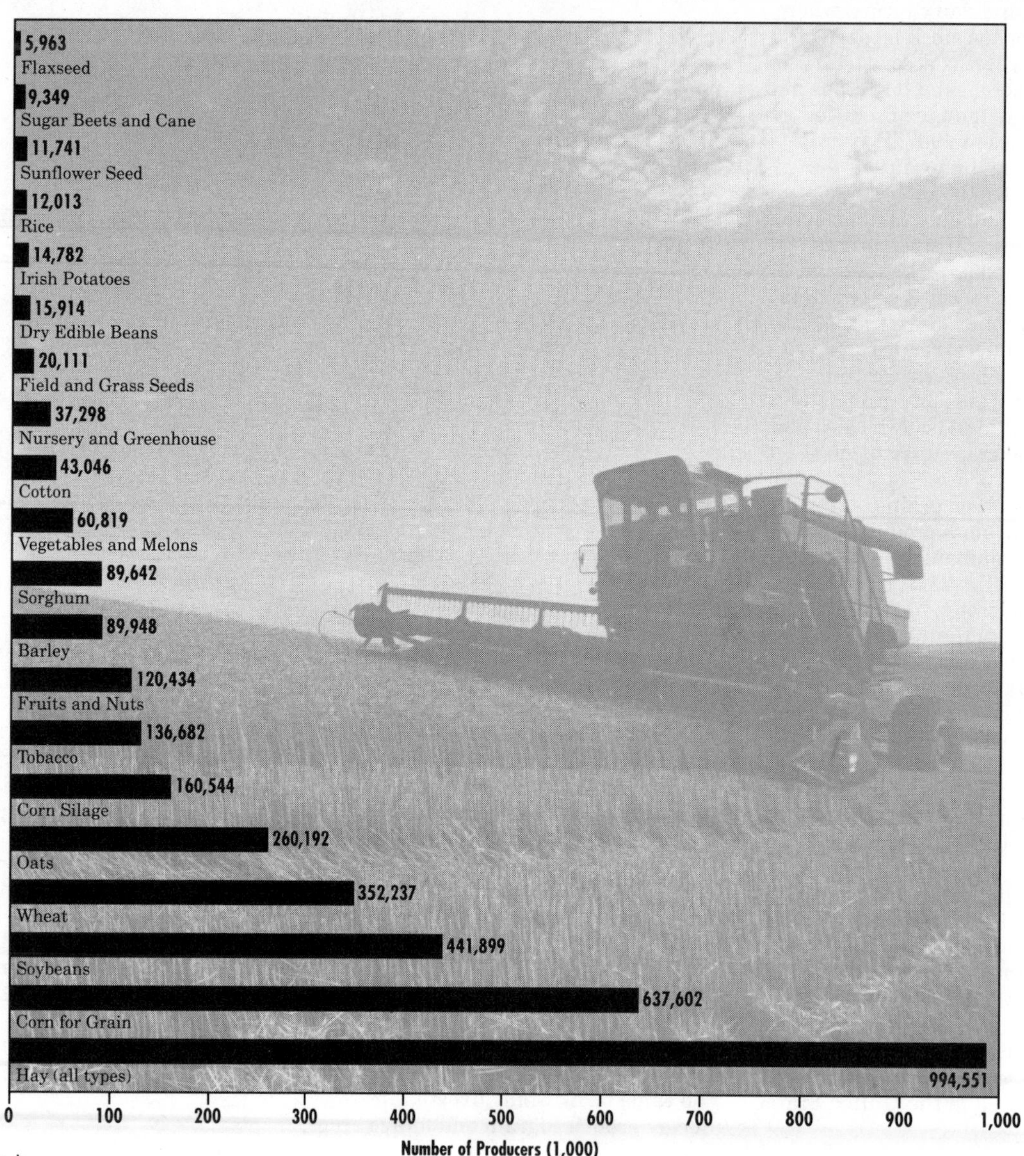

Source: 1987 Census of Agriculture

half the value of products sold is classified as a general farm—either general crop or general livestock, depending on whether crop or livestock products generate the most sales value.

Using this scheme, the Census of Agriculture classifies U.S. farms into 14 different types (see table). Beef cattle operations (excluding feedlots) and cash grain farms are the most common types. Together, beef cattle and cash grain farms account for more half of all farms in the United States.

The specialization ratio is the proportion of a farm's commodity sales that are generated from its primary commodity or commodity group (specialty). General farms, both crop and livestock, are the least specialized, because they produce a variety of commodities with no single commodity dominating their product sales. Among the specialized farm types, cotton and tobacco farms are the least specialized. On average, they obtain the smallest proportion (less than 80 percent) of their total sales values from their primary commodities. The most highly specialized farm types are horticultural specialty, animal specialty, fruit and tree nut, and poultry farms. These farm types, on average, obtain over 96 percent of their total sales values from their primary commodities.

Number of farms by type and specialization ratio, 1987

Type of farm	Number	Specialization ratio
Cash grain	458,396	0.863
Cotton	27,674	0.796
Tobacco	87,776	0.793
Other field crops	128,178	0.811
Vegetable and melon	28,801	0.873
Fruit and tree nut	88,323	0.963
Horticultural specialty	31,469	0.985
General, primarily crops	57,888	NA
Beef cattle (excludes feedlots)	643,831	0.879
Livestock, except dairy, poultry and animal specialties (includes feedlots)	248,436	0.865
Dairy	138,311	0.842
Poultry	38,494	0.963
Animal specialty	87,855	0.966
General, primarily livestock	22,327	NA
All farms	2,087,759	NA

NA, Not applicable.
Source: *1987 Census of Agriculture.*

David F. Warren/USDA 067-10-27A

Profiling the Diversity of America's Farms

What is the typical American city—Carson City, Kansas City, or New York City? Just as it would be difficult to typify the American city, it is equally difficult to typify the American farm.

When they think of the "typical farm," many picture a family farmhouse, a barn, and some cows, or a wheatfield extending as far as the eye can see. But farms are so diverse across this country that it is hard to generalize about them.

To look at this diversity, this chapter uses 1987 Census of Agriculture data (the most recent available) to profile five classes of farms, based on their annual farm product sales. We examine farm numbers and amount of farmland, product sales, asset values, expenses, type of organization, participation in Government farm programs, and several operator characteristics for each of five classes of farms (see table 1). These are:

I. Rural residence: less than $25,000 in sales
II. Small commercial: $25,000 to $99,999 in sales
III. Moderate commercial: $100,000 to $499,999 in sales
IV. Large commercial: $500,000 to $999,999 in sales
V. Very large commercial: $1 million or more in sales

Class I. Rural Residence Farms

Rural residence farms make up the largest share of all farms in the United States (almost 65 percent), but account for only a small share of the value of all farm product sales and acreage, with 6.4 percent of sales (fig. 1) and just over one-third the acreage of the average U.S. farm.

Average value of farm assets (including land, buildings, machinery, and equipment), annual farm product sales, and expenses for this class of farms—all indicators of economic status—lag behind others nationwide (table 1). The average rural residence farm loses almost $1,000 annually when expenses are deducted from sales. However, only 20 percent of these farms receive Government program payments and less than 5 percent have Commodity Credit Corporation (CCC) loans.

Rural residence farms are usually individually run operations ("sole proprietorships"), managed by one person who makes the decisions about such things as planting, harvesting, feeding, and marketing. Most operators are full owners of their land; only one out of every four rents any of the acreage farmed. Full ownership, once considered the ideal for a farming operation, is now associated with farming on a moderate or small scale.

The typical operator of a rural residence farm has a principal occupation other than farming. This is the only farm class to have a majority of its operators primarily employed off the farm. Half report more than 200 days of off-farm work, while only about one-third report none. Those with no off-farm work include a large number of retirees.

The median age of rural residence operators (53.4 years) is above the national median of 52.0 years, undoubtedly reflecting the large component of retirees. In fact, one fourth of all rural residence operators are 65 years of age or older, which is nearly twice the proportion in the commercial farm classes.

Many of the rural residence farms serve primarily as residences for individuals with nonfarm occupations or retirement income who are attracted to rural living. The farming activity for them is normally an avocation or hobby. Others are small farming enterprises whose proprietors typically need to supplement their farm income with off-farm earnings.

Class II. Small Commercial Farms

About 438,000 small commercial farms are in the second largest class of farms. As with the rural residence farms, the share of farms in this class is larger than their share of product sales (fig. 1). These farms have more land than the national norm, but the numerous rural residence farms included in the national statistics heavily weight national averages and distributions in the direction of smaller farms. However, in relation to the farms discussed below, which produce the bulk of the Nation's agricultural output, small commercial farms are truly small in acreage.

Unlike rural residence farms, average asset values for small commercial farms exceed national levels, and average product sales are slightly higher than expenses; on the average they net about $12,000 annually (table 1). Still, these farms have comparatively low economic status in the farm sector, lagging behind all but the rural residence farms. This class has the second highest participation in Federal farm programs, but the average Government payments and CCC loans per participant are below the national averages because of the much larger payments to bigger farms.

Small commercial farms are most often individually run. Like most of the

by Nora L. Brooks and Judith Z. Kalbacher, Researchers, Economic Research Service, USDA, Washington, DC

Figure 1. A small share of the Nation's farms produce most of the food and fiber

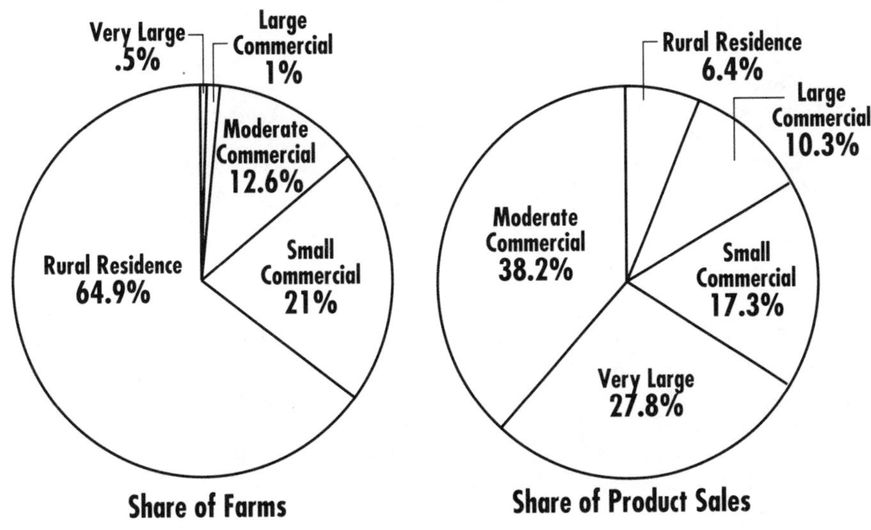

Nation's farm operators, except those of rural residence farms, these operators are likely to rent some of the land they farm. Renting additional farmland has become a common way for farmers to enlarge their operations without tying up large amounts of capital.

The typical operator claims farming as a principal occupation, and is much less likely than a rural residence operator to report any off-farm work. Operators of small commercial farms are slightly younger (averaging 50 years old) than most other operators; only those on moderate commercial farms are younger (averaging 48.2 years old).

Some small commercial farms, like rural residence farms but to a lesser extent, are part-time operations whose proprietors combine off-farm earnings with farm income. Others are full-time commercial ventures, whose proprietors depend primarily on income from farming.

Class III. Moderate Commercial Farms

Moderate commercial farms account for the largest share of farm product sales, but constitute a much smaller share of the Nation's farms than rural residence or small commercial operations (fig. 1). The average farm in this class has 1,284 acres, nearly three times the national average, and many more of these farms are in the larger size categories than is the case for rural residence or small commercial farms.

Average asset values ($750,000 in land and buildings and $114,000 in machinery and equipment) are well above the national average, and product sales exceed expenses by an average of $50,000 annually. These measures show the competitive edge of this size of farm over the smaller farms. Moderate commercial farms have the highest participation of all farm classes in Government farm programs, although payment and loan levels are higher for large and very large commercial farms.

Moderate commercial farms are most often individually run operations. Sole proprietorships in this and the small commercial farm class fit the traditional concept of the "family farm." However, this class has a larger share of other types of organization than smaller farms; 17 percent are partnerships, 9 percent are family-held corporations, and almost 1 percent are other than family-held corporations. About three of every four operators in this class rent some or all of the land they farm, which is the largest share for any farm class.

The operator of the moderate commercial farm, at 48 years, is the youngest of all classes. This operator is very likely to claim farming as the principal occupation (92 percent) and report no off-farm work (74 percent). The average moderate commercial farm is a full-time commercial venture, but this class also contains some smaller commercial operations whose proprietors rely on off-farm sources of income.

Class IV. Large Commercial Farms

Only 1 percent of the Nation's farms are large commercial operations, but they account for just over 10 percent of all product sales (fig. 1). Over half of the farms in this class have over 500 acres (fig. 2); the typical farm has 3,000 acres.

Based on farm assets, product sales, and expenses, the relative prosperity of these farms is exceeded only by those in the very large commercial size class. On

Characteristics of U.S. farms

	Farm class					
	I Rural Residence	**II Small Commercial**	**III Moderate Commercial**	**IV Large Commercial**	**V Very Large Commerical**	**All Farms**
Value of products sold	**Less than $25,000**	**$25,000-99,999**	**$100,000-499,999**	**$500,000-999,999**	**$1,000,000-or more**	
Number of farms	1,354,352	437,686	263,698	20,930	11,093	2,087,759
Percent of all farms	64.9	21.0	12.6	1.0	0.5	100.0
Average sales value	$6,386	$53,760	$196,884	$672,543	$3,414,401	$65,165
Percent of all sales	6.4	17.3	38.2	10.3	27.8	100.0
Average value of:						
Land and buildings	$136,671	$341,322	$741,348	$1,637,088	$3,940,143	$289,387
Machinery and equipment	$17,358	$55,194	$114,222	$188,143	$435,140	$41,227
Expenses	$7,323	$41,440	$146,233	$526,880	$2,828,884	$51,797
Government payments:						
Farms participating	264,211	252,426	168,242	10,309	3,822	699,010
Average payment	$3,825	$12,180	$27,799	$56,257	$79,660	$13,800
CCC loans:						
Farms participating	61,638	130,800	101,401	5,444	1,626	300,909
Average loan	$5,304	$18,386	$47,137	$106,251	$149,541	$27,693
Farms by acre size:						
Less than 10 acres	158,483	15,406	8,032	937	399	183,257
10–49 acres	372,792	24,640	12,091	1,820	1,094	412,437
50–499 acres	755,999	262,841	96,011	5,354	2,938	1,123,143
500–999 acres	45,455	76,604	72,887	3,517	1,595	200,058
1,000 or more acres	21,623	58,195	74,677	9,302	5,067	168,864
Average size of farm	168	623	1,284	3,002	5,655	462

Characteristics of U.S. farms (continued)

Value of products sold	I Rural Residence Less than $25,000	II Small Commercial $25,000-99,999	III Moderate Commercial $100,000-499,999	IV Large Commercial $500,000-999,999	V Very Large Commerical $1,000,000-or more	All Farms
	Farm class					
Operator characteristics:						
Tenure:						
Full owner	985,608	168,124	72,945	7,214	4,656	1,238,547
Part owner	246,163	194,274	152,954	10,904	4,717	609,012
Tenant	122,581	75,288	37,799	2,812	1,720	240,200
Organization:						
Sole proprietor	1,234,120	370,155	191,957	9,968	3,124	1,809,324
Partnership	96,218	50,529	44,933	5,261	2,618	199,559
Corporation:						
Family held	14,401	13,453	23,802	4,938	4,177	60,771
Other than family	1,822	1,137	1,700	551	988	6,198
Principal occupation:						
Farming	513,950	353,250	242,209	19,021	9,749	1,138,179
Other than farming	840,402	84,436	21,489	1,909	1,344	949,580
Farms by days of off-farmwork:						
None	406,302	233,856	180,818	15,344	8,156	844,476
200 days or more	633,573	78,461	22,212	1,832	1,128	737,206
Average age of operator	53.4	50.0	48.2	50.0	51.7	52.0

the average farm, product sales exceed expenses by $146,000.

Half of the operators of large commercial farms receive direct Government payments; average payments per participant ($56,000) are four times the national average. One-fourth receive CCC loans, also averaging about four times the national average. Note that although these farms are typically managed by more than one person, the farm itself is considered the participant in these programs, and multiple operators are not included in the averages.

The primary operator of this class of farm is 50 years old (slightly younger than the average U.S. farm operator), is principally employed in farming, and has no off-farm work. Although about half are in sole proprietorships, a larger share of these commercial farm operators are in partnerships and corporations than is the case for smaller farms. The farms are operated as small businesses and are run like small businesses in other parts of the economy.

Figure 2. Most of the Nation's farms have fewer than 500 acres

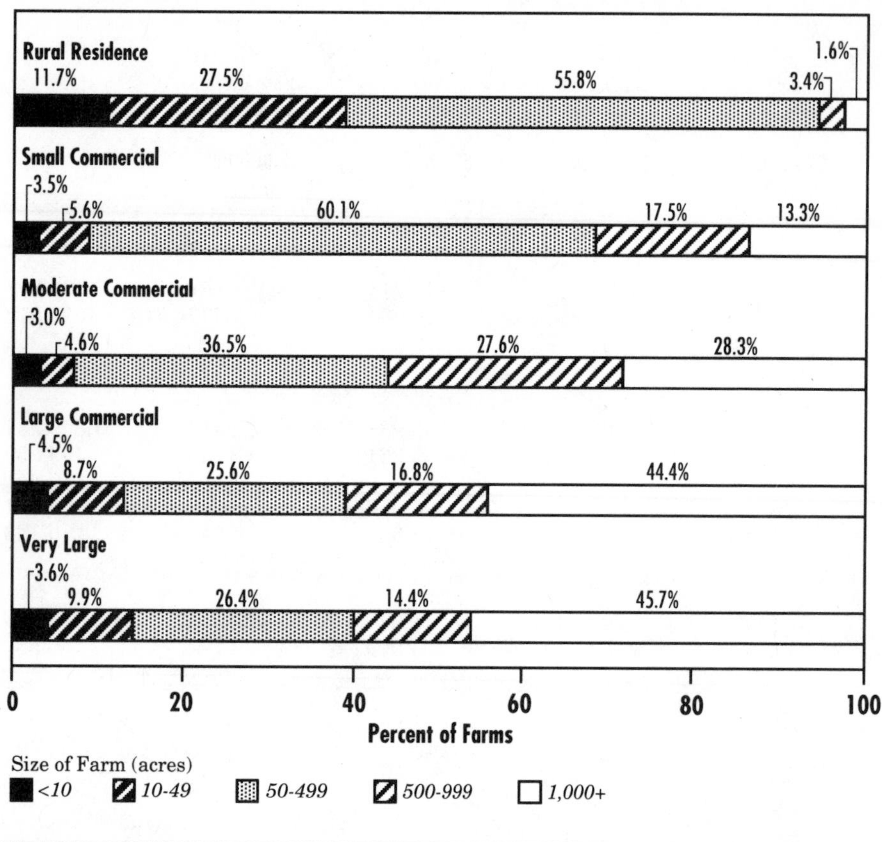

Class V. Very Large Commercial Farms

Very large farms account for only half of 1 percent of all farms, but they receive 28 percent of farm product sales (fig. 1). The size distribution for this class (fig. 2) closely resembles that for large commercial farms. However, because some of the very large farms have vast amounts of land, their average size is nearly double that for the large commercial class.

A comparison of farm assets, product sales, and expenses illustrates the extent to which these "superfarms" surpass other farms on these counts. Average asset values are more than double those for Class IV farms, and sales exceed expenses by $586,000 annually.

Participation rates in Government farm programs are the lowest of any commercial farm class, but the payments are the highest of all classes. Again, the farm is the program participant and the payments are divided among multiple operators.

The very large commercial farm is most often a family-held corporation. The operator is equally likely to be a full or part owner of the land. In comparison with the other commercial farm classes, the share of full owners is large, and the share of part owners is small.

The average operator of the very large farm is 51.7 years old, slightly older than other commercial farm operators. Typically, this full-time operator reports no off-farm work (79 percent) and claims farming as a principal occupation (88 percent). These are large-scale business enterprises, frequently involving several people in their management and functioning like moderate-size corporations in the nonfarm economy.

Two Kinds of American Farms

In comparing the five classes of farms, a clear pattern emerges. Rural residence farms far outnumber other classes, but lag behind in measures of economic status. Undoubtedly there are operators in this class who are "commercial farmers" trying to make a living at the business of farming. For most, however, the farm appears to be more a residence and hobby than a business venture. The profiles of other farm classes depict commercial operations of varying size and degree of involvement, ranging from small, part-time farming ventures to large, full-time operations.

PART II

farming

Candor, NY:

Alternative Farming, Alternative Place

Facts and fashion prompt policy advocates and professors to speak of "farming alternatives" as a key to both rural development and environmentally responsible agriculture. For dozens of agricultural entrepreneurs in Candor, NY, however, farming and the rural town are themselves the deliberately chosen alternative.

While Candor is a place, it's also an idea in our cultural heads. Once branded the archetypal *Small Town in Mass Society* by a rural sociology casebook about the town, Candor endures as farm town turned commuter dormitory. Nine-to-five jobs 20 and 30 miles distant largely have supplanted family dairy farms as the fount of Candor's cash-flow.

Changing times have left only 18 full-time dairy farmers in Candor.

Perry A. Rech/USDA 90BW0730-14

Rob and Darlene Howland, along with their daughters and a herd of Holsteins, call Candor home. Following a farming tradition, the entire family is involved in the Howlands' dairy business.

by Alan R. Knight, Farming Alternatives Program, Cornell University, Ithaca, NY

Eighteen others have quit since 1985, and probably three times that many have quit since the publication of *Small Town in Mass Society* shook Candor in the 1950's. Nevertheless, new ventures sprout like volunteer white pines in an old pasture.

Candor is home to a surprising array of farms, most of them small and supplemented with off-farm income: a fish farm, a roadside vegetable and pick-your-own market, five sheep farms, a growing goat farm, a market garden growing crops for sale at a small city farmers' market, a wholesale florist serving distant metropolitan markets, a firewood producer, four small-scale maple syrup and sugar producers, two Holstein beef producers, a hunting guide business, and at least five Christmas tree plantations.

Raising Kids

It is a 5-minute walk from the Candor Village Library to Rita Kellogg's goat farm. She got there by a much longer route, winding through time from Highland Park, NJ. Her uncle owned a weekend retreat in nearby Spencer, NY, and her family would drive the 6 to 7 hours from central New Jersey to visit.

"It was wonderful," Rita recalls, "miles of nothing. We kids would go off and play in the creek."

The memory never left her. After 12 years of working at a grocery chain store in New Jersey, she decided that she had had enough. City life, even the suburban variety, had grown unbearable. She moved out and took a job at the small grocery store on Candor's Main Street.

Perry A. Rech/USDA 90BW0733-10

After 12 years of working in a suburban grocery store, Rita Kellogg decided that she had had enough. She moved to the country to begin anew, and with her husband, Russ, and children, she has created a successful goat milking operation that continues to expand.

Then came the goats, starting with just one for the children as an afterthought when she and her husband went to buy a few beef cattle. Then they had to have a companion for that goat, then two bred yearlings, and then a kid. By 1982, they had become the proprietors of Kellogg's Goat Farm.

Rita, her husband, Russ, and their children Kelly, 16, Karen, 15, and Robert, 11, now rise each morning at 4:30 to milk 120 dairy goats, feed them, and push around some manure. The farm has not stopped growing. Rita expects to be milking 150 goats by the end of 1990, and the Kelloggs' shipping contract to a goat's milk ice cream manufacturer just increased from 750 to 4,000 pounds per week. The manufacturer, in turn, is to supply a leading upscale New York chain store and a food service supplier with the new product. Rita thinks that she will be milking 300 head by 1993.

If some dairy farmers have been heard to proclaim a preference for gravedigging over twice-daily milking, what is it that motivates the Kelloggs? Why would Russ work another job all day at Candor High School and then go home to more work in the barn? Why would Rita give up suburban New Jersey and bloody her knuckles digging a trench to get ready for pouring a new floor for an expanded milking parlor?

"You raise different kids this way," Rita says, referring to her children, not the livestock. "It's important. Oh yes, it's important. Parents who work away from home don't see their kids the same way. They get home and they're worn out. They may pick up their kids at the day-care center at 5 o'clock, and then the kids are off to bed at 8. They might see them for three stressful, frustrating hours. It's sad, isn't it?"

"This is a family business," asserts Rita. Goat farming is not easy, but for Rita Kellogg, farming, her family, and Candor fit together into a life that makes sense in a way that her life in suburban New Jersey never did.

Perry A. Rech/USDA 90BW0732-33

John Baust's farm life in Candor is worlds away from his challenging research position at the State University of New York in Binghamton. The quality of life offered in rural America is the setting in which the Bausts want to raise their family.

A Matter of Choice

Frank McDonald runs an 85-ewe sheep farm in the hills above the village. He used to operate a small heavy-equipment and bulldozing company on Long Island and would pass by Candor as he traveled to a hunting cabin in neighboring Spencer. As the years passed, he and his wife, Flo, decided to start anew in the country. They found a long-obsolete dairy farm and bought a starter flock of sheep from a young couple whose marriage and sheep-farming dreams had eroded. Failure is a part of life in these hardpan hills that run south to the Susquehanna from the Finger Lakes.

Frank's machinery experience comes in handy for putting up 80 acres of hay a year. Some goes to his sheep, and some goes to wholesale buyers who truck it to New Jersey horse owners or Pennsylvania mushroom growers for mulch. Flo works evenings at a nursing home 15 miles away. A daughter and a son are away at college, and another daughter lives close by.

Frank says that he is not looking to make a living with his sheep. It is where he wants to be, the way he wants to be: in Candor, on a farm, farming.

Norman Rockwell, Were You There?

John Baust looked over his shoulder for Norman Rockwell the first summer he moved to Candor. Given a chance for a challenging research position at the State University of New York at Binghamton, John and his wife, Judy, eagerly left Houston, TX, to return to part-time beef farming in south-central New York.

Within weeks the new arrivals were contacted to judge the homemade floats in the Candor Fourth of July parade. "Wow," John thought. "What a friendly community." But when he accepted, the caller said, "What a relief! I couldn't get anybody else to do it!"

"Still," says Baust, "I was struck by her unvarnished honesty. No pretensions."

While the American Legion honor guard lined up for the parade and the high school band strained to behave,

John and Judy looked at each other and shared the same thought: "This is straight out of a Norman Rockwell painting."

"Moving to Candor was a matter of values for us," says John. "We believe strongly in the importance of closeness of family, of developing the minds of the next generation, and we think a rural environment is the best place to do it."

The Bausts acted on their values by bringing three young teenagers and 100 head of Holstein beef steers to an out-of-business hilltop dairy farm. They used the Holsteins as a cheap way to build equity, and they now are cashing them in for about 25 to 30 Angus, which are more expensive.

The biggest enterprise on the farm is hay, 160 acres of it, most of which is wholesaled. The Bausts put up 10,000 bales their first summer and 25,000 the second. They aspire to 50,000 bales.

Son John does morning barn chores. Daughters Jessica and Christy take the afternoon shift. "We try to reward the children well," says John. "They see the payoff from their work."

The Bausts planted 9,000 pine and spruce trees in the spring of 1990 with the help of a tree-planting machine rented from the local soil and water conservation district. They plan to plant more. Also keeping this family farm in business is the sale of cutting rights to two commercial firewood sellers and the sale of hunting rights for 2 months a year during turkey and deer seasons to a hunting guide business recently established in Candor by a school-teacher turned entrepreneur.

Dad Always Wanted a Farm

Henry Del Mauro thought he had retired from his East Paterson, NJ, wholesale greenhouse and florist business. However, as his son Alan recalls, "Dad always wanted to have a farm, and I always encouraged him."

When Henry bought retirement property in Candor and built a house "on the mountaintop," Alan and brother-in-law Clark Rickens wished aloud that they might share utopia. So Henry cut a deal for the younger generation. He started Del Rick Farms, a new greenhouse business for all three families. Clark built a new home there, and Alan built a log home and planted Christmas trees.

That was in 1972, the eve of the shortages and price rises for fuel, so essential for heating greenhouses and for transporting plants and flowers the 5 hours from Candor through the Poconos to New Jersey and Manhattan. Cost-of-production analysis told Henry that growing for the Easter market, once an attractive winter proposition, was running him into the red. The family decided to shut down for the winter. Alan says that the decision saved the business, but it meant a kind of layoff for Clark, who withdrew and moved his family back to New Jersey to accept a job in the corporate world.

"I could have stayed in New Jersey," says Alan. "I had a good-paying job in a steel mill. But it's not what I wanted. It's peaceful here. The whole point of this business is to be here, in the country."

Henry Del Mauro, of Del Rick Farms in Candor, began a wholesale greenhouse and florist business in the quiet hills outside of town following his move from urban life.

Fish Farming

Buying a place in the country and starting a fish farm was Rick Musa's American dream.

Prompted by a passion for fishing, the young IBM executive bought some hilltop land with a 4-acre pond in Candor and simply enjoyed it. He decided to put in some pickerel. He went to a big hatchery in Pennsylvania, and while waiting for the fish, he had a look around and got talking to the elderly founder of the hatchery, who had built the business from nothing to worldwide marketing.

"For the next 2 years," recalls Musa, "I was thinking, 'Why can't I do this?' And then I got my hatchery license. Those first few years, all I did was build cages, chase the fry in a boat, net 'em, throw 'em in cages, and sell 'em. I didn't do anything, really."

Marketing was remarkably easy and "pretty helter-skelter," Musa says. As part of the licensing process, the State developed and published a licensed hatchery list. Anyone who wanted a few hundred fish for a pond simply would call him up. He also put a small advertisement in a local newspaper. In 1984 a nearby county soil and water conservation district placed a bulk order with him for its cooperating landowners. By 1987 two more conservation districts had signed on, and three more joined in 1988. Today he says, "I really don't want any more. I just want to perfect what I'm doing."

A milestone in his attempt to perfect his technique came in 1985, when he won a research and development grant from the New York State Department of Agriculture and Markets. The money went into bulldozing and piping for a series of four knee-deep raceways into which ordinary livestock fertilizer is cast to promote plant and fish growth.

Musa is enthusiastic about the future of fish farming: "I think there's a lot of potential in this fish farming business, but you gotta have capital. It's like anything else. Nothing's easy."

As busy as fish farming has kept Musa, it is not everything: "This isn't my living. I don't have the time. What I'm doing is what I have the time to do. It's not just money that I do this for. It's for some money—and fish."

Farmers' Market Sales

Earl Bolton has been selling honey and "anything else we could find" at the Ithaca Farmers' Market for about 15 years. "I'm technically retired," he says, but he finds it hard to say just when he made the transition from one job to the other or from farming to retirement.

As a schoolboy, living on his father's farm at Tuttle Hill, Bolton did the usual array of farm chores. He and his brother would go out in the dark of the morning to light gas lamps to regulate day length for their 500 hens. They had no electricity then. He remained on the family farm until World War II gave him a chance to leave Candor. If the Wehrmacht had aimed better, he might not have had the choice of returning, but after recuperation in England, in 1945 he came back to the family farm.

It was not long before Bolton discovered that he had to supplement farming with other jobs. He drove a schoolbus; worked part time and full time at a school, a sawmill, a foundry, a freezer plant, and a hatchery; and for 4 years he drove 20 miles a day to work as a janitor at Cornell University. Bolton finally got laid off, but he says that he was ready to quit anyway.

During those later years Bolton began to sell as often as he could at the Ithaca Farmers' Market. He takes honey to market twice a week, sometimes some beeswax. He makes a little maple sugar, too, and grows a few parsnips for the early season markets "just to help the market along, so's they'll have something to offer." When spent hens are ready for retirement, they end up butchered and offered at the market, but these days just a few—nothing like the numbers he had years ago. He still shows exotic poultry at the State fair and hatches out some to sell.

"My daughter helps me at the farmers' market every week now on Saturdays. She started with fudge, then added some cookies and doughnuts. Most of them are bought and eaten as snacks right at the market. "Once in a while I'll make a few wooden belt buckles or something. Might as well. You have to have a shop on a farm anyway. Might as well make use of it."

Across the road, in what was once an ornate showplace Victorian barn, Bolton keeps a couple of Jersey cows for home use. A dozen sheep are up on the slope, mostly to keep the brush down. He does not know whether they are paying their way or not. It doesn't matter: "Whatever is up there for feed is what they get."

Bolton recognizes that farming Tuttle Hill has its disadvantages: "Oh, it's a hard farm to work all right, most of it being hill the way it is. There's a certain amount of inconvenience with that. I remember a neighbor saying his place was too small to farm and too big to garden. Sounds about like this place."

Nevertheless, he remains attached to the place: "Guess I never saw a place I liked any better. It's awful pretty here, the different seasons and all. I like having everything all fresh and new in the spring after a hard winter."

Perry A. Rech/USDA 90BW0739-18

Skip Jackson keeps needing to expand his greenhouse business, Iron Kettle Farm, to keep up with customer demand. During various times of the year the Jacksons also operate a "pick-your-own" business for various types of produce.

Cliff and Debbie Van Till:

A California Family Finds Out What "Organic" Really Means

One day in late March 1990, a weak Pacific storm is breaking up over central California. Starch-white cherry blossoms are in full bloom. And Cliff Van Till is figuring out how to deal with a gopher problem.

"They like the onions," Cliff sighs. "I think that's their favorite food."

The San Joaquin County farmer certainly won't stay in business very long with an army of underground thieves stealing his crop, so he must get rid of them.

A number of synthetic rodenticides might do the job, but Cliff has to find something else.

Cliff is a "certified" organic farmer.

Either he sticks to the strict requirements of his trade association—the California Certified Organic Farmers—or he loses his certification. Under a 1979 California law, farmers like Cliff Van Till can become "certified" by trade groups like CCOF simply by adhering to the organic code of conduct.

Essentially, "organic" in California means that most synthetically compounded materials cannot be used in the production, harvest, storage, transport, or retail process.

Strychnine, a highly toxic substance, can be used to "organically" poison Cliff's gophers. Ironically, less toxic compounds cannot be used by organic farmers simply because they are synthetically derived.

"The logic seems to be that just because it's 'natural' it's somehow better, safer," he says. "There definitely are some head-scratchers, but you've got to play by the rules."

by John Stumbos, Public Information Representative, University of California, Davis, CA

Such is one of the many dilemmas in the evolving world of organic farming. But Cliff and his wife Debbie are committed to making it work.

So far, they've been very successful.

Going Organic

The Van Tills have not always been organic farmers. In fact, they would be more aptly described as "transitional" farmers. In addition to 40 acres of strawberries, garlic, onions, radishes, sweet corn, broccoli, tomatoes, and other organically grown crops, they also conventionally farm 150 acres of almonds and 120 acres of feed crops for his family's dairy.

Cliff's grandfather immigrated from Holland and started a dairy just outside of Ripon, in the valley—long before anyone made distinctions between organic and conventional. The Van Till dairy, now run by Cliff's father, is surrounded by orchards and vineyards. It is just down the street from Cliff and Debbie's organic onions.

Debbie grew up in Orange County, where a thriving citrus industry was being squeezed out by relentless Southern California urban sprawl. She "always knew" she wanted to be a farmer, so she studied farm management at California Polytechnic State University in San Luis Obispo. Upon graduation she took a job at a seed company in Yolo County. There, she met Cliff through her involvement in the Farm Bureau's young farmers and ranchers leadership program.

"I always wanted to do something more dynamic than raise corn and alfalfa for the dairy," Cliff says. "But I didn't have much experience with vegetables, let alone think about growing them organically."

Ten years ago, as Cliff completed a farm management degree at California State University, Fresno, few people in the Nation's agricultural colleges and universities were taking organic agriculture very seriously. Fortunately for the Van Tills, an idealistic and dedicated group of believers had begun an organic demonstration farm in nearby French Camp.

"Cliff and Debbie came by and started asking a lot of questions about insects and fertility," recalls Mark Van Horn, who at that time comanaged the 17-acre site. "I'd describe Cliff as 'skeptically curious.' It was pretty obvious he wasn't at all convinced that organic was going to work, but he's resourceful."

Cliff apparently had seen enough to give it a shot. "Cliff came home one day and said, 'You're looking at an organic farmer,'" Debbie remembers.

A Tough Start

"We started with broccoli," Cliff says. "I distinctly remember it didn't do well."

The Van Tills just leveled the ground and planted the broccoli. But they planted too many seeds and they planted them too deep. Cliff had to go back later and virtually weed out the extra seedlings with tweezers.

One thing farming organically means is that none of the convenient herbicides that modern agriculture has come to rely on are allowed. So Cliff and Debbie learned how to deal with weeds the old-fashioned way.

"In the beginning I was out there every day, 6 hours a day, hand hoeing," Debbie recalls.

The same nonsynthetic stipulation also means no quick nitrogen fixes for the soil. "I couldn't just go out and pump it full of fertilizer," Cliff says of the land.

Cliff has since planted blackeyed peas, vetch, and crotalaria, a tropical legume. It's part of a University of California study on sustainable agriculture. One day the neophyte organic farmers met the harlequin bug, an insect most commonly found in backyard gardens, but a voracious consumer of broccoli. "It ate the whole plant," Cliff recalls. "It would take a nice big plant and chew it right down to the stalk."

Help came from another organic farmer in the area. He told Cliff and Debbie that a common soap would take care of the bug problem. So Debbie went out and bought four boxes of the stuff. Cliff mixed it up in the spray rig . . . and it worked!

A Volatile Organic Marketplace

The Van Tills were able to harvest a crop—even though the harlequin bug had eaten half of it. "It's probably safe to say it was disastrous," Cliff says, "but the price of organic broccoli was high."

The Van Till family, of San Joaquin County, CA (L-R: Jason, Cliff, Jamie, and Debbie) believe in, and practice, organic farming. In California, produce is "organic" when most synthetically compounded materials are excluded from use in the production, harvest, storage, transport, or retail process.

John Stumbos/University of California-Davis

The Van Tills were told that the "gravy years" of super-high market prices were over when they went organic, but that did not stop them. Indeed, organic produce still fetches a significant premium over conventionally raised fruits and vegetables, prompting growers large and small to hang up their farm chemical caps for good.

"Some of those prices I've been embarrassed to ask," Cliff says, "even though I've needed to."

Originally, Cliff and Debbie sold their broccoli through the Stockton Farmers' Cooperative, which filled a void created when a number of local wholesalers went out of business. But the cooperative disbanded. Now the couple sells either to farmers' markets in the area or directly to wholesalers and retailers throughout the State.

The lack of an efficient distribution system for organic farmers in many areas continues to hamper the industry.

Desmond Jolly, a consumer economist with the University of California, found that one of the main things that turned off retail supermarket chains to organic produce is inconsistent supply. Consequently, some retailers who only recently began offering organic and other "pesticide-free" produce have begun scaling back their organic offerings.

"In retrospect, I think I would have started more slowly," Cliff says. "People told us to get as big a mix as we could, but as far as the wholesalers are concerned it's easier to deal with one pallet of broccoli than a dozen different vegetables."

The Van Tills continually work on finding the best mix of vegetables for them, and undoubtedly that will change along with the market.

"From an efficiency standpoint," Cliff says, "we're better off with fewer vegetables, since each one has its own nutritional requirements, water needs, and pest problems."

The Predators Cometh

There is little doubt the Van Tills will continue to grow organically. They are also exploring alternative methods of growing their conventional crops. Cliff nods toward his almond orchard.

"With an annual crop like nuts you can't play games. You've got to make intelligent decisions, but I wouldn't be surprised if eventually we're organic over there."

Indeed, they have already begun to wean themselves from pesticides—synthetic or otherwise—in their almond orchard.

"We're going on a predator release program this summer," Cliff says. A new agricultural consulting firm in the area will release parasitic wasps, lacewings, and predator mites to control the Van Till's biggest almond pests—mites, navel orange worm, and peach twig borer.

In neighboring Merced County, a University of California farm advisor has been monitoring two brothers who grow almonds—one with pesticides, one without. The advisor determined that while the organic grower harvested less crop, his costs were also lower. The bottom line is that financially they were in about the same position.

Cliff hears this and shakes his head.

"If you're not forced to go organic, then why go through all the headaches to get to the same point?" he asks. "These are the questions farmers are asking themselves."

Why Bother?

Why do the Van Tills farm organically? "We have a religious perspective," Cliff says. "And we want to be good stewards of the earth."

There is also a good, secular reason to farm organically. "The day is going to come when we won't have chemicals," Cliff believes. "We may not have the political clout to farm the way we do now. We need to be farsighted."

Like most farmers—organic or conventional—Van Till is frustrated with the public's lack of understanding about what those who till the earth really do and why they do it.

"Farmers didn't start out buying chemicals 'just because.' The bottom line is that we're dealing with economic realities and you'd better make a profit at the end of the season or you're going to be out of business."

Agricultural chemicals reduce the need for labor, which is the biggest single cost for most farmers.

"I can't see the whole Salinas Valley being hoed," Debbie says. "Fewer people are willing to do manual labor, and it takes a certain amount of time to do these things."

"Agriculture needs to keep seeking alternatives." Cliff adds. "But we're not going to get off the chemical bandwagon overnight."

Meanwhile, people like the Van Tills often find themselves making "seat of the pants" decisions. "We just take our lumps and keep stabbing at it," Cliff says. "Every year it gets a little easier."

Leroy Werremeyer:

Keeping a Record on an Illinois Grain Farm

Sunday morning, 11 a.m.: Five of the farmers who work the Sidney United Church's farm ground are debating whether to sell a portion of it.

"How many bushels did we get off the east piece last year?" asks Carl Nussmeyer.

"I'm not sure," says Kenny Katterhenry, another of the farmers who plant, cultivate, and harvest the church land. "But Leroy's probably got it down." To which Leroy Werremeyer responds, "I'll look that up when I get home."

Werremeyer has been "keeping track of things" for almost 40 years, maintaining a journal of daily events since he graduated from high school. Do you want to know when the devastating hailstorm of 1974 hit? (June 29 at 5:30 p.m.) Or how about the big ice storm? (January 1967) How many weeks did it take to restore phone service after the storm? (Four) Ask Leroy. And people do ask. More often than not, he says, people call on him to help settle an argument.

Keeping the journal helps Leroy plan for the coming season. "It's hard to remember just how well a particular variety of corn did. A guy tends to forget over the winter how well it shucked. Plus, it's fun to look back and see what I did a year ago today," he says. Werremeyer usually takes a few minutes at the end of each day to write down the highlights—a short paragraph, sometimes two.

Leroy Werremeyer, his wife Joyce, and their two sons (Randy, 27, and Tim, 25) farm approximately 875 acres near Sidney in Champaign County, IL. Theirs is a grain operation, with approximately 400 acres in corn and about the same acreage in soybeans. Forty acres of wheat and another 40 acres of Government set-aside make up the rest of the farm.

by Kevin Erb, Senior in Agricultural Communications, University of Illinois, Urbana, IL

Kevin Erb/University of Illinois

"I intend to be here as long as I'm able to drive a tractor, and then some," says Leroy Werremeyer of farming his 875 acres near Sidney, IL.

The Werremeyer farm is a family farm. Clarence, Leroy's father, lives just up the road and still helps out, although he retired from farming for health reasons in 1976. Tim and Randy also lend a hand, although Tim works full time in nearby Champaign and Randy farms another 400 acres of his own. Randy can be seen at work on the tractor or combine during the planting or harvest season. Joyce, Randy, or Tim can be seen hauling the corn to the elevator.

Twenty percent of the Werremeyers' corn acreage is under contract to Frito-Lay, which has a processing plant nearby. When the plant first came into the area, the family planted about 50 percent of their corn crop for it. Although Frito-Lay pays a premium for food-grade corn, Leroy says that the extra work and lower yields make it impractical to commit all corn production to it.

Beginnings

Leroy Werremeyer does not work the same land as his grandparents and great grandparents did. Compared with some of their neighbors, the Werremeyers are newcomers. Leroy's parents worked as hired hands on several farms near Sidney from the time they were married until 1945, when Leroy was 10 years old, and they began farming on their own.

Like other local farmers, the Werremeyers maintained a diversity of livestock. They milked five Guernsey cows until the early 1950's, when they switched to raising Angus. In high school, Leroy raised sheep for his FFA and 4-H projects. "Livestock's OK," says Leroy, "but they're too much work. There's one thing about livestock I don't miss—making hay."

Kevin Erb/University of Illinois

Ironically, making hay is what Leroy did after graduation from high school. He joined the National Guard, which gave him some time at home, so he purchased a baler and did custom baling during the summer. After serving in the Guard, he decided to become a farmer. "Actually, I never thought about anything else—never considered another vocation," Leroy says.

The following spring, 1955, Leroy rented 20 acres, planting it all in corn. "I got an awfully small check for 20 acres of corn," he recalls. He rented 240 more acres the next year. "Labor was my main expense," he says. "It wasn't near as expensive to start farming then. Plus, you could do custom work for those who hadn't yet bought the newer equipment."

Staying Out of Trouble

Some 30 years later, the first "Farm Aid" concert was held 20 miles from—and in sight of—the Werremeyer farm, at the University of Illinois Memorial Stadium. Yet the farm crisis was not severe in Champaign County. Leroy does not remember hearing about more than a couple of foreclosure sales in the entire time that he has been farming.

Leroy believes that what kept him and other farmers out of trouble during the farm crisis was the ability to resist temptation. "I'd drive by Allerton, see a new tractor, and say, 'Boy, I'd like to have that.' The guys who got into trouble said, 'Boy, I'd like to have that,' and then went out and bought two of them." The key, Leroy says, is to stay out of debt: "If you can't afford it, you don't really need it."

Leroy has seen a lot of changes in farming and in his community in the past 38 years. He sold the two-story farmhouse where his sons grew up, and it was moved 2 miles west. The barn has been replaced by a tool shed; the old workshop, by a new one. Good times, bad times, easy decisions, and hard ones are all a part of life, he says.

Lending a Helping Hand

In 1986, Leroy's church and another church inherited a 120-acre farm. Leroy and the members of his congregation farm the whole thing, renting the other church's half. Each farmer donates time and equipment. "It didn't take long to get the corn in with six combines going at once," Leroy remembers.

Joint farming means sacrifice. "There were several times when any of us would rather have been working our own ground," Leroy recalls, "but when the call came saying we'd be plowing at 8 the next morning, that's what we did."

Seeing a half dozen tractors working the same field is unusual in Champaign County, but local farmers have worked together before. When a neighbor broke his leg in a farming accident in 1983, Leroy was one of several neighbors who worked the ground and put in the crop, for free. Leroy says that it was nothing special—he was just doing a good deed for a neighbor in need.

Farming and the Environment

"When I started farming," says Leroy, "nobody'd heard of herbicides. When they first came out, we thought they were the greatest things—until we actually used them." He found that using chemicals increased the uncertainty of farming: Rain or lack of it within a few days, or working the soil too deeply or not deeply enough could render the chemicals ineffective. Chemicals "may work fine on one field, but not the one next to it," he says.

Today, Leroy does not put full faith in chemicals, but he admits that they are an essential part of modern farming. "Sure, we could go back to farming without them. But you couldn't make a living at it," he says.

To help control erosion, Leroy gradually has gone to a reduced tillage system—leaving part of the crop residue on the surface to prevent erosion. Although not all of his farmland requires minimum tillage, he uses it on all his acres. This system also saves moisture.

Kevin Erb/University of Illinois

Leroy Werremeyer has seen a lot of changes in farming and in his community in the past 38 years. "The key," Leroy says, "is to stay out of debt: If you can't afford it, you don't really need it."

Farming and the Future

Another thing that has changed over the years is how a farmer gets started. Leroy says that a prospective farmer needs someone to set him or her up these days. Land, tools, and machinery cost a lot more than they did in 1953. Therefore, Leroy is helping his son Randy get started. Currently, Randy is farming 400 acres previously rented to his father. Leroy says he intends to turn over the entire operation to Randy, though he will continue to run the homeplace. Leroy does not intend to retire and leave the farm.

"At my age," he says, "I don't have the experience or desire to go back to school. I intend to be here as long as I'm able to drive a tractor, and then some."

Randy Teeter:

Young Cotton Grower Finds Farming a Choice Occupation

If he could not be a farmer, there are several other things that 31-year-old Randy Teeter of New Deal, TX, could be.

He could be an automobile mechanic. He ran a garage in that farm community of 700 while he was still in high school.

He could be a drummer in a country-western or rock band. He and some buddies get together now and then to entertain at parties or reunions.

He might be in law enforcement. "I always used to think that might be my option, but that was when I was younger," grins the wiry young man, lean and bronzed from hours of work on his 800-acre cotton farm.

Then again, he might be a full-time, paycheck-earning firefighter instead of the State-certified volunteer that he is.

"What would I do if I had to go out of farming?" Teeter muses, shifting his wriggling, 6-year-old son Clay from his knee to the floor of the family room. Clay's 3-year-old brother, Shane, maneuvers toward the empty knee. The Teeters live in a comfortable brick home bordered by cotton fields and one neighbor. "If I could pick what I'd do, I'd be a firefighter, but I'm not intending to quit farming."

A Farming Tradition

Randy's family have always been farmers, "as far back as anybody knows." Randy is the third generation of Teeters to farm in New Deal, 11 miles north of Lubbock. His grandparents moved there from Arkansas in the mid-1940's. Randy's late father, Clayton, produced cotton, grain sorghum, and soybeans on much of the same 800 acres that Randy tends today on the broad, flat, high plains of West Texas.

by Joseph J. Bryant, Communications Specialist, Texas Agricultural Extension Service, Lubbock, TX

Bob Nichols/USDA 90BW1033-18

Farming the arid west Texas landscape north of Lubbock is nothing new to the Teeter family. Randy Teeter is the third generation of Teeters to farm in this area.

"Overall, it's about the same operation," Randy says. In addition to the land owned by his widowed mother, Randy farms other acres that he leases. Randy plants proven cotton varieties, uses soil tests to determine precise nutrient needs, and uses furrow dikes in his fields to retain the area's limited rainfall. He carefully scouts his fields for insects and uses integrated pest management to cut down on pesticide use. He works with his County Agent, testing varieties and demonstrating new methods to other producers.

Growing Up

Randy was part of the family operation from an early age. "The first thing I did was probably hoe cotton," he recalls. "I started driving the tractor when I was about 12."

At New Deal High School, Randy played drums, trumpet, and baritone in the band. "They had FFA, but I wasn't involved. I wasn't an athlete, and I sure wasn't a scholar," he confesses. "No, he was a rebel," laughs his wife, Gayla, shifting just out of reach, her eyes sparkling. Throughout high school, Randy continued to help out on the family farm "when I had time."

"I was a mechanic," he explains. "As a matter of fact, I ran a garage here in New Deal my senior year of high school. I had this '69 El Camino. It was green—a light, kind of apple green. Well, it ended up dark green . . . ." It is apparent that Randy remembers that El Camino better than his father's cotton crop.

"When I graduated in 1976," Randy says, "I tried some 8-to-5 work at a garage in Lubbock. About 6 months was all I could take. In December, my dad's hired hand quit. I told him he didn't have to look for another; he already had one. I'd had all that other life I needed."

Choices

In 1977, smalltown farm boy Randy met city girl Gayla in Lubbock, metropolitan "Hub of the Plains" with a population of 190,000. "He was cruisin' the Sonic," Gayla laughs, referring to a drive-in restaurant that was a popular meeting place for teenagers. Actually, they were introduced by one of her Monterey High School classmates who knew Randy.

"My parents were from farm families," says Gayla. "My dad farmed years ago, but had quit before my two sisters and I were born, so we were never around it." Her introduction to farm life came when she and Randy married in 1979.

"The first year was the hardest," she recalls. "The year before we got married, Randy hardly had to work at all; he had lots of time for me." That brings a snort from Randy, who explains, "That was one of those years it rained. We didn't have to water much." And without wells to check and irrigation pipe to move, he did have a little extra time for courting.

"Then, the first year we were married, it was dry, dry, dry. We ran the wells all summer," Randy recalls. "And on weekends," Gayla frowns, "he always had to run the sandfighter" (tillage equipment used to reduce erosion of the sandy soils by the strong West Texas winds). The hardest thing to get used to that first year, she says, "was the uncertainty about money—and the strange hours."

"Now it's 7 to 7 some days, and some days it's later, some days earlier," Randy observes. "And some days, it's not at all—maybe that's what I like most about farming, right there." He turns to see whether Gayla has risen to the bait. She lets it pass, observing, "I think what he really likes most is being his own boss."

Now Randy is assistant chief of the well-trained, 20-member New Deal Volunteer Fire Department, president of the Lubbock County Volunteer Firefighters Association, and an instructor on transport fires for the regional schools conducted at Lubbock by Texas A&M University. Three-quarters of his Tuesday nights belong to the fire department—business meetings and training.

For serious relaxation, Randy grabs his rod and reel and looks for the nearest bass tournament. He is a member of Lubbock Bassmasters, an organization that holds tournaments at nearby lakes. "The best lake I've fished—but I hate the driving, I hate the driving, I hate the driving—is Lake Amistad," Randy muses. Lake Amistad is on the Mexican border near Del Rio, TX, 360 miles from New Deal.

The family enjoys a lot of activities together, including some of the bass tournaments. But all the activities—except answering the fire alarm—take second place to the whims of King Cotton.

Making Cotton Work

Since 1983, Randy has farmed on his own and known the uncertainties of the West Texas wind, hail, drought, and deluge.

The Texas South Plains, which produce almost a fourth of the Nation's cotton, enjoyed a near-record year in 1988. That year Randy averaged almost 800 pounds of lint to the acre. "And 1987 was pretty good, too," he recalls.

"But 1989 was lousy. I harvested half what I did the year before." A June 1 hailstorm took 110 of Randy's acres of young cotton, and continuing rain prevented replanting until June 8, when he "tracked through mud" to put in a shorter-season variety with good yield potential. More cool, wet days caused blight.

It is because of years like 1989—which sometimes come in bunches—that Gayla has kept her job as assistant office manager at the Texas A&M University Agricultural Research and Extension Center just down Interstate 27 in Lubbock. Nevertheless, neither Gayla nor Randy would swap the challenges and the opportunities of the farm, not even for a 40-hour workweek or the regular paycheck of a fireman.

Bob Nichols/USDA 90BW1033-31

An employee of the ARS Cotton Gin in Lubbock, TX, inspects a cotton sample from a recent harvest.

Carroll and Evelyn Kepler:
Dairy Farming Where the Glaciers Parted

Carroll Kepler, Jr., was born and reared on a family farm near Sabin in western Richland County, in the heart of the unglaciated region of southwestern Wisconsin. Evelyn Getter grew up in the next county. Carroll and Evelyn were married in 1947. In this challenging, demanding farming region they have been successful as a family, as dairy farmers, and as citizens of their community. Their five children are all married, and the two sons are taking over leadership in the family's farming corporation.

Perry A. Rach/USDA 90BW0817-7

Carroll Kepler, Jr., and his wife, Evelyn, have weathered the demands of dairy farming in southwestern Wisconsin to create and maintain a successful dairy business large enough to effectively employ all interested family members.

Farming in Southwestern Wisconsin

Where Wisconsin, Minnesota, Iowa, and Illinois lock together like pieces of a giant jigsaw puzzle along the Mississippi River, some 40 counties lie untouched, or nearly untouched, by the leveling and smoothing of the last North American glaciers some 14,000 years ago. The glacier parted in west-central Wisconsin, to merge again about 200 miles farther south in northwestern Illinois and eastern Iowa.

The topography of that former island in the sea of ice now ranges from merely hilly in the lightly glaciated fringes to downright steep in the untouched "coulee region" near the Mississippi.

The broader ridgetops are cultivated, almost always on the contour, with strip crops to reduce soil and water loss. Rotations emphasize alfalfa, small grains, and corn. The wider valleys are also cultivated, but the steeper hillsides are maintained in permanent pasture or woods. Less than half the farmland in the area is in cultivated crops.

by William E. Saupe, Professor of Agricultural Economics, University of Wisconsin-Madison, WI

This part of Wisconsin is difficult to farm successfully. Yet Carroll and Evelyn Kepler and their family have succeeded.

"Getting started in farming here probably never has been easy," reflects Carroll. "When I was growing up on our home farm it seems like we had a little bit of everything—cows, hogs, chickens, a big garden. We even made our own maple syrup. Being self-sufficient probably was important back then, and that's the way all the farms were. But in this area, a good dairy herd is the way to get ahead."

Why Farming Is a Challenge Here

Topography in this area demands the raising of forage crops in order to conserve the land. But forage crops are difficult to market because of their bulkiness and weight. Such crops are usually fed to ruminant animals on the farms where the crops are harvested, because ruminants, particularly dairy cows, consume large quantities of forage crops.

To add to the challenge, it costs more money to set up a dairy farm in this part of the Midwest. Sizable investments are needed, not only for the dairy cattle, but also for a variety of farm machinery. With a relatively short growing season, the Keplers also needed to invest heavily in silos and other structures to store the 7- or 8-month feed supply needed between the end of summer and the next harvest season.

Winters are cold in southwestern Wisconsin, with temperatures commonly dropping below zero degrees Fahrenheit. Thus, the Keplers' dairy animals must be housed in substantial (expensive) barns or sheds for protection. Inside these buildings is an expensive and complicated-looking system of specialized equipment for milking and animal care, and for cooling and storing milk.

But that is not all.

Dairy farming is also labor intensive. People who are knowledgeable and skilled in animal care and dairy husbandry must be actively involved with the herd every day. As on most dairy farms, milking on the Kepler farm takes place twice a day, every day, year-round. Including feed production, it takes one full-time worker for about every 40 cows on a Wisconsin dairy farm.

Growth of the Kepler Family Farm

As was expected of all farm children in the area where he was born, Carroll helped out on his parents' farm while growing up. He climbed onto the lower rungs of the "agricultural ladder" as a young adult, when he became a wage worker on the farm.

After Carroll and Evelyn were married, they rented the home farm from Carroll's parents. They became owners of their own dairy farm in 1952. Evelyn taught school then, before the children arrived.

The children, as they became old enough, acquired purebred Holstein heifers as 4-H projects. These were the first purebreds in what is now an all-registered herd. As Ron and Kevin increased their involvement in the farm, their parents expanded operations, and the farm was incorporated in 1979.

"Not many young people are getting started in dairy farming now," says Kevin. "The way we're doing it, getting started with our dad, is probably how new people are going to get into dairying."

Expanding a farming business by consolidating nearby farms into one operation does not work as well in hilly southwestern Wisconsin as it does in the cash grain areas of the State and elsewhere in the Midwest. Roads follow ridgetops and valleys, so access to fields on the "second story" of a typical ridgetop and valley farm may involve considerable travel. Reaching cropland on an "adjacent" farm may in fact involve extensive travel, with machinery and equipment.

There are other difficulties in consolidating dairy farms.

On grain farms, economies of size are readily captured by acquiring more land to farm with an already mobile set of tractors and crop machinery. However, combining two adjacent dairy farms provides little economic advantage without extensive additions to the set of specialized buildings and equipment on one farm or the other.

For the Keplers, putting together a dairy farm business large enough to effectively employ all interested family members meant creating a new farm in the early 1970's, with a new set of buildings that could accommodate the scale of operation needed.

"When we knew we had to expand," Carroll said, "I looked around a lot. Then I bought the two adjacent 160's (160-acre farms) where we're located now.

"We laid all 320 acres out in strip crops on the contour. The soil is a loess, blown in by the wind a long time ago,

William Saupe/University of Wisconsin-Madison

The ramschackle farm that Carroll Kepler, Jr., purchased to help create his family's successful dairy business is a far cry from the modern operation the Keplers have developed over the years.

and it was laid down like drifts of snow. Some places it's shallow, but in others it's several feet deep. If you take care of it and farm it right, it will do well for you."

The only usable building was the former dairy barn. That was remodeled to house young heifers. A silo was added to store feed for those animals. In several stages, the construction project included a machine shed, a new dairy barn with 119 stanchions, four silos, and a mechanical feeding system, not to mention three new houses.

Over time, two additional contiguous farms were added, plus some land farther away.

The farm now contains about 600 crop acres, with from 150 to 200 acres of corn each year and the remainder in alfalfa and nurse crops. The Kepler herd is about four times the size of an average dairy herd in Wisconsin. Production per cow is 30 percent above the State average.

The Keplers' dairy herd is among the largest 3 or 4 percent in Wisconsin. Their breeding cattle have been sold in many other States and in Brazil, Japan, China, Korea, Taiwan, Saudi Arabia, Egypt, and other countries. Visitors have been welcomed to the Kepler farm from around the world.

Community Leaders

The Kepler family has served the Richland community in many ways. Carroll has served as a director for the production credit association and the Land-O-Lakes dairy cooperative, as an elected member of the Richland County Board, and as a member of the tri-State breeders sire selection committee. He was an Extension farm management aide for 9 years in the University of Wisconsin Extension program for small, beginning, and limited-resource farmers.

Evelyn Kepler returned to school 9 years ago—teaching kindergarten in the Kickapoo School in Viola. Both Keplers have been active as 4-H leaders and in Extension activities.

Maynard Nelson, former area Extension farm management agent, says, "Carroll helped a lot of younger farmers figure their way through the tough financial times in the mid-1980's. A lot of people were able to stick it out and make it because of the advice and encouragement they got from his visits."

Carroll still is sought out for advice and counsel by many young farmers.

Carroll and Evelyn live on the headquarters farm, as do Kevin and his wife Joan. Ron and wife Julie live about halfway between the farm and Richland Center, where Julie is director of the medical technology department in the hospital.

The Keplers' oldest child, Connie, and her husband operate their own dairy farm a few miles away, near Richland Center.

Perry A. Rech/USDA 90BW0744-5A

Holsteins are the predominant dairy cow in the Keplers' area of southwestern Wisconsin.

Two other daughters, Julie and Jill, are also married. Julie and her husband live in Iowa, and Jill and her husband live in northcentral Wisconsin.

"The grandchildren—five of them—are too young to help much or take responsibility on the farm now," reports Ron. "But when they get older, and if they're still interested, I guess there will be a place for them."

Joe Jagger:

Portrait of a Wheat Farmer

His white muttonchop whiskers make Joe Jagger stand out in a crowd. So does his enthusiasm for farming.

"I've never been bored," the 69-year-old Jagger says. "I've been overwhelmed a few times, but never bored."

Now he is getting out of farming. His machinery should be sold by the time this Yearbook is published.

Joe is the third generation of his family to work this north-central Kansas farm. None of his three sons—John, Jim, or Craig—wants to work the 1,600 acres. So, the machinery is being sold and the land leased to others.

That's all right with Joe. His own decision to farm was made only after careful consideration.

John operates a farm-based T-shirt company. Jim is a "circuit rider" for the Kansas Arts Commission's rural arts program. Craig is an agricultural economist with the Agricultural Stabilization and Conservation Service in Washington, DC.

"I had the privilege of doing what I wanted to do in life. They should too," Joe muses. "I wanted to be a farmer. They don't.

"For me, it was always a challenge to get up in the morning and see what the day brought."

But many of those days can be all-consuming.

"During planting in the fall and harvest in the summer, the wheat takes priority over everything," Joe says. "They are intense periods. Fourteen-hour days are not unusual.

"When our three sons were at home, we kept the machinery running longer than that in shifts, as long as we could. You never know when the next cloud will come up."

Joe was one of only a few from his Depression-era high school class to attend college. He left Kansas State University in 1943 with a bachelor's degree in agriculture, majoring in agronomy. He was also interested in radio and theater, and played the lead in one college play.

After college he served in Europe during World War II.

Perry A. Rech/USDA 90BW0816-31

Joe Jagger is the third generation to work his family's farm in north central Kansas. When asked about his life on the 1,600 acres he calls home, the 69-year-old Jagger replies, "I've never been bored. I've been overwhelmed a few times, but never bored."

Poetry in the Pasture

The Jagger family has a literary tradition, and Joe recalls his father, Fred, quoting from Shakespeare as they worked together fixing fence in a quiet pasture. This tradition is carried on by Joe's wife, Margaret, a writer and retired teacher. The entire family contributes to John's "Pipe Creek Newsletter," which is circulated to aficionados of his T-shirt business.

The Jagger farm was homesteaded in 1866—5 years after Kansas achieved statehood—by Captain Joseph Dawson Jagger and his wife Catherine, a Tennessee farm girl who taught the city-bred Joseph to farm.

The site of the homestead is along Pipe Creek—which but for a mapmaker's typographical error would have been named "Pike's Creek," for Lt. Zebulon Pike, who in 1806 passed through the area on his way to discovering Pike's Peak in Colorado. The creek holds an important place in Jagger family lore and traditions, and it contributes to the richness of the bottomland that is farmed.

Joe has grown wheat, sorghum, soybeans, and alfalfa commercially, and has raised certified wheat and soybean seed for sale.

In addition to grain farming, Joe had a cow-calf operation from 1947 to 1983. "This area of Kansas is good for raising wheat and cattle," Joe says. "And that's

by Carole A. Jordan, Public Information Officer, Kansas State Board of Agriculture, Topeka, KS

what we should concentrate on." But a heart attack helped him decide to get out of the cattle business.

The farm lies geographically on the border between the tallgrass and the shortgrass prairies of Kansas—or eastern and western Kansas.

"In Kansas," Jagger explains, "rainfall ranges from an average of 36 inches a year in the east to 15 inches in the west. With our area a transitional one between the west and east, we couldn't predict which kind of rainfall we would get in a given year. So we had to learn to farm both ways.

"With cattle and wheat both, if prices were down on one, the other would save you most years. Having cattle distributes the labor, too," he observes. "It gives you something to do every day."

Educated Wheat

Joe's interest in and even fascination with wheat—he can talk about wheat for hours—come to him naturally. His father began participating in the land-grant university's program of plant variety test plots for wheat in 1914. This program of planting different varieties at the same time in side-by-side plots allows farmers and researchers to see both differences and similarities in performance, yield, and disease and insect resistance. The family called it "the educated wheat."

The Jagger farm was home to wheat variety plots for 75 years—a record to which no one else in the State comes close. Years of experience with the test plots and his own business of growing and selling certified seed wheat have left him wary about pronouncing any variety better or the best.

"The best variety is always the next one," he says. "It's a moving target. At one time a variety from Texas called TAM 105 looked like it might be the best. It had some of the highest yields ever—73 bushels per acre—at one time. But 3 years later it was one of the poorest varieties, because it was susceptible to rust and leaf diseases, and we had a damp year that encouraged those diseases. Another variety, Newton, was developed with rust resistance—but within 5 years the rust itself had adapted so it could attack that variety."

Planting decisions for a Kansas wheat farmer today include waiting to hear from the Agricultural Stabilization and Conservation Service (ASCS) on Government programs.

"When we get our ASCS notice, then we decide whether to summer fallow [take out of production] or continuous crop," he explains. "Traditional farmers around here still do a lot of plowing. Continuous cropping tends to work better here.

Conserving the Soil

"I've always been interested in soil conservation. We were in the Dust Bowl when I was in high school.

"I've farmed since 1946, and we had a pretty severe drought in the mid-1950's, when you had to keep an implement ready to immediately roughen the soil if it started to blow."

He's always been reluctant to burn straw in the fields after harvesting. "When you plow a field the next year after turning straw under," Joe says, "you can see the humus and where the moisture had been held in the soil better."

At the same time, he sees the benefits of leaving fields fallow during summer. He would summer fallow his set-aside land [removed from production under USDA's wheat acreage reduction program] to build up moisture reserves and the soil.

Joe is active with the Wheat Quality Council, an organization that unites growers with other elements of the wheat industry. Its goal is to improve the quality of the Kansas-grown wheat available to industry. It sets up testing procedures for new varieties to make sure wheat is of optimum quality for milling and baking.

Joe is a man with a sense of history and a vision for the future, as comfortable sharing a story about his English grandfather as he is speculating on the importance of certified seed wheat or why hybrid wheats have not come into use.

Joe's retirement (he'll continue to live on the farm) will not be total. In addition to a long list of organizations and interests, he will continue to serve on the board of the Delphos State Bank (a small but healthy agricultural bank), and to be a member of a new company, AGSECO, with exclusive growing and marketing rights to some new wheat varieties. He will continue to sell certified wheat and soybean seed as he has for many years.

In 1989, the year of Joe's last wheat harvest, the Kansas Association of Wheat Growers named him its "wheat man of the year."

Grady Auvil:

Golden Rule Produces Golden Profits

Grady Auvil's 10-year-old, four-wheel-drive American Motors Company Eagle claws up a narrow, steep, sandy trail cut in the side of a mountain on the east side of the Columbia River near the small town of Orondo, WA. The 84-year-old's steady hand guides the vehicle to a vista several hundred feet above the river. There Auvil stops to show his visitor the 200-acre home orchard where he has farmed for 62 of his 65 years as a grower of apples and other fruits.

As principal owner of a corporation that owns two orchards totaling 600 acres and that has an operating budget of $9–12 million a year, Auvil could be squiring his guest around in a new pickup. The fact that his personal "get-around" is a dusty, old car is vintage Auvil.

"I get used to a car, I like to keep it," he says. Judging from the way the vehicle purrs, he must treat it like a friend when it comes to maintenance.

For 30 years, his orchard get-around was a Model A Ford. He says that his company has not bought more than four or five new pickups since it was formed. "We buy used pickups," he explains.

Auvil is not tight or lacking an appreciation for the latest technology. Auvil Fruit Company is a completely modern operation, from its orchards through packing and storage to its marketing facilities. It is fully computerized and communicates by facsimile machines. On a given day, its offices may transmit several messages between the two orchards, which are 70 miles apart, and send or receive facsimile messages from buyers in New York, Chicago, Dallas, or even New Zealand or London. Auvil's adrenaline surges when he contemplates the prospect of technological advances and other opportunities ahead.

by Terence L. Day, News Writer, College of Agriculture and Economics, Washington State University, Pullman, WA

Overcoming Obstacles

Few of the State's apple growers have coped with the adversity that Auvil has conquered, and few can match his influence on Washington's $500-million-a-year apple industry.

He was just getting started when the Great Depression hit. It bankrupted his father and many other farmers, but he survived.

He also overcame tree-killing winter freezes in 1950, 1964, and 1968. He had to relocate houses, buildings, and part of his orchard when the Douglas County Public Utility District built Rocky Reach Dam on the Columbia River, and he lost more orchards when the utility district developed a public park along the river in the late 1970's.

There have been major changes in the U.S. and world fruit markets, and now Washington's apple industry is in the midst of severe market woes. Through all of these crises and more, not only has Auvil survived, he has also thrived.

Grady Auvil was born December 7, 1905, in West Virginia. He came to Washington with his parents in 1908 and got his start in his father's apple orchard near Entiat. In 1924, at the age of 19, he had bought his own 5-acre orchard at Entiat. He sold that in 1928 to buy his first land at Orondo, where he still farms. He was in business with his father and two brothers for many years, and after his father and the younger brother died, he bought out the other brother—who still farms with a son just a few miles down river.

Auvil's business philosophy boils down to three strategies: Practice the golden rule, have an inquiring mind, and take advantage of opportunities.

"The world's troubles would be very simple if we all followed the golden rule," he says. "If you're a fruit grower and you follow the golden rule, you'll

Terence L. Day/Washington State University

"An honest product, an honest price, uniformity, and consistency—when you do this, it's a piece of cake," says Grady Auvil, the principal owner of the Auvil Fruit Company.

Doug Wilson/USDA 0584X660-26

put that fruit out the way you personally would like to eat it, and if you do, and deliver it to the consumer that way, you'll have no problems. An honest product, an honest price, uniformity and consistency—when you do this, it's a piece of cake."

Data and facts spew from his memory, and his conversation is sprinkled with frequent, easy chuckles.

Changing Times

Washington's apple image was built on the Red Delicious variety. The State still sells 60 million packed boxes of this popular apple each year. Auvil, who has marketed under the Gee Whiz trademark since 1949, still has about 10 percent of his land in Red Delicious. However, that variety is on its way out.

Most people in the Washington apple industry associate Auvil with new apple varieties. He was the State's leading proponent of the now popular green Granny Smith. In 1966 Auvil planted a few Granny Smith trees to get some personal experience with that variety. He grew the apples, ate them fresh, made applesauce out of them, stored them, and scrutinized them at every step. He even traveled to New Zealand for a firsthand look at mature Granny Smith orchards.

When Australian and New Zealand production increased sufficiently, the Safeway grocery store chain put Granny Smiths in all its western supermarkets. Within 2 years, Auvil says, every other supermarket chain had to follow suit, and he was ready. He harvested his first commercial crop in 1973 and was prepared to go full bore with the new apple.

"We had been trained all of our lives to believe we couldn't sell a green apple," he chuckles. Today, Granny Smith apples account for about 6 percent of Washington's apple production, and they occupy 70 percent of Auvil's acreage.

Auvil is not standing pat. He is among the orchardists who have introduced Gala, another newcomer to Washington orchards, which he first planted in 1985 and which now accounts for 10 percent of the Auvil orchards. The Gala variety comes from New Zealand and competes in the Golden Delicious market, which Auvil believes will continue to grow for some time.

In typical Auvil style, however, the orchardist already is pursuing yet another variety—Fuji. He believes that Fuji will be bigger than Granny Smith and Gala combined, dominating world apple production for the next 50 years or more. Fuji is a Japanese variety created from Red Delicious and Ralls Janet.

"There have been hundreds of apples developed all over the world with various breeding programs. This is the only one that has the capacity, I think, to fill the sweet apple gap," Auvil says. Auvil Fruit Company will not be the first to market Washington-grown Fuji apples, however; a neighbor will beat Auvil to the market by a year, in 1990.

Auvil's apple trees do not grow straight up like most people's. In Auvil's orchards, row upon row of trees grow outward at a 60-degree angle, in closely planted double rows supported on trellises. He believes that this arrangement makes better use of light and produces more and higher quality apples.

Cultivating Employees

Just as Auvil looks for the best apple and the best technology, he seeks the best people and cultivates them with all

Doug Wilson/USDA 0584X666-35A

The efforts of Washington's apple producers have created a $500-million-a-year industry in the State.

the care he gives his orchards. Auvil Fruit Company averages about 100 employees, with peak employment during the packing season exceeding 200. About 30 families live permanently on company property, and this housing is supplemented by more than 50 trailer homes and air-conditioned apartments for seasonal help.

Auvil's commitment to the golden rule is nowhere practiced more rigorously than in its application to employees. "Everyone who works for Auvil Fruit Company is slightly overpaid, including myself," he chuckles. "I call it Fat City. We pay a higher minimum and higher wages than anybody I know of." In addition to hourly wages, Auvil furnishes housing and utilities to employees. There are also profit sharing, stock options, and even a pond stocked with about 4,000 trout for his employees and their families.

Maintaining a Healthy Business

Another vital part of Auvil's success is the structure of his business. Most of Washington apple growers lose control of their fruit when it leaves the orchard, although they retain ownership of it until it is paid for by wholesalers or retailers. Thus, they remain exposed to risk. The Auvil Fruit Company began packing its own fruit in 1946. Three years later, it obtained a trademark for its "Gee Whiz" label. But in 1978 Auvil extended corporate integration to marketing his own apples.

Auvil was familiar with fruit marketing because he had always marketed the cherries, peaches, and nectarines that he grew. He also knew that by marketing his own fruit, he could benefit more fully from his reputation for quality.

Auvil fruit is sold all over the United States and in many world markets today. Auvil ships on a weekly basis to London and frequently sells apples to Taiwan.

Auvil's business is in excellent shape, but other apple growers are not doing so well. The entire Washington State apple industry has been reeling from the twin punches of 1988: the Alar scare and the State's largest crop in history. A Washington State University economist has estimated that the State's apple growers lost $130 million in sales when the 1988 crop's market was disrupted by consumer fears triggered by a television program on growers' use of Alar. (Apple growers have since quit using the chemical.) Still, Auvil tells anyone who asks that making money in the apple business is easy: "If you're doing the right thing, the orchard industry is a piece of cake." He said 1989 was one of the best years he had ever had.

Still No Retirement Plans

"To me, this is the most fascinating life in the world," says Auvil. "I'll be in this business until I die, and if I die under an apple tree, who cares? What's the difference? I enjoy working with people, I enjoy the fruit business, and I have a wonderful group of people to work with in this company. I still say it's a piece of cake."

Carmen Jorgensen:

Goodwill Ambassador for U.S. Agriculture

She is not a hog farmer, but she is no stranger to hogs.

She has farrowed sows alongside her husband. She has paid her dues to farming with calluses and sleepless nights worrying over finances.

Her contribution to agriculture today is that of bookkeeper and market forecaster, but promoting agriculture is what puts a sparkle in her eye.

Carmen Jorgensen of Dover, AR, is unique.

Attractive, articulate, and savvy, Carmen knows the ropes. Her blue eyes are direct and her voice is a well-modulated marriage of Southern and Midwestern dialects.

Carmen is as much at home in an airplane going to Hong Kong as on the farm. She has represented U.S. agriculture and women in agriculture in both Europe and the Far East.

It does not seem likely that the portals of world travel lie in a small Ozark foothills community, yet that is where Carmen started her career as a professional woman of the land.

University of Arkansas Cooperative Extension Service

Carmen Jorgensen and her husband, Wayne, have established themselves in the swine industry through their efforts in farming as well as related business enterprises.

Establishing a Name

Reared on a farm in Iowa, Carmen met Wayne Jorgensen just as she started a teaching career. Seven months later they married. The Jorgensens have been perfecting a partnership of complements for 33 years.

The foundation of their current success was built 20 years ago when Carmen, Wayne, and their two children, Sonja and Wade, then 12 and 10, respectively, moved to Dover. By then Carmen had retired from teaching.

by Denice A. G. Gray, Communications Specialist, University of Arkansas Cooperative Extension Service, Little Rock, AR

And she had begun trading commodities futures on the Chicago Mercantile Exchange.

After establishing themselves on a swine farm with related business enterprises, the Jorgensens became active in the Arkansas pork industry. A former army cook, Wayne won the 1978 national pork cookoff contest in Seattle, WA. (To this day, the Jorgensens serve barbecued pork to attendees of Ozark Memory Days, a local celebration.) For a while Wayne was the Arkansas director for the National Pork Producers Council and Carmen was the president of the National Pork Council for Women.

The 1980's were a time of change, and Carmen was in the forefront. The name Porkettes was no longer acceptable. Carmen was instrumental in getting it changed to the National Pork Council for Women.

If Carmen was heavily involved, so was her family—because family unity is important to her. Sonja was crowned Pork Industry Queen in 1976. Both Sonja and Wade were national 4-H winners in the swine project area.

Active in 4-H activities, Carmen also edited *Arkansas Pork Producer* magazine, which included selling advertisements as well as writing, addressing, wrapping, sorting, and mailing each issue.

Throughout the family's involvement, Carmen learned the art of networking.

"I take advantage of the opportunities given me," she says. "I get to know people. At any meeting I don't just say hello and goodbye; I want to know who I'm sitting by. Acquaintances are valuable."

Acquaintances Pay Off

Carmen has served on the National Advisory Committee on Meat and Poultry Inspection. Her time spent on State and other national boards has led her into conversations with Members of Congress, lobbyists, and USDA employees.

She was one of the few ambassadors of good will named by the Secretary of Agriculture. As such she traveled to Europe in 1984 and to Japan, Korea, China, and Hong Kong the following year.

Carmen revealed some of her philosophy in an address in Verona, Italy, in 1986, when she represented the farm women of North America at a conference organized by the International Federation of Business and Professional Women. Carmen pointed out the professionalism inherent in a farm woman's work:

Farm women, she says, have organized to draw greater attention to their own roles, to educate consumers about agriculture, and to lobby on behalf of their family farms. The farm woman has a career focus—the farm and its development. There is an opportunity to expand her role on the farm to whatever she wants it to be. Professionalism, then, is inherent to the position of farm woman.

Fred S. Witte/USDA 0581W524-2

The Jorgensens' swine operation encompasses some 400 acres; they sell 10,000 to 12,000 head a year.

If "professional" is a key word in Carmen's life, then her home office exemplifies it, fax machine and all. She spends many hours in that office. Her foreign travels are over, at least for now. She will tell you that one of her main regrets is that there are not enough hours in the day to accomplish all she wants to do.

Not only is there the swine operation that encompasses some 400 acres and sells 10,000 to 12,000 head a year. There is also the gift shop the Jorgensens purchased, appropriately named the Copper Pig. Carmen and daughter Sonja have parlayed their flair for interior design—along with Carmen's network of foreign and domestic acquaintances—into a successful operation. Recently they opened another store.

Timing has been everything in Carmen's life. She knows the ropes, and she knows how to make the system work for her.

Grant and Jo Anne Hill:

A Part-Time Professional and a Full-Time Farm Manager

Bob Nichols/USDA 90BW0936-26

Checking the aroma of new hay helps Grant Hill, of Ellicott City, MD, to determine if his crop is ready for baling. Farming is a second life for Hill, who also maintains an active dentistry practice.

The road slices through lush rolling hills covered with a mixture of field crops and residential housing developments. The landscape holds a smorgasbord of economic activity and is the home of urban, suburban, and rural residents. The scent of sun-dried hay is in the air. Baltimore is just over the next hill.

Howard County, MD, lies between Baltimore, MD, and Washington, DC. It is the location of Columbia, the county's new hub of commerce with a population of 72,000, and Ellicott City, the historic county seat. The land surrounding these communities is under tremendous pressure for development.

County residents have mixed opinions about the future. Some people want to keep farming, and others want new residential housing and business centers. Farms, in addition to providing food and fiber, also provide open space to people in areas of high population density, natural beauty spots in altered landscapes.

I pass a tractor that pulls a baler coughing up bales of hay onto a trailing wagon; then I turn off the highway to TaHill Farm, the home of Grant and Jo Anne Hill and their three sons. Grant is a dentist and farmer, and Jo Anne is the farm manager. Everyone is busy when I arrive, some loading bales of hay onto the conveyer that takes them into the barn, others loading hay onto a customer's pickup truck.

The 133-acre TaHill Farm includes 65 acres in hay, 35 in small grain, and the balance in pasture, woodlot, and homesite. The farm crops for a typical year amount to 7,500 bales of timothy, 2,000 of alfalfa, 2,000 of alfalfa-orchard grass mix, and 2,000 of straw. The farm's production is rounded out by 10 acres of corn, 25 to 40 acres of soybeans, and 10 acres of pasture.

I watch the pickup carry the load of hay out the farm lane. The clatter of the conveyor stops, and the dust settles. Grant and I now have the quiet time to talk about the dual roles of a part-time professional.

The Part-Time Professional

Grant works 44 hours a week, Monday through Thursday, as a dentist. The rest of the time he spends farming. "I need the heavy physical labor of farming after the many hours of doing the fine art of dentistry," he says.

"Practicing dentistry and farming complement each other," says Grant. "Every day brings something new." A diverse clientele use the services of the dentist, so he keeps in constant contact with the local community.

Some problems can arise from working two professions. "You must learn how to respond to any crisis and manage it well, in order to minimize the damage and possibly come out ahead," says Grant. Not unlike dentistry, equipment breaks or wears out and repairs must be made. Sometimes problems can be anticipated; however, more often there is no warning, and instant repairs are necessary if time is limited.

The Farm Manager

Jo Anne joins us and reminds Grant that he needs to get ready for a 4-H hay club meeting that evening. While Grant goes to prepare for the meeting, I ask Jo Anne to describe her job as the farm manager.

During the growing season, the main job of farm manager is to market the hay—to do whatever is necessary to sell

by Howard W. (Bud) Kerr, Jr., Director, Office for Small-Scale Agriculture, Cooperative State Research Service, USDA, Washington, DC

the crop, and to sell as much hay as possible "on the ground."

"That is trickier than it sounds," says Jo Anne. "It all begins with the maturation of the crop and a favorable weather forecast. We are currently growing three types of hay: timothy, alfalfa, and an alfalfa-orchard grass mixture. The timothy hay is our best seller; the alfalfa hay is the queen of the hay crops; and the alfalfa-orchard grass is very popular in a smaller market."

"We do not sell any hay that is not of the highest quality," says Jo Anne. Timothy hay is harvested twice per season. The hay is cut and dried and then baled. Alfalfa hay is cut or harvested four to five times a season. The current crop of alfalfa is 12 acres and will produce anywhere from 450 bales on the first cutting to 300 bales for subsequent cuttings. The alfalfa-orchard grass mix is much the same as the plain alfalfa.

The Next Generation

The two older Hill boys are in the 4-H Club and have had their own alfalfa fields. The oldest has won a 4-H Club trip to Chicago, IL, based on his record book in plant and soil science. The next oldest is following a similar path.

Jo Anne and her oldest son went to a Pennsylvania State University alfalfa seminar in Lancaster, PA, when they were first establishing the farm's alfalfa fields. Jo Anne recalls that they learned "everything you always wanted to know about alfalfa but were afraid to ask. We were the only female and only young man at the seminar, but we held our own, and our stands of alfalfa today are still being taken care of the way we learned in Lancaster."

The part-time professional and the farm manager both believe they should never stop learning. Grant has continued his dental education and his farm education. He has taken a course on diesel mechanics and welding to help him repair machinery on the farm.

Grant has used some of his spare time to acquire and restore a collection of John Deere tractors. The tractors date from 1935 through 1960, and Grant uses many of them on the farm.

What Makes It Worthwhile

Why do the Hills do this? "It's the best possible way to raise children," says Grant. "They can stay beside their parents and learn to be productive and skilled individuals. They can observe nature when it is kind and when it is cruel. They get a picture of the great circle of life—the beginning, the middle, and the end. They witness birth and life at early ages. They know what it means to be responsible for another living creature."

On weekend mornings in summer, Grant and Jo Anne often get up very early and have their coffee out on the front porch, which has a wonderful view of the farm and overlooks a 4-acre pond.

"We don't even talk sometimes, we just sit and look," says Jo Anne. "It is such a wonderful feeling to look out and see the hay you have cut lying in windrows gleaming with the morning dew."

Bob Nichols/USDA 908W0936-21

"I need the heavy physical labor of farming after the many hours of doing the fine art of dentistry," says Grant Hill. Balancing the demands of two occupations is a challenge that Hill believes is worth the effort.

José Reyes Reyes:

Winter Farmwork in Western New York

José Reyes Reyes is one of the relatively few farmworkers who work in western New York during the winter. Most farm employment (other than dairy work) in western New York is seasonal—May through October—with the majority of the demand for labor attributed to the harvest of apples, which takes place between late August and early November.

José's situation is also different because historically most farmworkers in western New York have been blacks from the Southeastern United States, Haitians, and Jamaicans. Only during the 1989 apple harvest did workers from Mexico and South Texas begin coming to western New York in substantial numbers. Hundreds of thousands of workers from Mexico are in the United States as Special Agricultural Workers—legalized U.S. residents under a provision of the Immigration Reform and Control Act of 1986. José was a legalized resident before the Act; his wife, Maria Oralia Medina, obtained her legalized status through the Special Agricultural Worker program.

From Mexico to the United States

José was born in San José de Bernalejo in the State of Zacatecas in central Mexico in 1954. He has three brothers and four sisters, and most of his family still live in Mexico. He first came to the United States in 1971 and worked in Texas and New Mexico, primarily as a day laborer in vegetable and onion harvesting. For a number of years he moved between the United States and Mexico and considered himself a not-so-serious migratory farmworker.

In 1975, José married a Mexican-American woman from San Angelo, TX, and eventually settled there, where they had two children, a boy born in 1977, and a girl born in 1982. Unfortunately, they were divorced after 10 years of marriage. Divorce is uncommon and unacceptable in Mexican culture, so it caused considerable anguish—not to mention considerable economic loss.

Having lived in Texas for about 12 years, José returned to his hometown in Mexico after his divorce. He spent 2 years there before entering the farmworker migrant stream again. In 1984, he went to Florida to work in the orange harvest. Typically, the Florida orange harvest season runs from October through April and is the source of employment for many migrants during the winter. In Florida, José worked primarily with other Mexicans, and he made new friends, who had an established migratory pattern. Like his friends, he returned to his hometown in Zacatecas at the end of each orange harvest season.

During one of the returns, José met a young woman, Maria Oralia, and after 2 years of courtship they entered the migrant stream together. In 1989, they

Perry A. Rech/USDA 90BW0731-30

Working through a labor contractor, farmworker José Reyes is able to find consistent employment throughout the year. His situation is different from that of many other farmworkers; for many areas of the United States, farm labor is a seasonal occupation.

by Enrique E. Figueroa, Assistant Professor of Agricultural Economics, Cornell University, Ithaca, NY

were married. Unlike his migrant friends from Florida, José and Maria traveled to Tennessee rather than California or the Midwest, and they spent most of the summers there, working in the nursery industry. Maria particularly liked nursery work because it was not as physically demanding as other day-laborer work. Depending on the weather, they would leave Tennessee during August or September and travel to Michigan for the apple harvest season. The apple harvest season would last into October, and thereafter they would then go back to Florida and begin the migrant cycle again.

Maria Oralia Medina has done farmwork in several States, including Florida, Tennessee, and Michigan. She settled in western New York in 1989 to prune apple trees.

Settling in Western New York

In 1989, the first year that western New York employed substantial numbers of farmworkers from Mexico during the apple harvest, José, Maria, José's cousin, and two friends went there instead of to Michigan. They worked in the apple harvest under contract to a labor contractor.

One factor influencing the Reyes' decision to live and work in western New York was the housing arrangement for the family. The labor contractor recently had received a loan to construct new housing for migrant workers, and the Reyes family moved into a brand new home. José made a good impression on the farm labor contractor, and at the end of the season he offered José, Maria, and their friend Misa Mendoza work through the winter —mostly pruning apple trees. Having a baby—José Javier, born September 1989—may have influenced José and Maria to stay in New York.

Typical Winter Workday

José's typical working day during the winter begins at 6 a.m., with breakfast and making the day's lunch. José and Misa, who lives with the family, drive in José's pickup truck to the day's work site. They are paid by the number and sizes of the trees they prune.

The labor contractor selects the work sites, but José works independently. The labor contractor goes to the site the first day and may visit the site again when the work is done at that particular orchard. Mostly, though, the contractor checks with the farm owner by telephone to confirm that the work has been done to the owner's satisfaction. The contractor provides the workers with the necessary tools, equipment, and clothing to do the job.

José and the labor contractor say that there is more work available than there are people able and willing to do the work. The workday is over by 6 p.m. The Reyes usually spend their evenings at home, watching television or listening to audiotape cassettes of Mexican music.

The labor camp in which they live is deserted during the winter; they are the only residents. José is a quiet person, and it is clear that life in western New York during the winter for the Reyes (or any other people from Mexico) is socially isolated—they have no other friends. Even though José's English is good enough to communicate with almost anyone, the same is not true for his wife and his friend.

José likes what he does—especially because he is basically his own boss once he has been given a task to do. His income varies through the year, but he has aspirations similar to those of most other Americans starting a family.

It is difficult to know whether José will settle in western New York. His decision will depend on whether year-round work is available and also on whether more people from Mexico choose to settle in the area. One advantage of working for a labor contractor is the network of potential employers that the contractor can tap into. This is particularly true of José's contractor, who has deep roots in the area.

Another important factor that will influence the Reyes' decision to stay will be the degree to which the community accepts people from Mexico. Extension agents who work with farmworkers in western New York suggest that the community has a growing interest in accommodating farmworkers like José and his family. Only time will tell.

José is not very different from most other farmworkers, but he is distinguished by three characteristics: He does not drink or smoke, he chose to settle in a socially and geographically isolated area, and he lives in relatively good housing. His situation is similar to that of many farmworkers in that he works for a labor contractor. José recognizes that the labor contractor makes money from his work, and he would prefer another arrangement. His family's social acceptance by the community during the winter is tenuous at best, and he and his family yearn to be among family and friends.

In many ways the Reyes family is very similar to the other families in western New York—hard-working, family-oriented, serious, and mindful of their responsibilities—but in the small town where they live, they also feel different from their neighbors.

Perry A. Rech/USDA 90BW0745-5

Farmworkers José Reyes and his wife, Maria Oralia, share a quiet stroll through an orchard in western New York before beginning their day's task of trimming apple trees.

Berta White:

A Lifelong Dedication to Agriculture

Not many individuals who leave school and marry at age 14 have the chance to lunch with presidents, serve in a State legislature, or earn a college degree when a grandmother. But Berta Lee White, or "Bert" as she is best known, of Bailey, MS, has done all this—and more.

On State Highway 493 in Mississippi, Bailey is little more than an isolated post office serving a rural community north of Meridian. Yet Bert, who has traveled around the world several times on behalf of agriculture, calls it home.

Bert proudly proclaims she is a farmer. She has been a farmer all her life. She eloped when she was 14 to marry her school sweetheart, the boy next door, who was then 18. The marriage joined two neighboring 100-acre farms—parcels farmed by the couple's parents and grandparents.

During their early married years, Bert and her husband Gordon maintained the farm, but they worked off the farm to supplement their income. Gordon worked as an engineer. Bert served as a "hello girl" and assistant lineman for the telephone company founded by her parents in 1911.

"In many ways, we actually grew up and matured together," Bert recalls.

She drove a school bus for 7 years in the 1930's. There were unscheduled stops on Bert's bus routes during those years—stops she made to help breast-feed two children—one black, one white—whose mothers were unable to nourish them. The Whites had four children of their own. While many people look back on the Depression years as a difficult time, Bert says it was a time of sharing and pulling together for rural Mississippians.

"We shared what we had and made the best of conditions," she recalls. "We didn't really think of ourselves as doing without. There was no electricity in rural Mississippi, so we weren't forced to do without conveniences.

"We had food from our gardens. We had a milk cow and our own livestock and chickens. No one in our area went hungry. You knew what your neighbors had and what they needed. There was an understanding that your garden was there to be shared."

Her Career as a Leader

Soon after the Depression years, Bert became actively involved in community activities. She joined the Lauderdale County Farm Bureau, where she became a volunteer leader.

Bert's leadership abilities and motivational strengths were soon recognized. She was appointed chairman of the county Farm Bureau membership committee and built the roster from 17 to 75 families during her first year.

Many other volunteer activities followed, including membership on several local boards. Once she was named the top 4-H leader in Mississippi. In 1982, the State of Mississippi officially recognized her for "outstanding contributions to programs and support for the aging."

Her neighbors voted her into Mississippi's House of Representatives in 1964. Four years later they elected her to the State Senate, where she served until 1975.

While serving as a State Senator, she also enrolled at the University of Southern Mississippi in Hattiesburg. Following the close of the day's legislative session, she would drive 100 miles to attend classes; when the legislature was in recess, she would enroll as a full-time student. After 5 years of study, Bert earned a bachelor of science and arts degree in political science.

"College was one of the most interesting periods of my life," she recalls.

Representing Farm Women

Bert used her political experience and knowledge to get farm women's input into the legislative debate over the 1985 farm bill. As a result of her prodding, State Farm Bureau women's committees generated 45,000 letters to elected officials in Washington, DC.

> Believing that agriculture's future also depends on continued technological advances, Bert helped create the Farm Bureau's "adopt a scientist" program. Now in its third year, the program establishes exchanges between scientists from agribusiness companies and individual farm families.
>
> The scientist lives on the farm for several days, exchanging information over the breakfast table, doing chores, and walking the fields. While no technological breakthroughs have been discovered yet through the program, Bert says the scientists involved have almost unanimously said they gained a far better appreciation for the pursuit of practical solutions and applications in their research.

by Jack King, Director of News Services, American Farm Bureau Federation, Park Ridge, IL

She currently serves as chairman of the Mississippi Farm Bureau women's committee and as national chairman of the American Farm Bureau Federation's women's committee, a position she has held for 10 years.

In an effort to create better public understanding of agriculture, the Farm Bureau women, under Bert, meet with the editors of the major consumer magazines. At these luncheons in New York City, farm women talk with writers who help shape public opinion.

Bob Nichols/USDA 90BW1074-7

Playing many roles is nothing new to Berta White. Although a wife, mother, farmer, and chairman of the American Farm Bureau Federation Women's Committee, White remains active as a lobbyist on rural issues on local, State, and Federal levels.

"Farmers don't fully recognize the importance of their communication role with the public," Bert says. "They work hard at what they do, but too often they assume the public automatically understands their role and why they operate the way they do.

"Farmers don't recognize their need to help the public develop a better understanding of agriculture. We have no choice. We have a responsibility to get involved and to relate to the public in terms they can understand."

Bert strongly emphasizes "Ag in the Classroom" projects (see Chapter 46) and is a tireless fundraiser for local programs in Mississippi. One of her pet projects now is promoting "The Choice is Yours," a computer program developed through the Farm Bureau's research foundation. Aimed at students in seventh through ninth grades, the software shows agricultural career paths. In describing the program, Bert says, "The future of agriculture depends on attracting capable youth into the industry."

It was through her work in the Farm Bureau that she became involved in the Country Women's Council and Associated Country Women of the World. She would eventually meet with Presidents Reagan and Bush to present the viewpoint of rural women on various issues. She has frequently testified before Congress, Federal agencies, and her State legislature, offering a statement for all of agriculture.

She has visited each of the 50 States and nearly 2 dozen foreign countries to rally women as defenders of agriculture. She wants to help farm women develop leadership abilities.

The Whites were married 54 years before husband Gordon's death in 1986; Bert has 10 grandchildren and 12 great-grandchildren. Since Gordon's death, Bert and their son Gordon have jointly managed the farm operation, raising crops and white-faced herefords on 250 acres.

Despite her 60 years of involvement as a wife and mother, a legislator, and a community and national leader, she still has a mission and a sense of work unfinished. She is driven by what she describes as the need to encourage farmers to become better communicators, to create better public understanding of farm issues.

To do this, she stresses that action must begin at home. Solutions to all issues will originate first with the people, she insists, not government.

Bert has participated in three trade missions coordinated by USDA. On these missions, she spoke to government leaders and farmers in the European Community, Asia, Hungary, Yugoslavia, and Turkey. In addition, she led a delegation of Farm Bureau women to Sweden, Germany, and Austria in 1988 to address foreign trade concerns.

"The goals and desires of farm women are the same around the world," Bert says.

The Carpenter Family:

Farming Vegetables and Fruit Keeps Their Dream Alive

Most people in Grady, a small community in southeastern Arkansas with a population of about 400, boast often about a unique farm family in their midst. This family has survived, living on the farm and growing vegetables and small fruit, for the past 15 years, while many others around them have failed at farming.

What is it that makes this family so special and so successful? Why have they succeeded at farming while others have not?

Abraham Carpenter and his wife, Katie, are the nucleus of the family's expanding produce operation. From meager beginnings, the Carpenters have built a successful family business through a mixture of technology and traditional family values.

Abraham Carpenter, Sr., his wife Katie, and members of their family were close to losing their farm during the early 1970's, attempting to grow cotton and soybeans as a means of survival. They managed to secure a few dollars to keep their heads above water by selling peas grown on a quarter-acre plot adjacent to the family home. Then the Carpenters bought a small tractor and expanded the garden plot to 3 acres.

"In 1973, we were selling our produce out of our old car on a department store parking lot in Pine Bluff," Katie recalls. "We sold peas to roadside markets, but at that time we could only get about $1.75 per bushel." Today, peas bring between $4 and $12 per bushel, depending on the variety and time of year.

by Arthur L. Allen, Associate Dean/Director, Research and Extension, University of Arkansas at Pine Bluff, AR

Extension Lends a Helping Hand

Times would get better for the Carpenters, as people at the Cooperative Extension Program at the University of Arkansas at Pine Bluff (UAPB) played a vital role in helping them toward upward mobility. More important, Extension helped them keep alive their dream . . . that of staying on the family farm. "Everybody in the family wants to stay on the farm," says Katie. "The kids enjoy it and they make a living."

Abraham, Sr., who started this operation some 15 years ago, has turned the day-to-day marketing and other managerial aspects of the family business over to Abraham, Jr., who joined the business full time 8 years ago. But in this family everybody knows that Abraham, Sr., is still the boss. He presides over operations on the farm. "I decide who works in the fields and who goes to market in Pine Bluff and Little Rock," he says. "I usually stay in the field and monitor the irrigation of produce, along with other duties."

Over the years, the UAPB Extension program has helped the Carpenters stay on the farm by assisting them in expanding and diversifying their meager 3-acre farm into a thriving 450-acre operation. Extension specialists and agents advised them on which vegetables to plant, when to plant, how to fertilize, and which pesticides to use for weed and insect control, as well as the latest irrigation techniques, how to keep records, and the importance of soil testing. They also helped the Carpenters select the best kind of land to buy when the family made the decision to expand the operation.

The Carpenters now produce and market an impressive array of high quality vegetables and small fruit—including turnip greens, peas, okra, squash, Irish potatoes, sweet potatoes, blackberries, muscadines, spinach, broccoli, carrots, peppers, cucumbers, onions, peanuts, radishes, and mustard—to various markets throughout the State.

"We secure most of our own markets, which include the Pine Bluff and Little Rock farmers' markets, supermarkets, local restaurants, and some out-of-State outlets," says Abraham, Jr. The supermarket connections provide the volume and cash flow the Carpenters need to support an operation of this magnitude. Even though they have established themselves with the larger buyers, they

University of Arkansas Cooperative Extension Service

Although their produce business has expanded greatly since its origin, the Carpenters remain active in farm markets throughout Arkansas. The family's togetherness and strong work ethic, combined with a willingness to update their operation as new technology becomes available, help keep their farm a success.

still remain loyal to the farmers' markets, which account for about 55 percent of their income.

A Hard Act To Follow

The Carpenters are an exception rather than the rule among vegetable farmers. Although many vegetable operations are family oriented, the Carpenters are probably in a class by themselves, as they involve all family members in cultivating, harvesting, and marketing vegetables and small fruit from their 450 acres. About 5 years ago, the Carpenters farmed 50 to 60 acres, all in vegetables.

"The decision was made to expand substantially when my younger brothers finished high school and decided to join the family business," recalls Abraham, Jr. "Our total family income is generated from our vegetable and small fruit operation."

With the help of UAPB Extension, the Carpenters have been able to grow in an organized manner. They have purchased a state-of-the-art vegetable washing and cleaning machine and four late-model refrigerated vans to carry their produce to market. They have devised an innovative method of cooling their vegetables, using an ice machine prior to going to market, and have had their land leveled using a precision laser technique that has reduced runoff and thus improved their irrigation system. Their watering system—a 160-foot well and tractor-powered pump, pipe for furrow irrigation, and a sprinkler system for spot irrigation—paid for itself in 7 years.

The Carpenters are a close-knit family and dedicated to their family business. The dedication is evident as it takes 16-hour days on the part of most family members to keep their large operation going. Most work days begin at 2:00 a.m. for the working crew, which numbers about 25. Abraham, Jr., his seven brothers and sisters, and other relatives by marriage make up this unique group. Katie prepares the meals while one or two of the younger daughters babysit the young.

The Carpenters' success can be traced to the family's work ethic, togetherness, a willingness to listen to recommendations from the Extension Service, and the insight to update their production and marketing techniques as new technology becomes available.

However, it is their unique family structure that contributes most to the success of the Carpenters. It is something special that is rarely found among American families today.

University of Arkansas Cooperative Extension Service

Ed McGrew:

Putting His Shadow on His Land

Positive about the present, enthusiastic about the future, Edward I. McGrew personifies what it takes today to successfully farm the irrigated desert lands that provide this Nation with most of its fresh, cool-season vegetables each winter.

He is a man of the times. Skilled in farm management and active in community affairs, Ed is sensitive to his area's economic pulse. His personal involvement and investment are helping his community prepare for a decade of change.

Ed, 52, is the sole owner of MAGCO AG, a diversified farming operation headquartered in the Meloland area of Imperial County—nestled in the southeast corner of California. Meloland lies between El Centro, the county seat, and Holtville, MAGCO's mailing address. It was Meloland when Ed, a native of the area, started MAGCO and still is Meloland to him today despite the postal designation.

Desert Oasis

The county's Imperial Valley, a Sonoran Desert oasis, accounts for about $1 billion yearly in gross income to agricultural producers. The odds are that the lettuce, cauliflower, broccoli, carrots, and asparagus you see displayed in your supermarket from January through March were grown in the Imperial Valley. El Centro's chamber of commerce boasts that, acre for acre, the valley is the most agriculturally productive area in the Nation.

by Forrest D. Cress, Communications Specialist, Cooperative Extension, University of California, Riverside, CA

Bob Nichols/USDA 90BW1036-21

Ed McGrew, owner of MAGCO AG, a vegetable farming operation in the Imperial Valley area of California, is a regular fixture in his company's fields. Speaking of the importance of remaining active in his business, McGrew says, "My father told me the best thing you can put on your land is your shadow."

People in the valley, though, are looking to the 1990's as a decade of change. They see diversification of business activity, spurred by investments from urbanized, coastal southern California.

MAGCO farms about 4,000 acres in the Imperial Valley and another 4,000 acres around nearby Yuma, Arizona. Ed also is the developer, builder, and co-owner of the new, $1.6-million Rio Bend RV Resort Ranch, a 270-space, full-service RV park west of El Centro.

Reinvestment, Not Flash

As one of his business associates puts it, "McGrew doesn't show a lot of flash. He reinvests in his enterprises, to the benefit of our valley and county."

Although Ed has been directly involved in farming his whole life, he is amenable to change, to diversification. His resort RV ranch venture attests to that. When life gives you lemons, make lemonade. That is what he says. "You must learn to make adversity work for your benefit," he notes. It's worked for him.

When Ed graduated from college there was no opportunity for him to go into business with his father, who had a small farming operation, so he went to work for a grower who farmed more acreage and made him a partner. They sold out to Purex in the late 1960's, and Ed served for 3 years as a regional manager for Freshpict Foods, a Purex subsidiary. When Purex pulled out of its farming enterprises, he bought back in and formed MAGCO.

Hands-On Boss

Here is another old saying that Ed follows: "The best thing a farmer can put on his land is his shadow."

Ed sees himself as a day-to-day, hands-on owner/operator. His home is but a quarter mile from MAGCO's office and headquarters. He is up at 4:30 a.m. and in his office by 5:30 a.m. each workday. His off time begins when MAGCO operations shut down for the day.

Each day by 10 a.m., his secretary reports what is going on in each MAGCO field, how many employees are involved, and how many people are staying at his RV park. A two-way radio keeps him in contact with his Yuma operations, and he makes much use of the mobile phone in his pickup. He believes that his presence and daily communications with key personnel are essential to his company's operations. "I want them to be self-motivated," he says, "and I value their input as to how we might improve what we're doing."

Management Team

His key personnel include a controller, a personnel manager, two area growers, three tractor foremen, three irrigation foremen, and two shop foremen. He also keeps a California certified pest control adviser on retainer to protect his crops from diseases, weeds, and insect pests. (He is setting a tentative goal of reducing agricultural chemical costs on MAGCO cropland by $50 per acre this year.)

Almost all of the land farmed by MAGCO is leased and always has been. "About 65 percent of the acreage I lease in the Imperial Valley belongs to absentee owners, which is fairly typical of land being farmed here," says Ed, "and the same more or less holds true for the Yuma area acreage we have under cultivation."

About 75 percent of the MAGCO acreage is planted to vegetables, such as lettuce, cauliflower, broccoli, carrots, asparagus, and onions, and 25 percent to field crops such as alfalfa, wheat, Sudan grass, and sugar beets.

"We double crop," he says, "and follow our winter vegetables with cereal grains or a field crop. We're working year-round. We have no slack time."

Coordination Critical

Coordination of cultural practices is critical to MAGCO's vegetable crop operations. "Shippers have to be guaranteed a steady supply for 100 to 120 days," Ed notes. "Production is very intense. For example, our asparagus harvest entails picking each acre every single day for 100 days or more. Winter vegetables are planted in late summer, and there's a very stringent schedule for planting. We also have fairly sophisticated field crop scheduling."

From his second-floor MAGCO office window, Ed sees hundreds of recreational vehicles, many pulling boats, streaming eastward each weekend on Interstate 8, bound for the Colorado River and its environs. "The low cost of food," he notes, "makes it possible for adults to have so many expensive toys."

The RV presence in his life, so visible from his office, so visible in Yuma each winter when thousands of "snowbirds" from colder climes flock there, led him to start making lemonade from life's lemons back in 1983. That's when he took his first steps toward developing an RV park on land he owned just south of Interstate 8 west of El Centro. At that time, agriculture generally was not doing well, Ed recognized the growing demand for high-quality RV facilities in the Imperial Valley, and he wanted to diversify anyway.

His Rio Bend RV Resort Ranch had its grand opening in March 1986. His wife Patty designed it and planned for it. Their daughter, Margo McGrew-Dubois, is general manager of the enterprise.

Valley's Needs

More general business during the summer months is a major need of the valley. Cotton once was a major crop there and an important one because it provided a cash flow in the valley during its slow months, summer and fall.

"We need to get cotton growing again," says Ed. "We also need a meat packinghouse somewhere in our area. It would be a significant economic shot in the arm."

Optimistic about the future, he sees great opportunities for the Southwest States to sell their produce and goods to Pacific Rim nations.

"A large percentage of our asparagus is already going to Japan," he notes. "All of our Sudan grass is begin shipped to Japan as dairy cattle roughage feed. It's being shipped in the same containers Japan uses to deliver new cars to Long Beach harbor. In 1991, we'll be exporting beef to Japan."

"Golden Triangle"

He sees the Imperial Valley as being in a "Golden Triangle" between San Diego and Palm Springs, CA, and Phoenix, AZ. "They're all rapidly developing into great metropolitan areas," he notes, "and we're seeing significant increases in housing construction, sales tax revenue, and more goods and service provided to El Centro residents and guests. El Centro is in the center of the center."

Leaders in many areas of community life, Ed and Patty are alumni of California Polytechnic State University, San Luis Obispo. Ed majored in farm management and Patty in home economics. Their daughter Margo is a Cal Poly graduate. Another daughter, Cindy, is a graduate of Scripps College, Claremont, CA. The baby of the family, Jennifer, is now attending Hope College in Holland, MI.

Ed takes pride in his family, his business enterprises, and his home—the Imperial Valley, where his presence is a low-key but constant, positive force for the valley's future.

Bob Nichols/USDA 90BW1031-17

Ed McGrew (left) and USDA onion inspector Chuck Bombarger (right) examine a random sample of onions harvested that day. The inspector checks the onions for size, weight, bruises, and dirt.

George Houk:
The Whole Is Greater Than the Sum of Its Parts

It is not easy to get in touch with Ohio farmer George Houk. Depending on the time of year, or time of day (or night), George is likely to be planting a grain or soybean crop, tending his Christmas tree operation, tapping maple trees for sap, working for the Agricultural Stabilization and Conservation Service (ASCS), coaching his daughters' soccer or softball teams, shooting photos for a magazine or a multimedia slide show, organizing a community activity—the list goes on. Phone messages are best left at the office where his wife Kathy and mother Irene share a dentistry practice. If anyone ever needed a beeper, it is George Houk. Here is how George describes himself as a part-time farmer —which is something of a misnomer:

"At 37 years old," he says, "I feel I have experienced about as much in life as anyone my age could ask for. This hasn't happened by accident, because I'm always seeking new experiences and the opportunity to be part of every aspect of life. I believe that while you only live once, if you do it right, once is enough."

Family Life Important

For George, life revolves around his family. George's wife and mother are both dentists—"they're the only daughter-in-law–mother-in-law dentist team I know of," he says. Daughters Annie, 7, and Katie, 4, are already entrepreneurs with their own business, "Kids Krops," specializing in pumpkins, gourds, and decorative corn.

Houk was born and raised in Mahoning County, Ohio, on the family farm, which he and his wife Kathy now own and operate. George says he could never picture himself as anything other than a full-time farmer. Houk earned his bachelor's and master's degrees in agricultural education and agricultural economics at Ohio State University. He says that during his 4 years there, his only dream was to return to his northeast Ohio home to take over the family farm.

Fulfilling a Dream

In June 1977, George and Kathy Houk fulfilled their ambitions and went into farming and dentistry, respectively, in partnership with George's parents.

In the agricultural boom years of the 1970's, farmers expanded their operations with relative ease and confidence. "I was able to get in on a part of this in the late 1970's," George says, "and with the help and support of my father, Albertus, we were soon farming nearly 500 acres of corn, soybeans, wheat, and oats. We fed out beef and hogs and sold them as freezer meats by the half or whole." George took over his father's 1,200-bucket maple sugar operation and later added a wholesale Christmas tree business, growing 5,000 trees on 4.5 acres.

To George, maple sugaring is an art, not just a process. In the last 50 years or so, maple syrup production has been associated mostly with the New England States (see Chapter 29). However, in parts of northern Ohio where Great Lakes weather patterns prevail,

George Houk

"We must realize we haven't inherited this good earth from our parents," says George Houk, "we're borrowing it from our children." Houk is bringing his daughters, Annie, 7, and Katie, 4, along in the family tradition of farming by assisting them with their own business, "Kids Krops," which specializes in pumpkins, gourds, and decorative corn.

by George Houk, Part-Time Farmer, ASCS Field Reporter, and Photographer, Poland, OH with Virginia Broadbeck, Public Information Specialist, ASCS, USDA, Washington, DC

sugaring is still carried on. "My father often reminisced about sugaring in his youth," he says, "when they tapped trees with wooden spiles [spigots used in taking sap from a tree], caught the sap in crocks, and then boiled the sap in kettles to make syrup that sold for $1.25 a gallon."

The Art of Sugaring. "For me, making maple syrup hasn't changed too much, but the tools we use have been updated to metal spiles and buckets. More recently plastic tubing has gained popularity as a means of gathering sap and carrying it to a central collection point. Boiling the 40 to 50 gallons of sap required to make 1 gallon of pure Ohio maple syrup is now done with an automatic continuous flow evaporator."

The flow of maple sap up and down the trees is the result of an equal blend of cold, frosty nights and warm, sunny days. Typically, this season comes to Ohio from late January through mid-March. A day's run of sap can range anywhere from 1 pint to over 4 gallons per tap. Sap from even a small run must be collected quickly and processed, as raw sap will tend to sour about as quickly as raw milk.

Nothing Added. Nothing is added to sap to produce pure maple syrup. Only water, in the form of steam, is removed until the sap reaches the proper density. A gallon of syrup weighs 11 pounds and recently has been selling for $20 to $23 per gallon, George says.

"That's a nice increase from the $1.25 per gallon my dad got years ago, but sometimes, when you consider slopping through the mud, and the hours spent gathering and boiling the sap, it seems that this is an art carried on for the sake of nostalgia, not profit."

After hearing all the stories shared in the sugar house by oldtimers, "You find the real art of sugaring hasn't changed—there's been no need for change," he says. "I can't help but feel a thrill as I head to the woods to gather sap, sap from the same trees that were tapped by pioneers, and just possibly by early Indians." As he goes about his sap-gathering chores, "I'm interrupted only by the honking of geese, as a giant V-shaped formation of Canadian geese heads north—another sure sign that spring is just around the corner."

Off-Farm Work

Since the late 1970's, George has worked part time for the Mahoning County ASCS office as a field reporter. This job involves measuring grain bins and fields for farmers participating in USDA feedgrain programs. "When I first started, this day or two every couple of weeks served as a nice bit of extra income," George says, "as well as an opportunity for me to get around the community and meet and serve other farmers." George has also served as an ASCS community committeeman in Mahoning County.

"But as times have changed," he continues, "Government programs have become both more complex and more financially attractive to farmers. This means the ASCS office has needed more field work in the past several years." At the same time, financial pressures have affected many farmers' cash flow. The combination of more ASCS work time available along with the need for more supplemental income led George to become a part-time farmer.

Houk still farms 400 acres, but the livestock operation is gone, and since his father's death in 1986, he farms alone.

While George now spends nearly 175 days off the farm as an ASCS field reporter, he says his duties enable him to be a "full-time" employee on the days he works for the agency, and a "full-time" farmer when weather and field conditions permit equipment to run in the fields.

"I don't really think of myself as a part-time farmer," he says. "When I do anything, I do it full time that day."

A Flexible Schedule

"I really enjoy the flexibility of my work and my life. There's no set schedule. If, for instance, I were driving a school bus like some farmers do for extra income, that's an everyday commitment during the school year. If you're working in the fields, you have to drop what you're doing to meet your schedule. I'm very fortunate in that I can organize my work pretty much as needed."

Most people would have their days filled with that much activity, but George Houk has two more jobs that he loves.

From Avocation to Vocation

Photography has been his major hobby since he was 8 years old, and, he says, "I photographed every bear seen on a family vacation to Yellowstone Park at least twice." Over the years, this hobby has evolved into another line of work. In his part-time photography business, George now takes several thousand photos every year for calendars, brochures, and magazine covers. He also specializes in putting together multimedia slide shows promoting American agriculture and patriotic themes for audiences throughout Ohio and neighboring States.

“A camera now seems to be a fixture of my wardrobe,” he says, “and I’m seldom without one whether I’m in my car, truck, or tractor cab. I have a unique opportunity to capture rural life on film and then share the results and help tell the story of American agriculture to others.”

Lights on Tractors

But by far his biggest job, and the one he values most, is being a parent. He arranges his work schedule around his family life as much as possible.

“I thought that’s why they put lights on tractors,” he chuckles. “If you’re willing to be flexible, you can coach your child’s soccer team, manage the baseball team, or attend a school or church function to see your children in their moment of glory, and still get your farmwork done. I’ve never seen a corn stalk grow upside down just because it was planted in the dark of night.”

He admits, however, that reasonable precautions must be taken to avoid shaking up the neighbors if the tractor is still running in the wee hours. Even so, it is not unusual for George to be out until 2 a.m. or later during planting season.

“There is no place like a farm to raise a family,” he says. “Country life affords lessons of birth, growth, and maturity; teaches the value of hard work; and, with the exception of weather-related interruptions, allows people to have a direct influence on their returns. When enthusiasm meets with opportunity, good things can happen.”

George Houk

“There’s no place like a farm to raise a family,” says George Houk, who farms 400 acres of grain, soybeans, Christmas trees, and sugar maples in Mahoning County, OH.

Into the Next Generation

Farming may well continue into the next generation in the Houk family. Katie and Annie Houk’s “Kids Krops” is already a thriving venture, complete with business cards George had printed for the girls. “They’re busy raising money to help defray college expenses when the time comes,” he says.

But life is not all work for the Houks. “We love to play hard, too.” During the winter, the Houks enjoy downhill skiing at resorts throughout Ohio, Pennsylvania, New York, and New England. With his daughters by his side, “or usually out ahead of me,” George says skiing is not only great exercise, it also offers opportunities to be one with nature and see sights shared by a fortunate few. The summer months find the Houks swimming or playing softball, and George coaching his daughters’ sport teams.

George also finds time to be active in business and professional organizations, including the Mahoning County and Ohio Young Farmers’ Associations, the Farm Bureau, the Northeast Ohio Forestry Association, the Youngstown Photographic Society, the Photographic Society of America, the Ohio State University Alumni Association, and the National Association of State and County Employees of ASCS. He is also active in community and church activities.

A Good Life

Pausing to reflect on his life and his work, George says, “We must realize we haven’t inherited this good earth from our parents, we’re borrowing it from our children.”

“We pass through life so quickly when we enjoy what we do. I never get bored by doing one job all the time—I have so many. I love people, I love the great outdoors, and I love my family. I’m a lucky person. I feel I’m experiencing life to its fullest, and life is good to me.”

Judy Berg:

Volunteer Helps Manage Maine Woodlands

Ever since she was a child roaming the forested paths of Manhattan's Inwood Hill Park, Judy Berg has liked trees.

"I grew up a city person, but that didn't keep me from being in the woods. Inwood was unspoiled in those days." she recalls, describing the urban forest at the northern tip of Manhattan, near the Hudson Bridge. "In fact, I remember going to Native American powwows there every year. They commemorated the smoking of the peace pipe with Henry Hudson."

Judy's love affair with the woods is now practically a full-time occupation. In addition to managing her family's 200-acre woodlot, the Buckfield, ME, resident is a woodland volunteer for the University of Maine Cooperative Extension's woodland volunteer program.

This program is a joint venture of the University of Maine Cooperative Extension, the Maine Forest Service, and the Small Woodland Owners Association of Maine. It provides information, resources, referrals, and motivation to Maine's 80,000 people who privately own woodland of 10 acres or more. In the tricounty (Oxford, Androscoggin, and Sagadahoc) area where Judy lives, more than 1.5 million acres of woodland are privately owned.

"Forest management" means different things to different woodland owners, depending on the types of woodlands that they own and the uses that they want to make of them. For some owners, it may mean thinning—clearing out some trees so that other trees can have more sunlight and grow to full maturity. For other owners, it may mean a "selective cut," in which misshaped, unmarketable, or unhealthy trees are harvested so that more valuable trees have adequate nutrients and light to grow. Whether it is part of a management plan or not, many small woodland owners rely on their "backyard" woodlands for firewood to heat their homes throughout the long winters.

by Melanie Spencer, Publications Editor, and Frank Wertheim, Oxford County Extension Educator, University of Maine Cooperative Extension, Orono, ME

Perry A. Rech/USDA 90BW0747-28A

Judy Berg's love for the woodlands is an asset in managing her family's 200-acre woodlot in Buckfield, ME. Woodland volunteers, like Judy, are trained to help small-scale woodland owners assess possible uses for their land and plan management practices for the future.

One-to-One Help

Maine's woodland volunteers are trained to help small-scale woodland owners assess possible uses of their land and plan for the future. A volunteer will walk the land with a client, helping to define what he or she wants to do with it and providing information on programs, such as the tree growth tax law. Judy and the other volunteers can also connect the client with professionals for more information on forestry, soils, wildlife, recreation, environmental protection, or other issues.

"It's very rewarding for me to walk through a woodland with a small woodland owner and help him or her understand what were formerly mysteries of the forest," says Judy. "On a one-on-one basis, I help landowners identify tree species, calculate a tree's age and size, and point out signs of wildlife. I also like to explain how good management not only improves the quality of timber growth but also attracts wildlife, protects watersheds, and provides for hiking and cross-country ski trails."

Judy is one of 18 woodland volunteers in the tricounty area. All of Maine's woodland volunteers are local people who believe in multiple-use management and are willing to share their knowledge and enthusiasm with others.

As a busy wife, mother of three grown children, free-lance editor, and member of the Buckfield planning board, Judy is well aware of how hard it can be for a private woodland owner to juggle priorities and make time to care for what could be viewed as a very large backyard.

"I understand how some people feel they don't have the time for forestry management," she says. "But making contact with a woodland volunteer is well worth the time, for it helps people realize they don't have to do it all alone."

Judy's foray into forestry began in 1985, when she attended Yankee Woodlot Forestry Camp, a weeklong forestry management program sponsored by the University of Maine Cooperative Extension. The annual event, held at Tanglewood 4-H Camp on the Maine coast, draws participants from all over New England.

"I came back from camp euphoric," she says. "The camp was like a college silviculture course all in 1 week. We focused on trees from 7:30 a.m. till 10 p.m. When I got home, I immediately had my whole family running around in the woods measuring trees, pacing off distances for a management plan, and looking for signs of wildlife."

Judy's camp experience led to her involvement with the woodland volunteer program and to her participation in the Small Woodland Owners Association of Maine, which she now leads as president. Judy hopes to inspire other landowners to manage their woodlands.

Benefits of Management

"One of the worst things one can do with land is to neglect it," she says. "A dense, poorly growing forest doesn't benefit anyone, even most wildlife. But simple management techniques can improve the health and vitality of the forest, increase wildlife habitats and food, and improve the esthetic value of the land simultaneously."

Judy cites a Hebron, ME, couple who are recent converts to private forest management. The couple had owned 150 acres of woodland since the early 1960's, yet they had never managed it and did not know where to start. They saw a sign for the woodland volunteer program, and one call brought Judy to their home.

"I sat down with them at their kitchen table and explained the variety of programs and opportunities. This came at a critical time, because development was taking place all around them and they didn't wish to develop their property," says Judy. "Since then, they've had their property surveyed and they developed a management plan for timber stand improvement and trails. They were aware that programs existed, but weren't sure how to find out about them."

A management plan is a statement of the owner's goals and objectives, an inventory of the land, and a schedule of activities, according to Extension educator Les Hyde, who helps coordinate the annual Yankee Woodlot Forestry Camp. For example, a small-scale woodland owner notes that her objectives are "to encourage wildlife habitats and support a harvest of 15 cords of firewood each year."

In Their Own Woods

Judy and her husband, Charles, an engineering professor, own a 200-acre tract of land, and much of her expertise evolved from managing it. Their land had been cleared for farmland in the 1800's, but gradually it had reverted to forest.

Under a Federal cost-sharing program of USDA's Agricultural Stabilization and Conservation Service and with the help of a Maine Forest Service forester, Judy and Charles planted 8,000 white pines and improved 5 acres of hardwoods. Working with a forester and a logger, the couple recently thinned an oak stand and sold the harvest to a lobster trap manufacturer. They selectively cut two tracts that were overstocked to allow remaining crop trees greater access to sunlight, soil, and nutrients.

Sometimes Judy and Charles do the work themselves, taking to the woods with hard hats, heavy boots, safety goggles, and chain saws. At other times they work with a crew of loggers, particularly on large-scale or dangerous projects. Judy notes that in either case, woodland projects are like gardening, but on a much larger scale.

"Selective cutting is like thinning carrots and radishes in your vegetable garden," she explains. "It just takes longer and requires heavier equipment, and you don't enjoy the results the same season. What I do enjoy right away are the trails for hiking and cross-country skiing, and so do my neighbors and local snowmobilers."

Ole Nissen:

Adaptability Is the Key

Pete Packett/Florida Department of Agriculture

By adapting to market pressures, Ole Nissen has been able to plant his company in a profitable niche. The success of Nissen's Sun State Carnations, Inc., stems from production of uncommon flowers that are difficult for his competitors to ship long distances.

Born and reared in Denmark, Ole Nissen now works among 90 acres of flowers in southeastern Florida.

It is pleasant and rewarding work—Nissen and his three sons gross $2.5 million a year—growing, packaging, and selling such familiars as snapdragons, iris, and phlox along with such less common varieties as liatris, white dill, didiscus, allium, and scabiosa.

If there's one word that describes Nissen it's "adaptability."

Shortly after he opened his first 40 acres of flower production at Hobe Sound, FL, to produce cuttings for carnation growers, Kenya leaped to international leadership in the cuttings field.

Nissen switched to the cut-flower market. Then Colombia shouldered its way into the lion's share of the U.S. cut-flower market and Nissen adapted again.

Now he grows uncommon flowers that are hard for the Colombians to ship long distances, even by air.

Nissen is adaptable. But nature does impose limits. Ten acres of the Nissen farm is under plastic cover, and another 10 acres are shrouded in plastic film. Still, in the freeze of December 1989, Nissen's son Eric estimates the firm lost $500,000, mostly in snapdragons grown in the open air.

At Nissen's packinghouse, millions of colorful cut flowers are bunched into plastic buckets bound for welcoming tables throughout the Eastern United States. But Nissens' Sunshine States Carnations pauses to serve its upscale residential neighbors, too. The firm's retail outlet just north of West Palm Beach does a brisk and profitable business 7 days a week. Hobe Sound homeowners think nothing of spending $150 a week sprucing up their homes with Ole Nissen's flowers.

Many of Nissen's competitors in southern Florida have given in to the pressure of urbanization, sold their farms, and gone out of business. Instead, Nissen adapted.

Pete Packett/Florida Department of Agriculture

Shipping flowers to 300 wholesale accounts throughout the Eastern United States makes up the majority of the Nissen's business. The family also maintains a successful retail outlet to service the needs of individual flower seekers.

by Pete Packett, Information Specialist, Florida Department of Agriculture and Consumer Services, Tallahassee, FL

PART III

the business of agriculture

Carla Jo Payne:
Cropduster

Carla Jo Payne has a significant and unusual role in agribusiness. She is not only a pilot, she is a pilot in the agricultural aviation industry.

Only 25 years old, she has been flying since she was 16. At 17, she got her private pilot's license and her license to fly with instruments; at 18, she got her commercial license and multi-engine rating, as well as her instructor's certificate. For the past 3 years, she has worked as an agricultural pilot, flying a highly sophisticated airplane specifically designed for agricultural work.

Payne Flying Service owns two planes. Carla and her husband, Carl, share the pilot duties of one aircraft, and they hire a pilot for the other one. Both airplanes are Air Tractor A400's, powered by Pratt & Whitney PT-34 turbine engines. These planes are state-of-the-art equipment in the agriculture industry, costing more than $300,000 each. Many pilots with several years of experience do not have the expertise, or opportunity, to fly this type of aircraft, but Carla has the ability to fly them and to do aerial application work.

Bob Nichols/USDA 90BW1037-25

One of the two Air Tractor A400 turbine-powered airplanes the Paynes use in their business comes close to a rice field. Payne Flying Service operates out of Katy, TX, in the heart of rice country.

The Paynes own and operate their agricultural aviation business in Katy, TX, just west of Houston on I-10. This is in the heart of rice country, and the bulk of their work is seeding, fertilizing, and applying crop protection chemicals to rice. This is where Carla started learning agricultural flying from her husband and where she does most of her agricultural flying today.

They also do contract work that takes them throughout the United States. These contracts are for another type of agriculture flying—forestry work. Carla's duties on these trips are to help keep things organized on the ground for her husband and the other pilot.

There are several tasks involved in running a successful agricultural aviation business—including flagging where the airplane has been, loading, and answering telephones. Carla is usually busy even when she is not piloting an airplane.

The Paynes are involved in several agricultural and aviation organizations, including the Texas and Southwestern Cattle Raisers Association, Texas Agricultural Aviation Association, California Agricultural Aviation Association, and the National Agricultural Aviation Association.

The Paynes are dedicated to the professional agricultural aviation industry. Carla believes that agricultural aviation plays a role in providing food and fiber for the world.

Bob Nichols/USDA 90BW1037-11

Cropduster Carla Jo Payne is a busy person, but she still finds time to raise Texas Longhorn cattle and to train horses.

by Phyllis J. Jones, Past President, Women of National Agricultural Aviation Association, Benkelman, NE

Genita Cockrell and Lawrence Johnson:

Savoring Success in the Food Processing Industry

Genita Cockrell was only 23 years old when she landed her dream job. She figured she'd have to wait another 10 years before she was named director of research and development at Bee Gee Shrimp, a seafood processing firm in Lakeland, FL.

After just 6 months at Bee Gee, she won a promotion that placed her in charge of dreaming up new products and improving the quality of current favorites. She develops and tests new products for shrimp glazes, coatings, stuffings, sauces, and other seafood products.

"When people who have talked to me on the telephone meet me, they're surprised that I'm so young," says Genita. "They can't believe I have this job."

She says the food science program at the University of Florida's Institute of Food and Agricultural Sciences (IFAS) in Gainesville helped her advance in her field.

"The classes I took relate directly to the work I'm doing," says Genita. "And the rapport I had with professors enables me to call on them if I need help."

Genita received her food science degree in 1987 and is one of a number of IFAS graduates getting good jobs in all phases of the food processing industry, from quality control to research and development. The citrus and seafood processing industries, in particular, offer many job openings for new graduates.

The Right Training

To meet the challenges of the food industry, students are prepared by a rigorous course load that includes one semester of calculus, two years of chemistry, one semester of physics, and one semester of statistics. Courses in engineering and food analysis, processing, and chemistry are also part of the food science curriculum.

"IFAS gives students a strong foundation in the principles of food science and technology to fulfill requirements set by the National Institute of Food Technologists," says Marty Marshall, IFAS associate professor in the Department of Food Science and Human Nutrition. "Through work experiences, such as internships offered by food companies, students are better prepared to go out directly and work in the food industry."

A graduate may find a job as a food scientist or technologist, or sometimes both. Generally, a food scientist is concerned with the fundamental properties of food, such as nutritive value, caloric content, flavor, and color. A technologist works with product development, processing, and quality control.

Marshall says that a food science degree combined with a minor in marketing is good preparation for students headed for the food processing industry.

Many managers in processing plants have master's degrees in food science. Students interested in the research side of food science often pursue a doctorate for positions at universities or as leaders of research departments in industry.

In addition to possessing strong science and business skills, newcomers to the food science industry must also be articulate speakers and concise writers.

Bob Nichols/USDA 90BW0808-33

Genita Cockrell found her dream job—testing and developing new seafood products. Employed with the Bee Gee Shrimp Company in Lakeland, FL, Genita tests such products as stuffed crab Caribbean, pasta primevera, and oysters Bienville.

by Susan O'Reilly, Managing Editor, Impact Magazine, Institute of Food and Agricultural Sciences, Gainesville, FL

Typically, graduates entering the food processing industry start out in quality control and assurance programs, judging whether a product meets a company's standards and government requirements. Starting salaries in 1990 generally range from $19,000 to $25,000 a year.

New Products: From Laboratory to Supermarket

Lawrence Johnson, a 1977 IFAS graduate, is now director of research and development for Tropicana Products Inc. in Bradenton, FL. "For students willing to work very hard for a couple of years, not in a glamour job, but at something where they get their hands dirty every day, there definitely is a fast track," he says.

The thrill of creating a new product that winds up on a supermarket shelf attracts many food scientists to research and development. At Bee Gee, the research and development department is discreetly tucked away in the rear of a warehouse, behind ceiling-high stacks of seafood breading. "Authorized Personnel Only," warns a red sign on the door.

Inside, Genita and her assistants cook in what Genita calls "the laboratory"—a kitchen equipped with industrial-sized fryers and refrigerators. "We're developing two new product lines, but I can't talk about them—they're top secret," she says.

Developing a product from scratch takes a combination of know-how and creativity, plus a lot of patience. Lawrence says that launching the successful new "Twister" line of tropical fruit juices took about 2 years. Genita says she can work on a single product for a year.

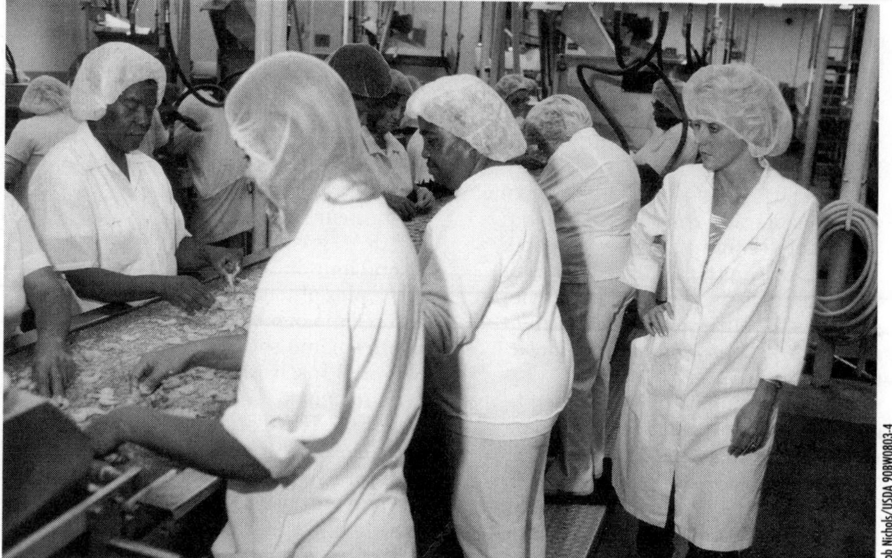

Bob Nichols/USDA 90BW0803-4

Besides doing research and development, Genita Cockrell also keeps an eye on the quality of product preparation.

"Sometimes it's frustrating," says Genita. "I can't schedule something as fast as people want it scheduled. I can't get it out fast enough."

Lawrence supervises a staff of 14 people. Tropicana, he says, prides itself on being an aggressive player in the marketplace. During the last 4 years, Tropicana has released a new product or packaging every 90 days.

"It's been terribly exciting to watch," he says. "I enjoy the satisfaction of watching something go from the bench to market."

Genita says she never forgets that she is competing against people with twice her experience. "I put in a lot of extra hours in the laboratory," she says. "There is always something on the back burner."

When she created a new glazed stuffed shrimp, Genita spent hours in her laboratory kitchen, trying to get just the right taste, texture, color, and aroma. She also had to make sure the shrimp would be juicy and tender every time it was cooked.

She makes it a practice to enlist colleagues, family, and even company repair workers to tell her what they think of her new culinary creations. Her family, she says, enjoys trying rejected products and trying to figure out what is wrong with them.

Once she works out the kinks in a product, she invites the company president and vice president to a taste-testing session in a formal dining room adjoining the kitchen. She usually presents several items at one time.

If her products are approved by company leaders, then Genita savors her favorite part of the job. "It's not easy, and it takes a long time, but when I finally get it right and I see it in production, that's a neat thing."

Murray D. Lull:
Rural Banker

The 20th century was 8 years old when a Kansan named Lull started banking in the geographic center of the continental United States. His son, a teacher, later asked to join the family business.

Lull warned his son that their rural service area was losing residents. In turn, that son warned his son. Then the third Lull in line warned the fourth.

But as the population dwindled from more than 15,000 to 5,000, the Smith County State Bank stayed in business. Today, Murray D. Lull is the fourth generation of his family to serve as the bank's president.

His wood-paneled office in Smith Center, KS, is filled with a mixture of mementos, books, and computer equipment. It is dominated by a carved seal of the State of Kansas, pictures of his predecessors, and an entire wall of windows looking into the bank.

His customers are people he has known all his life. They can always easily see if "Murray's in."

"My 12-year-old daughter comes in and says, 'I'm going to be sitting where you are someday,'" he says. "I have to wonder how she could have a 30- or 40-year career. I want more of a future for her, but the population of many rural areas is decreasing.

"I'm hoping the golden years are still ahead for us. In any case, as long as you're eager about getting up every morning and doing the best you can that day, you're going to last a lot longer than those who are fearful."

Despite his guarded optimism, Murray is fighting to ensure that the family bank remains viable. His methods address not only his children's future but also the futures of his home town and of agricultural banking.

by Kathleen Ward, Extension Communications Specialist, Kansas State University, Manhattan, KS

Kansas State University, Department of Extension Communications

With guarded optimism, Murray D. Lull is fighting to ensure that the family bank remains viable. Lull is the fourth generation of his family to serve as president of the Smith County State Bank, Smith Center, KS.

Murray believes that the successful banker is a good neighbor. It is just being a good neighbor to help secure Federal economic development grant funds to help a local travel-trailer manufacturer expand, to expand his bank's services into overseeing trusts throughout north central Kansas, to testify before the State legislature in Topeka, to help plan national and regional banking schools, or to meet with Federal officials on Capitol Hill.

"The worst indictment I could face is that I stood in the way of progress, of growth," he says.

Murray emphasizes he is able to be this involved in his community and industry only because the Smith County State Bank and Trust Company has outstanding employees and because his dad is still chairman of the board.

He encourages his employees' community activities too.

"If you chip in your part, whether you're a jeweler, a hardware store owner, a real estate broker, or a banker, the total of everyone's involvement keeps your community alive," Murray says.

Bank employees now serve as leaders in service organizations, the local Chamber of Commerce, and the zoning commission. The city even named one of Murray's coworkers to serve on the Smith Center Tree Board, which oversees the planting and care of community trees to maintain the town's overall attractiveness.

"Banking is fun," he admits with a grin. "I like being a positive part of so many different enterprises—the farm that prospers, the Main Street business that hangs in there, the homeowners who get the house they've always wanted. Banking is working with people and some of their fundamental needs."

The toughest part of banking is being unable to help some people, Murray adds. He worries that rural bankers are becoming even more restricted in the help they can provide.

"Two years ago, Kansas had 625 banks. Today we have 575. In another 5 years, you'll probably see the disappearance of at least another 100," he says. "The good news for us is that Kansas adopted a law that will allow many small banks to continue as branches of banking systems."

Even so, the handshake-and-a-promise days are gone, Murray says.

"It's been popular to say farming isn't a way of life any more, that it's a business," he points out. "Farming *is* becoming more and more businesslike. But if it weren't a way of life, there wouldn't be so many willing to live with the long hours, the heartbreaks, the rain that didn't come.

"That's why borrower character still is one of the paramount things we consider, even though it carries little weight when a bank examiner looks at that person's credit."

Kansas State University, Department of Extension Communications

"I'm just a Kansas banker who knows agriculture," says Murray Lull. Wherever rural bankers operate, they're serving farmers, he says, and "they are probably the cream of the crop, so far as people are concerned."

Changing Times for Rural Banks

In the past, rural banks could give producers some flexibility, Murray says. Bankers knew that repaying a tractor loan would take most farmers an average of 4 or 5 years, even if they paid less in bad years and more in good years.

Now farmers must prove their ability to make set payments and follow a strict schedule. And they must repay *all* their tractor debt—in 4 or 5 years.

"Examiners may decide a person's loan is substandard due to the probability of failing crops or the declining value of equity," he says, "but they don't often consider the fact that the farmer has always paid his debts for 40 years."

Murray is the only member of his family to train specifically for a banking career. He first spent several years, however, as an examiner, working from 1970 to 1972 for the Federal Reserve Bank of Kansas City, where he helped examine State-chartered banks.

"Dad had a couple of requirements before I could join the business. First, I had to work for someone else, so I could see if we were getting in a rut. And I had to let a little time expire, so people wouldn't see me as that high school kid they used to know," he says.

His experience working for the Federal Reserve gave Murray a good idea of the limitations and benefits of bank regulators' roles.

In Kansas, the U.S. Comptroller of the Currency sends examiners to all national banks; the Kansas Banking Department regulates and examines State-chartered banks. The Federal Deposit Insurance Corporation (FDIC) also sends examiners to State banks that are FDIC-insured, and the Federal Reserve Bank of Kansas City examines the other State banks.

"Banks need and appreciate regulatory review. It has kept us independent, relatively strong, and stable through a lot of tough times," he says. "We just want consistent and equal measurement."

Murray says well-run banks will always have a limited number of loans with more than ordinary risk.

"You don't serve your community without taking risk," he explains. "Still, the question is becoming this: How far should the bank expose itself to criticism by taking a chance on a customer? Should the bank play it perfectly safe, as some might want?"

A related question is, How can banks meet today's examiners' requirements for sound loans, yet also comply with the Community Reinvestment Act? This law, which was enacted in the 1970's and last amended in 1989, requires banks to address community needs, "especially those of residents making low to moderate incomes, which means agriculture generally," Murray says.

For rural bankers, the law is simply good business, he says. It is also a reason lenders have to know their customers' business. And this can create another dilemma.

"Customers come in looking for advice," Murray says. "I have to understand where they're going in their business management, yet not tell them how to manage their businesses. That's their job."

Murray is the third Lull to serve in leadership positions in both the Kansas and the American Bankers Associations. In 1990, Murray Lull was chairman of the ABA's agriculture division and one of 10 ABA Banking Advisors working with media across the United States, talking about banking-related issues.

According to Murray, agricultural banking is the most encompassing division in the ABA, spanning the United States and including the largest and smallest banks.

"Rural bankers in Virginia, Texas, California, and Montana all have about the same work to do every day," he says.

"It's been fun being their spokesperson for a few years. I'm just a Kansas banker who knows wheat, milo, and cattle. But whether you're banking where the product is cotton, oranges, salmon, or corn, you're still serving farmers, and they are probably the cream of the crop, so far as people are concerned."

Those bankers also are facing about the same problems: declining rural populations and increasing competition, not only from urban banks but also from nonbanking institutions that are being allowed to offer more and more banking services.

"You can measure the deposits in rural banks by looking at their quarterly statements," he says. "But it's a mistake to measure rural people's financial assets by that.

"It's amazing how many rural residents deposit their money in big towns, in other States, in savings and loan institutions. They're investing with insurance companies, brokers, and even those chain stores that sell everything from socks to stocks—companies whose services banks aren't allowed to duplicate."

Added together, though, those deposits and investments still do not give an accurate picture.

"Rural people's wealth comes out of the ground and from livestock. Every spring, new life sprouts in the fields. Baby pigs and lambs arrive. It's a renewal," Murray says. "Those raw products also generate new economic life that, through processing and packaging, multiplies their value and ripples out to enrich countless numbers of Americans.

"How long will rural America as we know it last? Who knows?"

Smiling broadly, Murray adds, "Anyway, *I'm* committed. We've built a home in Smith Center, and I've got a daughter who wants to go into banking!"

Kansas State University, Department of Extension Communications

Hoping that the golden years are still ahead, Lull is eager to do the best for his family, community, and bank.

Leonard Harris:

Spreading Electronic Market Data in North Dakota

In rural North Dakota, on a family farm with 2,200 acres and 10 cows, Leonard Harris is trying to spread a new technology that can help other farmers help themselves.

Bob Nichols/USDA 89BW2235-28

North Dakota farmers who are subscribers to the Data Transmission Network system receive up-to-the-minute marketing information. Futures and options prices are transmitted continuously to subscribers as they appear on grain and livestock exchanges, such as the Kansas City Board of Trade.

Marketing Information Systems

In 1987 Leonard's brother-in-law in Minnesota subscribed to a marketing information service that was beamed to Minnesota, Iowa, and Nebraska over FM radio towers. On a screen similar to a computer screen he could view up-to-the-minute information on futures, grains, livestock, local weather, and bids.

"When I saw it," says Leonard, "I thought that this technology could help us help ourselves in agriculture through marketing." He approached the Data Transmission Network Corporation in Omaha, NE, about receiving the service in his home in North Dakota. The company said that North Dakota's population was too sparse to make data transmission profitable.

However, the Data Transmission Network soon came out with a new satellite dish through which the service could be received in sparsely populated areas. Leonard called the company as soon as he heard about the new dish, and by January 1989 he had his own system on the way.

New System

The new Data Transmission Network system consists of a 34-inch satellite dish connected by a cable to a screen. A one-time fee of $295 covers all maintenance and repair costs, for as long as the owner subscribes.

Subscribing to the marketing service is similar to subscribing to cable television, Leonard says. The basic subscription rate includes 75 information screens (or pages) that cover five topics—futures, grains, livestock, local weather, and bids—plus a rural shopping service, all for $29.95 a month. The company updates the information periodically throughout the day. The futures and options prices are continuously transmitted as they appear on several grain and livestock exchanges, with a 10-minute transmission delay.

"It's strictly an information system," Leonard says. "No one tells you what to do. You make decisions based on the information at your fingertips."

Advisory programs are available through the system, but they are not included in the basic subscription rate, Leonard says. Thirty electronic newsletters are available, including advisory services on hogs, cattle, grain, weather, and trading, and these allow individual subscribers to tailor the system to their own operations.

Leonard stresses that computers are not involved. The owner simply uses two switches to go back and forth from screen to screen.

Within 2 weeks of receiving his own Data Transmission Network system, Leonard and his neighbor Don Bauman began traveling all over North Dakota and into Montana and South Dakota to agricultural shows, elevators, FFA

by Carey Neshem, Student Assistant, North Dakota State University Extension Service, Fargo, ND

chapters, and individual farms, telling people about the system and how it would enable them to compete in agricultural markets. Leonard and Don work on commission as independent sales agents.

"The future of farming is changing," Leonard says. "It's getting pretty competitive out there, and we're going to have to become marketers and get the most out of our marketplace. We want to help make the farmers marketers and managers, with good business skills."

Not only is Leonard concerned with helping today's farmers, but he also wants to help improve tomorrow's. He has convinced Data Transmission Network to develop a plan to place its system in schools for free.

"Vo-ag departments are teaching marketing, and this system brings it alive for the kids—instead of having them read about it in a 10-year-old textbook," Leonard says. "They're the future of American agriculture. If we can get them involved and interested, they will learn and they may find a money-making opportunity."

Bob Nichols/USDA 89BW2237-24A

Advisory programs are available through the Data Transmission Network system, but they are not included in the basic subscription rate. Advisory services on cattle, grain, hogs, trading, and weather allow individual subscribers to tailor the system to their own operations.

Developing the Programs

Leonard and Don have been working closely with Data Transmission Network since 1989 to develop programs for the northern Midwest. "We're not company representatives just out to sell units," he says. "We're trying to develop the programs for our area, because most of the programs are designed for the Corn Belt."

For example, Leonard and Don were instrumental in bringing into the service an hourly radar weather page for farmers in North Dakota, South Dakota, Montana, and Minnesota. "Originally, the page only showed the Corn Belt," Leonard says. "Don and I told the company that the weather down there was OK, but we needed weather for farmers up here as well. So they are designing a screen for farmers in our region."

Leonard and Don also helped regionalize the local elevator page for North Dakota farmers, and they designed from scratch a Minneapolis cash grain page that shows what is happening on the trading floor throughout the day. "We know each day at closing what all the elevators are paying, without making calls," Leonard says, "and that can make a difference in how we market our grain."

Reaching America's Farmers

Leonard's wife, Edith, is in charge of all the correspondence and bookkeeping. "We couldn't have done all this without her," Leonard says.

Leonard has spent many hours on the road and a lot of his own money trying to reach farmers, often at the expense of family time. "We have set a mission for ourselves, to help educate the American farmer to be more market oriented, and we think this system can help," he says.

He and Don work on commission and set their own hours. They also pay out of their own pockets for most of the advertising and mailings done to promote the Data Transmission Network service in North Dakota.

Leonard says that he likes to treat his customers on a personal basis as much as possible. He does so by providing a 24-hour toll-free number and, with Edith's help, sending out frequent mailings to all their customers.

In January 1989, Leonard became the first farmer in North Dakota to own a Data Transmission Network system. Since then he and Don have sold hundreds of systems in the State.

"We have what we consider the nicest part-time job," Leonard says, "because we're helping others to help themselves."

Sharon and John Gibbons:

Honey of a Hobby Sweetens Retirement Plans

Jim Curley/University of Missouri

Sharon Gibbons checks production in one of her 100 colonies of bees. Her bees produced the grand champion honey at the 1988 Missouri State Fair.

Sharon and John Gibbons are busy, busy, busy with the Gibbons Bee Farm in Ballwin, MO. Honey is the principal enterprise on their farm, but their bees also help pollinate orchard and field crops across much of eastern Missouri. Both Sharon and John hold off-farm jobs in the St. Louis area—Sharon as a dental hygienist and John as a free-lance executive recruiter.

by James D. Ritchie, Agricultural Journalist, Versailles, MO

The Gibbonses did not exactly fly into the beekeeping business without giving it a lot of thought. They began by purchasing a small farm in Crawford County, on the northeastern rim of the Missouri Ozarks, where they planned to make their home after retirement.

To provide an income supplement later on, they planted trees on the land. But trees are a slow-paying proposition. "We wanted to begin an enterprise that would start yielding income quicker," recalls Sharon.

Jim Curley/University of Missouri

Jim Curley/University of Missouri

In addition to her beekeeping activities Gibbons maintains an observation hive in the Florrisant School District's nature center.

The ancient art of tending honeybees, perhaps? Sharon read up on the subject and enrolled in a beekeeping workshop. Still, she was not convinced that bees and honey would mesh with her spare time and temperament.

"John fairly well decided the question one evening, when he came home with two colonies of bees and all the equipment we needed to get started," Sharon remembers. "We were in the bee business."

How Sweet It Is

The Gibbonses concentrated on producing quality honey that could be sold directly to consumers. Sharon sold honey from those first few colonies of bees through gift shops and specialty stores. As her expertise grew, so did the scale of the honey hobby.

Today, Gibbons Bee Farm has about 100 colonies, producing more than 4 tons of the natural liquid sweetener each year. All that honey is extracted and packed at the Gibbons home, and virtually all of it sells at retail.

Depending on what species of plants happen to be in bloom, the Gibbons' bees may range over a 50-mile radius, from the Mississippi River north of St. Louis to Augusta, well up the Missouri River.

"The most hives we put in any one location is 20," says Sharon. "Bees work an area within about 2 miles of the hive. If they must fly much farther than that, they waste too much time and energy. As a result, we spend a lot of time moving the bees to where the blossoms are."

The Gibbonses have learned to specialize by producing different types of honey. Early in the year, they place hives where the winged couriers can collect nectar from clovers, honeysuckle, black locust, and fruit tree blossoms. In late summer, the bees harvest asters, goldenrod, and other fall-blooming plants. Sharon processes and packages the two types of honey separately.

"Clover and fruit-tree honey is light-colored, delicately flavored, and ideal for table use," she explains. "The honey made later in the season—we call it Ozark Wildflower—is darker and stronger flavored and gives a more distinct honey flavor in cooking and baking."

The Gibbonses stress quality. The ribbons, plaques, and medals on their wall are testimony to how well they have succeeded. Gibbons Bee Farm honey has garnered awards at national competitions sponsored by the American Beekeepers Association, and it was picked as grand champion of the 1988 Missouri State Fair. A year later, Gibbons honey won blue ribbons in 10 of a possible 15 honey categories at the State Fair.

Processed Honey Products

Sharon has developed a variety of honey-based products to please the palates of her customers. She whips or spins honey and blends in pieces of fruit—apricot, peach, raspberry, apple, strawberry—to make a unique spread for toast, muffins, and other breads. Gibbons Honey Crunch is a light, honey-coated popcorn, packaged as a ready-to-eat snack.

"We have tried to come up with as many different honey-based products as we can adequately manage and market," says Sharon. "We also pack wooden crates and baskets with a variety of honeys and honey-related products to market to people as gifts for friends and relatives."

Most Gibbons Bee Farm honey still sells through gift shops, specialty food stores, and other retail outlets. In recent years, Sharon has also developed a direct-mail clientele, with a growing list of repeat buyers.

The direct-mail effort got a boost when Gibbons Bee Farm honey and other products were selected for the *Best of Missouri Farms* catalog, published by the University of Missouri-Columbia and University Extension. Products featured in the catalog are judged by the University's Food Science Department, and some 10,000 copies of the publication are distributed nationwide.

"The *Best of Missouri Farms* catalog put me in touch with buyers I would never have contacted otherwise," says Sharon. "We are selling honey to customers virtually from coast to coast."

Sharon admits to being concerned—not worried—about the effect that aggressive Africanized bees, which have been migrating north in recent years, may have on their enterprise.

"I've read that Africanized bees from South America are coming into the United States within the next year or so," she says. "I hope scientists will solve the problem. If not, I'll simply have to learn how to handle them."

The only other problem (if it is a problem) with the Gibbons' beekeeping hobby is that it has grown into a full-time enterprise before Sharon and John are quite ready to retire. "When we do retire," says Sharon, "we shouldn't be spending a lot of time in rocking chairs."

Jim Curley/University of Missouri

The honeybee, creator of a golden nectar that has grown into more than a retirement hobby.

John Harris:

Integrating Beef on a Large, Diversified Operation

There are two sights people remember most about driving through the San Joaquin Valley. One is the California Aqueduct; the other is cattle, thousands of cattle, roaming a giant feedlot near Coalinga.

This is the largest feedlot in California and part of one of the most sophisticated livestock and farming operations in the United States—Harris Ranch. Perhaps no other outfit illustrates just how much the beef industry has changed out West since the sun set on the big cattle drives of a bygone era.

Indeed, the structure of Harris Ranch more closely resembles the vertically integrated poultry industry, with which it competes in the protein marketplace. From the stocker operations that supply the feedlot with the raw material of sirloins, fillets, and New York strips to the refrigerated trucks that ship boxed Harris beef to upscale supermarkets throughout the West, the Harris organization focuses on monitoring the entire production process to ensure quality.

John Harris (left), cowboy foreman Howard Harshman (center), and pen rider Kelly Street (right) discuss the cattle in one of the feedlot pens on the Harris Ranch 600-acre feedlot. The feedlot holds 100,000 cattle in 400 pens. The pen rider monitors the herd for any signs of health problems.

Bob Nichols/USDA 90BW1254-17

Farming the Westside

John Harris doesn't quite fit the popular image of a craggy, saddleworn cattleman. His business attire, and that of his senior staff, consists of jeans, a blue cotton dress shirt, and cowboy boots. He has the weathered look of a man who'd rather be out riding fence with the cowboys who work for him than going to meetings and interviews.

"I didn't grow up roping cattle," John says. "My background is more in farming." In fact, his family did not even get into the cattle business until 1964, well before I–5 blazed its asphalt trail across the Panoche Plain. The freeway lies a stone's throw from the feedlot.

John can trace his family tree back through Texas to Mississippi. At the turn of the century, his grandfather moved to southern California's Imperial Valley and started one of the State's first cotton gins. John's father, however, yearned for his own operation and in 1937 started farming a half section of land on the unforgiving west side of the San Joaquin Valley.

According to University of California animal scientist Ken Ellis, John's father had his work cut out for him: "You had to know what you were doing. Farming the Westside in the early days was really tough. That part of the State can be a fairly inhospitable environment for agriculture, so it's still a challenge." Summer temperatures normally sizzle well above 100 degrees Fahrenheit, rainfall is scant throughout the year, and geological processes have cursed portions of the Westside with soil and water problems.

Until the 1960's, the Harrises grew cotton and grains. But the new aqueduct brought water from the mountains of northern California and changed the character of the San Joaquin Valley forever. The desert bloomed with fruits, nuts, and vegetables that would have been impossible to grow otherwise.

John now farms more than 15,000 acres, producing more than 30 different crops—everything from carrots, lettuce, garlic, onions, tomatoes, cotton, and melons to oranges, lemons, walnuts, almonds, and wine grapes—in addition to the beef operations. He also raises thoroughbred horses.

A Knack for the Niche

Diversification is not uncommon in a State that produces more than 250 different commodities commercially, and John oversees the production of

by John Stumbos, Public Information Representative, University of California, Davis, CA

enough agricultural bounty to feed several good-sized cities—a large farm by any standard. What really sets John apart is his ability to zero in on a market niche, something he just may have inherited from his father.

John recalls that his father got into the cattle business back in the 1960's because he spotted a good opportunity—there were not many feedlots in California. He started out small, with a mere 15,000 head in the feedlot. On any given day now there are about 100,000 head on the 600-acre feedlot.

The senior Harris died in 1981, leaving the entire operation to his only son. John, who earned a degree in agricultural production from the University of

Bob Nichols/USDA 90BW1249-12

A sample of the livestock at the Harris Ranch which includes Hereford, Black Angus, and Brahman cattle. Harris says, "The biggest challenge for us is to convince the consumer that we have a healthy, nutritious product that meets the needs of their eating habits."

California at Davis in 1965, had been running the farming operation since he and his wife, Carol, returned from 3 years of military service in Korea. Soon John put his own signature on the family cattle business by moving away from traditional marketing of live cattle toward carcass production, boxed beef, and eventually to his own name brand.

"He knew he had to take the operation into a new place if it were to survive," recalls Jane Anderson, executive director of the California Beef Council. "John has always been open to doing things differently. That's a compliment, because he works in an industry where people like to do things the way they've always been done."

Bob Nichols/USDA 90BW1248-14

Cotton accounts for two-thirds of the crop production on Harris Farms. The Harris family cotton operation moved from Mississippi to Texas and then to California.

Bob Nichols/USDA 90BW1252-10

Onions harvested and packaged in the field, ready for transportation to market.

John began the long process of building the Harris brand into one that people would recognize and associate with quality. That was no small task in the early 1980's, when beef suffered a serious image problem and U.S. consumers continued the trend of eating less red meat. Nevertheless, the poultry industry had long since embraced the idea of marketing a brand name product, so why not beef?

"One reason is that chickens raised throughout the United States are much closer to each other in genetic makeup," explains animal scientist Ellis. "With cattle we are dealing with 30 to 40 different breeds with variable types within each breed. Coupled with the fact that the cattle are raised in many different environments, it becomes more difficult to establish and maintain a uniform meat quality."

Because Harris Ranch is more vertically integrated than other western cattle operations, however, it can control many of the variables that might lead to a tender steak one day and a stringy piece of meat the next.

Meeting New Consumer Markets

Mindful of consumer food safety concerns, Harris Ranch is also one of the few cattle operations in the United States that have been able to meet the strict standards of USDA's residue avoidance program. No hormones, chemicals, or artificial ingredients are used in raising the animals for the Harris brand.

The key to ensuring residue avoidance is the expensive process of monitoring the specially formulated feed. The Herefords, Angus, Brahmas, and various mixed breeds in the 400 feedlot pens are fed different computerized rations of rolled whole grains, bran, molasses, alfalfa, vitamins, and minerals to meet the various specifications of different markets.

Japanese Yen for Beef

One niche that Harris Ranch has targeted successfully in recent years is especially worth noting.

The Japanese people do not eat much meat—about 13 pounds per capita per year. When they do eat beef, however, they often seek a highly marbled beef, Kobe beef, that can sell for $50 to $60 a pound. In Japan a special breed of cattle, Wagyu, is fed a high-protein, high-energy diet to fatten them well beyond USDA prime grade. The cattle are finish fed for up to 18 months and given massages and even a little beer in their diet to reduce stress.

While John hasn't yet tapped a keg for his cattle, he has bred a well-received Wagyu-Black Angus cross that is finish fed for up to 10 months. (Cattle bound for domestic consumption typically are fed for 4 months before making the trip to the packing house.)

The Japanese are as enchanted as anyone else with the California mystique. "California is perceived to be of higher quality for any agricultural product," John says. "Australia's beef may be cheaper, but ours is what they want."

Japan has had restrictive quotas on beef imports, which won't be completely phased out until April 1991. John discovered a partial way around the quotas by shipping live cattle. About 20 percent of the tonnage he will ship this year will be switching flies on the airport tarmac when they depart for Tokyo.

"I recognize this is the least efficient way of shipping," John explains. "But this is a tough business we're in, and we need to figure out any way we can to be different."

John and Carol Harris have figured out many ways to be different. They have developed an "oasis" hacienda a few miles south of the feedlot on I–5, with conference facilities, an inn, a pool, an airstrip, and three restaurants. The red tile roof, stately stucco archways, and pale turquoise trim are a tribute to the Southwest's rich heritage. More than 2,000 people visit the hacienda each day, and some spend time exploring the country store.

John is acutely aware of the public relations value the inn provides. "It puts a lot of pressure on us to keep the quality up," he says. But John has long been aware of public perceptions. In the early 1980's, he was instrumental in persuading his fellow cattle ranchers to extend a mandatory assessment program nationwide to save beef's faltering image through research and promotion.

His commitment to the industry through the years earned John the 1990 Cattle Businessman of the Year award from the National Cattlemen's Association. "That was more of a company award," he says with pride, sharing the credit with the 1,300 employees of Harris Ranch.

As much as nutrition research has helped to restore the position of beef in public opinion, John believes that the job is not done. "The biggest challenge for us is convincing the consumer we have a healthy, nutritious product that meets their eating habits," he says. With innovators like John Harris at work, the job will be easier.

John Barrientos:
Growing an Agricultural Career

Personnel work, critical yet often overlooked in much of agriculture, occupies many men and women in various roles. Most of these people are found within the production firms themselves, but many work through service organizations. One of these professionals is John Barrientos, a labor field representative with the Farm Employers Labor Service, an affiliate of the California Farm Bureau Federation.

Bob Nichols/USDA 90BW1258-14

Rudolpho Galindo (left), crew foreman, John Barrientos (center), and Steve Nishita (right), co-owner of Nishita Farms in Salinas, CA. Barrientos acts as an ombudsman for the farm laborers. A major challenge for Barrientos is "to handle the difficult situations without letting my own feelings interfere."

John helps agricultural employers improve relations with personnel, prevent labor disputes, and resolve conflicts as they occur. His clientele includes the operators of more than 100 agricultural businesses—farms, wineries, packing sheds, nurseries, and others—that employ some 2,000 workers overall.

John has been around agriculture for virtually all of his 37 years. He has had experience in a range of field and managerial jobs that have helped equip him for this important work that affects so many people.

Born in Salinas, CA, he still lives there with his wife and their four children (ages 10, 8, 6, and 5). His father was a lettuce harvest crew leader.

Before joining the Farm Employers Labor Service, John worked directly for a few vegetable firms based in Salinas. From 1966 to 1981 he was an artichoke cutter, tractor driver, irrigator, payroll clerk, employee service representative, lettuce processing operation supervisor, and safety manager with Sea Mist Farms and Bud Antle, Inc.

by Howard R. Rosenberg, Agricultural Labor Management Specialist, Department of Agricultural and Resource Economics, University of California Cooperative Extension, Berkeley, CA

Growing Interest

As employee relations manager at the Garin Company, John developed personnel policies, implemented the safety program, participated in union contract negotiations, handled grievances, and provided general liaison between management and employees. This experience led to a similar position with D'Arrigo Brothers Company. There, as personnel and safety manager, he conducted workplace safety audits, coordinated safety training, and supervised the handling of workers compensation insurance claims.

Having studied agricultural engineering at California Polytechnic Institute, Pomona, John did not become interested in personnel work until his payroll job exposed him to a range of employee concerns and labor relations problems. Since that time, he has found great satisfaction in helping people through personnel work.

Challenges...and Appreciation

A major challenge in John's position is the frequent need to separate personal sentiments from professional responsibilites—"to handle the difficult situations that arise in this kind of job," he says, "without letting my own feelings interfere. I have picked up some helpful techniques by working under the wings of a few seasoned, knowledgeable managers."

Although many contributions of personnel managers are subtle and thus unrecognized even by their beneficiaries, the appreciation that John does receive from others is very gratifying to him.

He enjoys the variety of working with multiple clients and situations in his present position, especially providing guidance to farm managers who want to build good relationships with workers. When called to deal with a problem that has already surfaced, however, John generally needs to begin by managing expectations. He says, "No third party can just come in and clear up deep-rooted problems that have been developing for years."

David Marvin:

Tapping into the Vermont Maple Business

For most of Vermont's maple producers, sugaring is a sideline business, a way to supplement farm income in an otherwise slow time of year. For David Marvin, owner of Butternut Mountain Farm, however, maple is his profession and his passion.

One of the State's top maple producers, Dave is also one of the few who have been able to make a successful living from the sticky, sweet, amber-colored syrup. Although he also runs a small forestry consulting service and wholesales about 3,000 Christmas trees a year, the nucleus of his business is maple.

Perry Reck/USDA 90BW0735-11

David Marvin is one of Vermont's top maple syrup producers. He has been able to make a successsful living from the sticky, sweet, amber-colored syrup.

Dave runs 11,000 taps on his 1,000-acre farm in Johnson, in northern Vermont. He produces more than 3,000 gallons of syrup in a good year. Unfortunately, in three out of the past four seasons production has been below average for a number of reasons, including unfavorable weather conditions, maple tree decline, and the pesky pear thrip. He has kept up with demand from wholesale and retail markets by buying local syrup. He notes that "many people like to produce, but not sell. I don't want to produce if I can't sell what I make for a profit."

by Lisa Halvorsen, Extension Press Editor, University of Vermont, Burlington, VT

Sugarbush Management

Dave considers himself a steward of the land, managing his timberland and sugarbush (the sugar maple trees used to produce syrup) to ensure profits but also to protect the individual trees and the land.

He is concerned about the effect of the environment on the maples, especially in the older stands. Many of Dave's trees already are suffering from premature loss of foliage, slow-healing tapholes, defoliation, and other signs of decline, and he can only speculate as to the cause. He blames the loss of vigor on acid rain and other airborne pollutants as well as recent infestations of a tiny pear-shaped thrip. His temporary solution has been to limit the number of taps per tree and to thin stands conservatively, particularly those containing mature sugar maples.

"We are losing a lot of trees, and this concerns me," he admits. "In young unmanaged stands there may be as many as 1,000 trees per acre, so loss of a few trees is not as critical. As a forester, I've always used thinning to improve the sugar-bush. But with the maple decline and the impact of a lot of stress, entomologists are recommending that producers don't thin now. There is strong evidence that heavy thinning adds another stress to already weakened trees."

Selection by Sweetness

One 60-year-old tree on Dave's property, a product of two genetically sweet parents, fertile soil, large crown, good exposure to the sun, and other ideal conditions, has registered an 8-percent sugar concentration on the refractometer, compared to a sugar concentration of 2 to 3 percent for the average tree. Dave has affectionately dubbed it "Champion"

Perry Rech/USDA 90BW0735-35

Dave checks the pipeline feeding into the storage tanks for possible leaks. He opted to go with plastic pipelines rather than the traditional system of taps and buckets. He has more than 100 miles of tubing set up through his woods to deliver sap to the storage tanks.

and hopes someday to have a mountain covered with trees as sweet as this one through selective thinning of the sugarbush.

"The traditional method of establishing a sugarbush involves working a stand of seedling- to sapling-sized trees to select those that show vigor, good form, and rapid growth," Dave explains. "I prefer to select trees based on sweetness. I measure the sweetness of individual trees, then determine how sweet each is in relation to its neighbors.

"If two trees are close together, and one tests 2 percent and the other, 3 percent, the tree testing 2 percent would require 43 gallons of sap to make 1 gallon of syrup. For the tree with a 3-percent sugar concentration, only 29 gallons of sap are needed for 1 gallon of syrup."

Perry Rech/USDA 90BW0743-22

He bases his thinking in part on the results of a study conducted by his late father, James Marvin, a botany professor at the University of Vermont, and the late Fred Laing, another well-known Vermont maple researcher. The study concluded that trees maintain their relative ranking in terms of sugar concentration in a mature stand. In addition, other research has shown that the sweeter trees also appear to produce a larger volume of sap.

Value of Research

Dave recognizes the value of research and so has participated in several studies throughout the years. He is now beginning his third year of participation in a cooperative research project with the Finnish Forestry Institute to determine the effects of some soil amendments, including commercial fertilizers, wood ash, lime, and organic fertilizer, on tree health.

He periodically collects samples of twigs from the crowns of trees on several test and control plots to send to Finland for nutrient analysis. Although the data still are inconclusive, Dave believes that information gathered through this research someday will help maple producers improve their production through better sugarbush management.

Staying Ahead with New Technology

Dave's interest in research and new technology also has helped him stay ahead of the competition. When he started managing his sugarbush in 1973, for example, he opted to go with plastic pipeline, a new concept at the time, rather than the traditional system of taps and buckets, which required many hours to collect the sap and haul it to the sugarhouse for boiling. He now has more than 100 miles of tubing set up through his woods, which, when conditions are right, deliver sap to the storage tanks at the sugarhouse at the foot of Butternut Mountain.

In 1979 he purchased a reverse osmosis machine that removes much of the water from the sap, at a rate of 1,000 gallons per hour, before it is boiled. With this process, sap going into the evaporator has a much higher sugar concentration, meaning that less time is needed to turn the raw sap into syrup.

"Before I make any decision, especially one involving a major purchase of equipment, I do some serious pencil pushing," he admits. "I look at how this piece of equipment or change in procedure can benefit the business as well as how it will affect my cash-flow over time. Although I was among the first in the State to purchase a reverse osmosis machine, it has proved to be a wise investment as it has kept fuel and labor costs down."

Forestry Consulting

"My forestry consulting business fits in nicely with the rest of my operation," Dave says. He trained as a forester, receiving a degree in forestry from the University of Vermont in 1970. He also put in 2 years with the U.S. Forest Service in Vermont in economic maple research before starting his own sugaring operation.

"In the beginning, I had many opportunities to set up the tubing, evaporator systems, and other sugaring equipment for others. As dealers became more familiar with the equipment, the nature of my forestry consulting work changed. I now consult more with private landowners, especially advising them on land use to meet the requirements of State environmental and land use programs.

"If I have clients who are interested in developing a new sugarbush or maintaining an existing one, I will help them get started. However, I will only bring them to a point where they can continue by themselves. Why? Because we, too, are in that business. The sugaring season is obviously a busy time for us, so we can't hold anyone's hand, but there's also a possibility of conflict of interest when it comes to marketing.

"I don't mind telling someone what not to do, based on my own experiences. But when it comes to telling them how to do it, I have to protect my own interest and theirs."

Marketing the Products

With Dave's continued success, it comes as no surprise that he would rather not divulge his marketing strategies. He started small, and until recent years he handled all the packing and shipping of syrup and maple products from his home on Butternut Mountain. A few years ago he opened a country store on Main Street in Johnson. His wife, Lucy Marvin, manages the store. There the Marvins sell many of their own maple products, along with other specialty food items, many maple related and most, though not all, from Vermont. The store also carries a complete line of sugaring equipment.

In 1989, after several months of planning, Dave opened a new plant in neighboring Morrisville to pack and ship maple syrup and other maple products. The expansion has made it feasible for him to go after overseas markets, including some in Great Britain, Japan, and West Germany.

The Future

What does the future hold for this 42-year-old entrepreneur?

"I think the key word for many people in agriculture is to diversify. Maple is what I know best and it works well for us, but one thing about our business that makes management hard and profits unpredictable is that every day is dictated by the season, the weather, or the customer. Because of this, I have considered expanding into other types of food processing."

He is also looking to the future with his Christmas tree farm. "Right now we're 100-percent wholesale, but years down the road we may make more money in retail sales. In anticipation of this, we have begun planting trees in more accessible locations for a choose-and-cut Christmas tree operation.

"Twenty years from now, development may reach us here on Butternut Mountain. Growth is inevitable, but to me it represents a challenge. However, I don't want to expand my operation for the sake of expansion. I want to be at a size where we can do all we do well."

Perry Rech/USDA 90BW0734-10

A display of maple products inside Butternut Mountain Farm Store. Dave sells his products here along with other products made by wholesale buyers of his syrup and other country-style products, many from Vermont.

Hildreth Morton:

Selling Herbs, Growing with the Times

A pleasant hillside with a beautiful view: That is the first impression of Bittersweet Hill Nurseries. The view is what attracted its owner to the property nearly 50 years ago. However, visitors today come not for the view but to purchase quality herbs or flowers or to choose from among 50 varieties of water lilies and lotus.

In 1940, Hildreth Morton and her husband purchased 120 acres of farmland in rural Davidsonville, MD. While her husband was employed off the farm, Hildreth took on the business of farming, beginning with a small chicken business and then venturing into hogs, cattle, tobacco, and then flowers. Now Bittersweet Hill boasts one of the best known herb plant inventories in the area.

Bob Nichols/USDA 90BW0990-13

"Herbs make 'scents and cents'" says Hildreth Morton of her business, Bittersweet Nurseries. For Morton, herbs have become a way of life. What most farmers regarded as a niche crop 10 years ago has quickly become a lucrative cash crop.

Starting Small

The nursery started small, graduating to larger and larger operations as profits and demand allowed. The first small greenhouse was built at one end of a block building that contained the water tank and the furnace for the house. Hildreth sold petunias and other annual plants from this small greenhouse, using a cigar box to hold the money.

In the 1960's house plants were popular, so Bittersweet Hill supplied them, stressing quality and variety. As nearby housing developments came, the farm built its reputation and credibility in the community. As the money became available, Hildreth built more buildings; today there are three large glass greenhouses, one plastic greenhouse, one fiberglass Quonset hut for cooling, and a potting shed.

During the 1980's, the popularity of herbs increased, and they are now a major part of the business. Although it is primarily a retail business, Hildreth sells some herb plants wholesale to garden centers. She also has given herb plants to the National Arboretum (part of USDA's Agricultural Research Service) in Washington, DC.

A Going, Growing Concern

The nursery, which is open every day, is managed and staffed by women. Customers often comment on the helpful and knowledgeable assistance they get from the employees. The nursery features seasonal additions of fall and Christmas specialties, such as chrysanthemums, poinsettias, and live green wreaths.

Herbal weekends have been held annually for several years, featuring demonstrations, door prizes, and garden displays with plants for sale. They are well attended by local customers as well as by garden and herb clubs from neighboring States.

by Carole S. Kerr, Small Farm Owner, Bowie, MD, and Howard W. (Bud) Kerr, Jr., Director, Office for Small-Scale Agriculture, Cooperative State Research Service, USDA, Washington, DC

Bob Nichols/USDA 90BW0989-13

All the employees of Bittersweet Nurseries are women. Here Hildreth and employees Elaine Lahn and Sally Listro tend to their herbs.

Bob Nichols/USDA 90BW0988-31A

Hildreth Morton working in her office, which is a desk and a bookshelf from floor to ceiling. Her knowledge of the plants she sells was acquired through continuous study, research, and experimentation.

There is nothing glitzy about Bittersweet Hill; it is a place for serious gardeners. In one greenhouse is a garden and gift shop selling how-to books, a few good tools and supplies, decorative pots, and packets of seed varieties not usually found in drugstores. In addition to posted prices, there are neat hand-lettered signs giving plants' scientific and common names, planting information, cooking instructions, and often history or interesting facts. A sign on a pair of garden clippers reads, "A good pair of clippers is hard to find. We use these all the time."

Hildreth's trademark is the colorful flower she always wears in her hair. With a friendly and outgoing personality, she communicates a love of her farm and a wealth of knowledge about the plants she sells—knowledge acquired through continuous study, research, and experimentation when no help was available. Business acumen, intuition, and common sense have kept this operation ahead of the current trends and have helped it survive growing competition and changing times. Hildreth goes on buying trips to find new varieties, makes appearances at community and State functions, and attends trade association meetings and seminars.

Ten years ago, most farmers regarded herbs as a niche crop, but they are becoming a more significant crop. The recent upsurge of interest in herbs may result from health-conscious consumers who choose fresh fruit and vegetables as the basis of their diet. Herbs, fresh and dried, add to this healthy profile. Growing and marketing all kinds of herbs, flowers, and ornamentals is becoming commercially feasible for all kinds of farmers in the 1990's.

The view from Bittersweet Hill now includes more houses, as well as the glistening roofs of competitors' greenhouses. Suburbia is encroaching. But Hildreth Morton will continue to operate her farm with an eye to the future. By offering plants of consistently high quality and by applying her insight into the business, she will maintain her small farm and grow with the times.

Ellen Dolan and Joy Jackson:

Exporting Value-Added Foods

Ellen Dolan and Joy Jackson, owners of American Trade Exchange, Inc., share a small-scale marketing company with global ideas.

Jeff Joiner/Rural Missouri

"Good day from Trenton, Missouri, U.S.A.!" So begins another fax transmittal from American Trade Exchange, Inc. (AMTEX), in its quest to export Missouri-produced food products to distant lands.

Similar messages are sent by thousands of export businesses throughout the United States, but AMTEX provides a little twist—both of the firm's principals are women. Ellen Dolan, Managing Director, and Joy Jackson, Assistant Managing Director, have been friends for more than 18 years and partners for nearly 5.

AMTEX is a trade company born out of the depressed farm economy of the early 1980's. In 1986 Ellen's husband, a farmer, joined with five other businessmen from Trenton (population 7,000) to form AMTEX.

"When the farm economy was poor and we were having financial problems, a high school friend suggested forming an exporting company," Ellen recalls. "Our friend, who is known as a visionary, asked my husband, Gary, if he would like to be involved."

The Dolans became two of AMTEX's original stockholders, and Ellen believes that the firm provided them with a healthy diversion from their financial problems. These problems ultimately caused them to file for bankruptcy and changed their lives forever, although Gary continued to farm.

by Sally Klusaritz, Public Affairs Specialist, Foreign Agricultural Service, USDA, Washington, DC

"In some ways, I don't think you ever get over it," Ellen says. "When you know you didn't pay your bills, you never get over that if you have any conscience. But after the firm's one salaried employee left to return to England, Gary suggested I channel my energies into the firm."

"I started out not knowing anything about business," she continues. "I have a degree in art education and I know about oil paintings, but I didn't know anything about business. I have a strong artistic and creative side, but I'm very slow when it comes to business; I just don't think that way."

After attending an exporting trade show with Ellen in 1987, Joy Jackson joined AMTEX. "At the show, I fell in love with the business," Joy recalls. "I had been a seamstress—making wedding and pageant gowns—for 16 years. The detail work that goes into wedding gowns parallels the details of developing a shipping price for a shipment of goods to a foreign port."

Learning Exporting Takes Time

Initially, AMTEX tried to market agricultural products, such as fertilizer, seeds, chemicals, and machinery. Ellen says that business was slow, not only because of the depressed world market but also because the firm did not know how to develop markets.

Staff in the Missouri Department of Agriculture advised the company to branch out into value-added foods. Today AMTEX represents more than 40 companies, working to export such products as gourmet sauces, hash browns, meals, flours, and USDA-graded pheasant.

"We saw the potential of value-added products," Ellen says. "Missouri manufactures all kinds of products. Now we've crept over into other States in search of products. We met a Kansan who manufactures his corn into a tortilla chip product, adding a lot of value to his commodity. That's a new product."

"We can't work with big companies because they already have their distribution set up and are so savvy about what they do," she continues. "We have to be able to give something to a company. We look for that little niche market where people are manufacturing on a smaller scale. We deal mainly with cottage industries—those that have 500 employees or fewer."

They also are willing to venture away from food items. "We had a request from a Japanese company that wanted to buy snack items," Ellen says. "At the bottom of the letter was a postscript asking for silk parachute cord, circa World War II. So we're looking for it."

Ellen's and Joy's day-to-day business experiences have provided nonstop learning opportunities. "When I first started, the Missouri Department of Agriculture advised me to call a company that might want to export," recalls Ellen. "When I called, the man asked what commission rate I charged. I didn't know what 'commission' meant. I know that makes me sound extremely ignorant, but if you're not in some sort of business, you don't know how the business world operates."

Joy agrees. Like Dolan, she had no business education or experience. "I've learned that anyone can do anything they want to do if they put their mind to it," she says. "I studied very little business in school. I studied foreign languages and that sort of thing. I didn't think I'd ever be doing anything like this."

One of the major lessons the two women learned is the value of networking. "I don't think locale inhibits you much," says Joy. "As long as you have a fax machine, a telephone, and a typewriter, you can run a trading company. I know the demand is there for our goods; it's just getting the connections made."

"If you're willing to learn, you can accomplish great things," says Ellen. "We sit on Main Street in Trenton with this great international business knowledge. We're doing fine. We're learning. We're aggressive. There are so many possibilities that we see. I know you can starve to death on possibilities, but they're here."

Operating in a Man's World

Both women agree that their individual styles complement each other and that the fact that they are both women provides an edge in some aspects of business.

"Ellen and I are totally different people," says Joy. "Ellen is creative. She has a degree in art education and the gift of gab. I am more of the nitpicker—the one who wants the facts. I want things put in order. She doesn't think in those terms. She doesn't think about getting a quote together. She thinks in terms of making the deal. Then I get the quote and the freight forwarding together. But we work well together. Otherwise we would have killed each other a long time ago."

Ellen agrees: "The concept of trade and the idea that we are ambassadors are exciting to me. But we know our limitations; we didn't go to Harvard Business School. But we have charm, honesty, and a sincere appreciation for other people's cultures. People trust us. We work out of one 9'-by-12' office, and we shared one desk and one phone for many months. These are the strengths of women—we've had to do more and sacrifice more. The strength of the company has been the femaleness of it."

That "femaleness" has created some interesting situations. Many men believe that the principals are Mr. Jackson and Mr. Dolan, says Joy, and some from foreign countries are especially surprised to find a woman on the other end of the telephone.

"It took one man from Pakistan almost 5 minutes before he would talk to Ellen," says Joy, "because he couldn't decide if he wanted to talk to a woman. He had called long distance and then got off the phone. We could hear him talking in the background, but he wouldn't talk to her. He wanted to talk to her husband—not her. He finally came back on and said he had decided to talk to her."

In another instance, a Saudi Arabian buyer said that he wished the two women would visit his country, but there would be some drawbacks. "He said my husband would have to come, too, and that he couldn't speak to me there," recalls Joy. "He can talk to me in the United States, but not in Saudi Arabia. He was embarrassed about that, but that's the way it is."

Career Advice for Their Sons

As the mothers of teenage boys, Ellen and Joy are raising the next generation of American agriculture. Because of their disappointing experiences farming in an economically depressed area, both have advised their sons to think beyond careers in production agriculture.

"Joy and I tell our kids that agriculture takes on many forms," says Ellen. "AMTEX is a form of marketing value-added goods. The knowledge we've gained is the creative part of agriculture. The advice I would give young people interested in agriculture as a career is to diversify. If they want to be farmers, then they should also have two other sidelines. Be flexible. Be a jack of many trades. I think that makes us strong and knowledgeable, and it also makes us compassionate. Sometimes if you know just one thing, you're too narrowminded. Also, be creative. I used to think I would never use my degree in art education. Now I know creativity in business is the key to business survival."

Ellen and her husband have emphasized that their sons should study agricultural journalism, marketing, or economics. "We want them to study something they can fall back on if they decide to farm," Ellen says. "Children need to understand that there's more than just planting the crop in the field or raising a pig or a cow. There's a lot of people who don't understand the value-added concept and how selling value-added products helps the rural economy."

Defining Success

The two women have given much thought to the success of AMTEX and their business partnership. In the fall of 1989, they exported their first full container load—a shipment of Missouri charcoal for a buyer in Japan. For a big company that would be minor, Ellen points out, but for AMTEX it was a big step.

"Joy and I have talked about what success is," says Ellen. "Is it financial? Well, financially the books are lean. It doesn't look good. But if we've been able to tell our four teenage boys about potential and give them a jump on the future, then we feel that we've been successful. I'd like to take home $40,000 a year—we're taking home nothing at this point—but it's hard to establish yourself internationally. It would take us just one good sale. It is out there. I just hope against hope that we'll make it. We may not. But if we don't make it in this business, we have had 4 of the best years of our lives."

In the meantime, the business is growing slowly. Now when they read their mail and fax messages, the responses to their "Good day from Trenton, Missouri, U.S.A.!" are "Good morning and a sunny day from Canada," "Exceedingly good day from Singapore," and "Good day, ladies, from Japan."

Ray Bergin, Jr.:

Bringing Fresh Produce to Minneapolis-St. Paul

Ray Bergin, Jr., born in Minneapolis, MN, in 1930, has just completed his 40th year in the fresh produce business in the Twin Cities area. However, he still has a way to go to catch up to his grandfather Carl Bergin, who was employed by Pacific Gamble Robinson, a food wholesaler, for 53 years, and his father, Ray, Sr., who at 83 still spends mornings in his office at Bergin Fruit Company, the family-run wholesale produce company that handles fruits, vegetables, and nuts.

Bergin Fruit was incorporated in August 1951, when "Junior"—as he is still known by everybody—joined his parents, Vernice and Ray, Sr., to start up the company. Loans from insurance policies and a gift from Vernice's father, Ed Collect, got the business off the ground. Ray, Sr., had developed rapport with everyone on Market Row, the old market in downtown Minneapolis, during his years at Pacific Gamble Robinson; these people generously offered business advice, which helped the company in the rough first years.

Volume developed quickly; within 2 years the company moved to larger facilities, and in 1958 it moved again, to the Crown Meat warehouse on North Sixth Street in downtown Minneapolis. By this time, Bergin Fruit had established itself as the only purveyor in town selling solely to the institutional market. Bergin Fruit also started processing fruit and vegetables during this period, starting with fresh sliced apples for pies and soon following with other processed produce items.

In 1987 Bergin Fruit created a new company, Market Food International, to serve the oriental restaurant trade, a rapidly growing part of the Twin Cities' institutional trade.

by James N. Morris, Jr., Industrial Engineer, and Richard K. Overheim, Marketing Specialist, Agricultural Marketing Service, USDA, Washington, DC

The family business of Ray Bergin, Sr., and Ray Bergin, Jr., has been distributing fresh fruit and vegetables in northern Minnesota for over 30 years.

Perry Rech/USDA 90BW0814-10A

Helping the Produce Industry Grow

The early 1960's brought new responsibilities. Junior, along with two other young leaders in the Twin Cities industry, Gene Katzmarek and Morrie Spizman, believed that the market needed a forum so that the industry could have a common voice on issues important to produce marketing. The three merchants therefore founded the Twin City Fruit Terminal Association in June 1963. Membership increased quickly, and today the association's membership is 45 companies.

The association soon found that a new market was essential to the continued health of the local produce industry, because the market at the time was split between two sites—one at Sixth Street and the other at the Rock Island Railroad Terminal. Junior, along with Gene and Morrie, helped identify sites for the new market.

Building a New Produce Market

The need for a new market facility was clear. Warehouses on the existing market sites had deteriorated, and sanitation and adequate refrigeration were major problems. The Minneapolis Industrial Development Commission supported the idea of a new market, and the cooperative efforts of the produce industry, the City of Minneapolis, and USDA's wholesale market development program made the new market possible.

After 14 years of planning, the Kasota Fruit Terminal opened for business in May 1977, with private funds from the local produce industry and public funds from the City of Minneapolis. The old market sites were replaced by highways and the Hubert H. Humphrey Metrodome.

The new market was an instant hit. Kasota became a first-class produce market, serving as home base for independent fruit and vegetable companies serving customers over a five-State area and Canada. Employment in the market has doubled since opening, and business has increased about 600 percent from opening day. About $200 million in produce moves through the market each year. Increases in the local tax base from Kasota's growth have more than returned city funds contributed to the project.

James N. Morris, Jr./USDA Agricultural Marketing Service

When warehousing and market facilities deteriorated, private and public funds were used to build the Kasota Fruit Terminal, where Bergin Fruit and other fruit and vegetable companies distribute their produce.

A Family Business

Bergin Fruit Company is a family business. It has three divisions, with Junior heading produce sales, his brother Tom handling processing, and his brother John running the nut section. Seven of the company's 80 employees are members of the Bergin family, including Junior's son Pete, the operational manager, and his daughter Paula, the comptroller.

One of the hazards of the produce business is becoming too involved with business to have time for the family. Junior and Grace, his wife of 37 years, work hard, but they also play hard. They and their four children, who have all graduated from college, participate in such activities as racquetball, badminton, tennis, golf, swimming, yacht racing, and downhill and cross-country skiing. The Bergins travel extensively when time permits. Junior is on the Board of Directors of the Metropolitan Medical Center, he has coached the local youth soccer program, and he has served as a committee member with the United Fresh Fruit and Vegetable Association.

Joseph M. Stewart:

An 1890's Success Story

Joseph M. Stewart beat the odds.

He was born in Louisiana in 1942 and grew up in a rural area. His parents had little schooling, they earned a mere $35 a week, and nine people lived in the family's three-bedroom house. Today, Joseph is the senior vice president for corporate affairs at the Kellogg Company and a highly respected member of his profession and community. He is proof to young people that, despite great odds, they too can be successful. But success did not happen overnight; it required years of dedication and hard work.

Early Years

Joseph attended Southern University, the 1890 Land Grant institution in Louisiana, where he studied food and nutrition. After his graduation in 1965, he spent 6 years working his way up through the ranks of the food service industry. His experience included positions at Alabama State College, Tennessee State University, and Howard University in Washington, DC.

In 1971, Joseph was appointed director of food services for the public school system and director for child nutrition programs for the District of Columbia. Three years later, he was awarded the Silver Plate Award for having the best school feeding program in the United States. In 1975 he was appointed to the Federal Energy Administration's Food Industry Advisory Council.

by Tom Willis, USDA Extension Service, Washington, DC

Mike Shoup

Joseph Stewart, a senior vice-president of the Kellogg Company, knows that success does not happen overnight; it requires dedication and years of hard work.

Climbing the Corporate Ladder

After nearly 2 decades of success in the food and nutrition component of the Nation's educational system, Joseph moved to the corporate world. He began his career with the Kellogg Company in 1980 as director of child nutrition programs in the Foodservices Marketing Department of the U.S. Food Products Division. Within a year he was promoted to director for corporate communications in the Public Affairs Division. In 1985 he was appointed vice president of public affairs, and in 1988 he became senior vice president of corporate affairs.

Joseph serves on the Board of Directors of Battle Creek Unlimited, Inc., and the board of trustees of the Battle Creek Health System, and he was fundraising chairman of the 1989 Battle Creek United Way Campaign. He is a member of the National Agricultural Research and Extension Users Advisory Board, the Directors Food and Nutrition Advisory Commission, and the State of Michigan Department of Health.

Mike Shoup

Joseph attributes much of his success in the corporate world to his alma mater, Southern University. The school helps foster pride and a goal-setting attitude. With Joseph in the Kellogg Company office of the Corporate Affairs Division are (L-R) Neil Nyberg, Tim Knowlton, and Hilda Harris.

Secret to Success

Joseph attributes his success, in part, to his alma mater. He learned firsthand of Southern University's commitment to fostering pride and goal-setting attitudes in its students. In an address to graduates of the university, he said, "Southern has helped each of us overcome tremendous odds. Some of the odds could have crushed our social and psychological well-being in this country. In spite of the odds, you and I and others have survived."

Although it has been many years since his graduation, Joseph maintains close ties with Southern. As a member of the university's agriculture and home economics advisory council, he was instrumental in securing a $200,000 grant from the Kellogg Company for the improvement of home economics programs in the food sciences department.

When Joseph was a student there, Southern University helped provide him with the confidence and support he needed to beat the odds. Now that he is at the top of his profession, he hopes to give back some of that support.

Ralph W. Ketner:

Give and Take of a Grocery Executive

Inspiration comes in different forms. For many young people in North Carolina and around the Nation, it comes from Anne and Ralph Ketner.

Ralph W. Ketner is a cofounder and the chairman of the Food Lion grocery chain, based in Salisbury, NC.

A humorous man, Ralph often tells how he got started in business, beginning with selling newspapers and ice cream in his spare time. He said he got an "early experience in marketing" when he persuaded a new teacher not to fail him in geometry. He had scored high in algebra, but geometry, which he took for a year, "took me," and Ralph argued that the teacher would not want to be remembered as proving other math teachers wrong by flunking him.

Food Lion Story

Early marketing and public relations savvy did not bring quick success for Food Lion. Ralph founded the chain, originally called Food Town Stores, along with his brother, Brown, and Wilson L. Smith in 1957. "For 10 years, business did not look promising," Ralph says. "We didn't find anything that worked."

The tide turned in early 1968 after he pioneered the low price concept that he called LFPINC (Lowest Food Prices In North Carolina).

Today, the Food Lion chain employs more than 40,000 people in 680 stores in 10 States; its sales amount to $15 million daily, or $5.5 billion a year, and stock originally worth $1,000 is now worth $15 million.

by Denise R. Miller, Director for Communications, National 4-H Council, Chevy Chase, MD

Food Lion is one of the 10 largest supermarket chains in the country, making Ralph one of America's largest agricultural product consumers. His chain buys food locally whenever possible, encouraging the stability of the family farm. "I don't want to see the family farm disappear," Ralph says. "Competition is good for the economy and the consumer. If all our acreage got into the hands of farming corporations, it would be bad for American consumers."

Ralph knows what he's talking about when he speaks of competition. He based Food Lion's success on going into a market and opening a store with greatly reduced prices. He believes that his customers eat better for less and says that, as a result of its lower price policy, Food Lion moves 5 to 10 percent more tons of food per year than its competitors.

Model for Young People

4-H is the largest voluntary youth educational program in the United States, reaching more than 5.1 million boys and girls. It is the youth program of the Cooperative Extension System of the State land-grant universities and USDA's Extension Service. The National 4-H Council is a not-for-profit educational organization that uses private funds to enhance and expand the 4-H program (see Chapter 50).

Ralph exemplifies the character, initiative, and ideals that 4-H develops in young people. His successes, from humble beginnings, have inspired thousands of young people. In sharing his story with young audiences, he says, "I learned early in life the value of some four-letter words: home work, hard work, team work, good Lord, good luck, and good idea."

Anne and Ralph became interested in 4-H when they learned through Rowan County 4-H members that 4-H is family oriented and provides leadership training.

Ralph has been involved with 4-H for many years, first working on a 4-H development program and now serving as a member of the board of trustees of National 4-H Council and as a board member of the North Carolina 4-H development fund.

Because of their belief in 4-H, the Ketners gave $1 million to National 4-H Council, so 4-H members nationwide will benefit from the Ketners' response to the youth of Rowan County.

The Ketners' gift, the largest personal gift ever made to National 4-H Council, helped to build a new educational facility at the National 4-H Center. The Center, where each year more than 30,000 young people and adults study citizenship and leadership, is located in Chevy Chase, MD. Ralph W. Ketner Hall is a four-story brick facility with conference rooms, residence space, and business offices.

The Ketners devote their personal time and energy to many community organizations in addition to 4-H, including a home for children in their community, a soup kitchen, and a shelter for the homeless.

Ralph has been honored many times for his service to business and young people. He has served numerous business directorships and won many community awards; he is a trustee of Catawba College, in Salisbury. Ralph has an honorary doctorate in business administration from Catawba, and from Tri-State University in Angola, IN, a diploma awarded to him 43 years after he dropped out for financial reasons.

Odonna Mathews:

Consumers on Her Mind

"I've always enjoyed foods and working with people."

That seems appropriate for the vice president for consumer affairs of a 150-store supermarket chain operating in Maryland, Virginia, and the District of Columbia.

Odonna Mathews, 39, runs a division of Giant Food, Inc., that responds to more than 15,000 consumer comment cards and letters each year, distributes 63,000 informative flyers each week, handles myriad telephone calls daily, and sells $10 million worth of party platters, flowers, and gift certificates over the telephone each year.

At Giant's headquarters in Landover, MD, just outside of Washington, DC, Odonna's office overlooks the company's huge warehouse. Inside, several files and a dictaphone are poised for Odonna's attention after an interview.

In an adjoining office, a secretary's voice alerts a customer relations expert that "a lady on the phone says she ordered carp but was given mullet by the store. She wants her money back." The soothing voice of the expert takes over.

Soothing. Patient. These are the trademarks of Odonna's office. And of Odonna herself, though just below the surface is an impatience to get things done . . . to explore ethnic restaurants . . . to go halfway around the world to see a solar eclipse.

Busy Schedule

On a typical morning, Odonna arrives at her office at 8:30 a.m. By 9:00 she has plunged into the details of customer concerns expressed to the Consumer Services Department, which handles more than 35,000 telephone calls a week.

From there, Odonna steps smoothly into a conversation with the senior vice president for operations—their biweekly review of consumer compliments and complaints.

Next, and still before noon, Odonna joins a meeting of the firm's environmental issues task force, which is completing plans for a new recycling campaign. The campaign's advertisements and brochures, like all Giant consumer brochures, will be written under Odonna's direction, with input from other areas in the firm.

Odonna is enthused about Giant's recycling initiative. For many years, Giant has been offering customers a choice of plastic or paper bags in which to carry home their purchases.

Lunch provides no opportunity to escape from the job—not that Odonna wants to. She has crabcakes made from a new recipe soon to be offered in the supermarkets. All of the recipes suggested by Giant are written and tested by Odonna and her staff. In this case Odonna approves of the result, though she personally prefers a little more spice. Marylanders like their crabcakes spicy.

After lunch, Odonna telephones consumers who have written to the company or called her office. Some days she works until 6:30 p.m. to reach them.

"They're always surprised when I call them personally," Odonna says. "The store manager calls them, too."

by John Crowley, Public Affairs Specialist, Office of Public Affairs, USDA, Washington, DC

Bob Nichols/USDA 90BW1073-8A

"To listen and to make the marketplace more responsive to customers" is a goal of Odonna Matthews, vice president for consumer affairs, Giant Food, Inc.

Listening to Consumers

Odonna's job, like that of her predecessor, Esther Peterson, is less to placate irate customers than to take the case of the consumer vigorously to others in the management of the $3-billion-a-year firm.

Under Mrs. Peterson, for instance, Giant introduced open dating, unit pricing, nutrition labeling, and even suggestions to buy cheaper foods. With Odonna as consumer advisor, the food chain has expanded into food safety, environmental issues, recipe cards, health publications, and cooperative programs with government on such issues as diet, cancer, and heart disease.

Odonna (named after her father, whose middle name is Odon, after a Norse god) was influenced greatly by the consumer movement of the 1960's. Born in Washington, DC, and a graduate of junior and senior high schools in Camp Hill, PA, Odonna was impressed by the work of Ralph Nader and Esther Peterson.

She enrolled in a new curriculum for management and consumer studies at the University of Maryland, and received a bachelor of science degree before joining Giant full time. Later she earned her master's degree from the same university, where she majored in marketing.

Although Mrs. Peterson was a great influence on Odonna's life, other forces shaped her career. Because her father had suffered from heart disease, Odonna became very conscious of the health aspects of food. And her mother "was always reading labels . . . she wanted to be a dietitian."

Giant Food selected Odonna as consumer adviser 5 years after she started with the firm as a student intern.

Odonna's staff of 45 includes two nutritionists, an assistant director of consumer affairs, a sensory evaluation specialist, and four secretaries. In addition, there are a manager, supervisor, trainer, and 34 telephone representatives in her Consumer Services Department.

"This office generates and handles a lot of paperwork," Odonna explains. "What our customers tell us, we tell the company president, its vice president, and many other people throughout the company so that they can respond to our customers' needs and wishes."

Never Entirely "Off Duty"

It takes Odonna longer to shop for food than most people. Customers recognize her (she appears in both newspaper advertisements and television commercials to discuss consumer issues), and store personnel suspect her, incorrectly, of inspecting their facility.

Odonna travels to exotic places not in search of food, but of solar eclipses and other skyward events, such as Halley's Comet. Her husband, Charles Simpson, is a research physicist. ("Can you imagine?" Odonna quips, "Physics was my worst class in school.")

Odonna and her husband raise vegetables in a home garden slightly larger than her office. Not every year is a winner in the garden: "Last year we had practically no tomatoes but loads of basil."

Nearly all of Odonna's activities are work related.

Active in many civic and professional organizations, Odonna represents Giant in the Washington, DC, Community Partnership for the Prevention of Homelessness. Her firm contributes more than 500,000 pounds of nonperishable goods and $1 million worth of perishable goods each year to food bank agencies in the area.

"The food bank agencies go to the stores two or three times a week to pick up food that we can't sell but which is still safe and edible," Odonna explains. "We also get suppliers and vendors to donate food."

Odonna does not run out of issues. There's food safety, for instance. And locally grown produce.

"We know consumers like locally grown food, and we're selling more and more of it," she explains, "but it is just not feasible for buyers to sell local produce if they have to deal with many small suppliers. The farmers need to get together in a cooperative or some other arrangement."

What is Odonna trying to do for consumers? "To listen," is her direct answer, "and to make the marketplace more responsive to consumers."

In addition to meat, chicken, and fish recipe cards developed in-house, Giant distributes 19 publications free of charge near the checkout counters. These are not stuffed in the grocery bags. People have to go a little out of their way to pick them up. And they pick them up at the rate of 63,000 a week.

"Only one of our publications is for sale," Odonna observes. "That is the *Eat for Health* food guide. We sell between 1,000 and 1,500 a week. And it's quite a job keeping it up to date. It lists more than 4,000 items that are low in fat, cholesterol, sodium, or calories or are good sources of fiber." Giant has special green shelf labels to identify these products for consumers.

Odonna takes job-related literature home to read. "Now, though, I'm reading more about pregnancy and childbirth," she notes. Charles and Odonna were expecting the birth of their first child in September 1990.

Bessie Beuchert:

Discovering Herself Among People and Peonies

by Craig Regelbrugge, Director of Regulatory Affairs and Grower Services, American Association of Nurserymen, Washington, DC

Bessie Beuchert had not planned on a nursery or garden center career, but she discovered by accident that working with plants and people is a rewarding way to make the most of her natural talents.

Craig J. Regelbrugge/American Association of Nurserymen

Bessie Beuchert hadn't planned on a career in a nursery and garden center, but discovered by accident that working with plants and people is a rewarding way to make the most of her natural talents.

Values and Hard Work

Bessie's interests and values have their roots in a traditional upbringing in a close-knit family. Her father managed a thoroughbred horse farm in the lush, gently rolling hills east of the Blue Ridge Mountains near Warrenton, VA; her mother attended to the tasks of raising seven children and "put three hot meals a day on the table."

Bessie developed a reputation early for enjoying hard work. Feeding the horses and cleaning their stalls were parts of her daily regimen. She remembers the meadow flowers and the hayfields, and she recalls proudly that she was the only girl her father allowed to pitch hay.

After finishing high school, the children went their separate ways, though most stayed in the area and still maintain contact. At 25, Bessie married Vinson Beuchert. Within a few years they had their only child, Toni. Bessie worked part time with her husband at an electrical supply store in Merrifield, VA.

Opportunity Knocks

Bessie still smiles as she recalls a beautiful Indian summer Saturday in September 1983, when she had set out to play a few games of tennis. She stopped in for a soda at a local convenience store and ran into Bob Warhurst, owner of the thriving Merrifield Garden Center across the street. Bob mentioned to her that he needed some help in the annual and perennial plant section of the nursery and asked if she knew anyone who might be interested.

"I enjoy working with plants and people, and I'd love to work outside again," Bessie answered. "If I took the job, when would you like me to start?"

"Right now," said Bob.

Bessie put her tennis gear in the car, walked across the street, and has loved her job ever since.

"I was so excited and interested in the job, I didn't even think to ask about how much money I would make. I wanted to work with the flowers again . . . they remind me so much of the farm."

Bessie found a special niche at Merrifield Garden Center. When she started, she knew little about the plants she was to work with. Each night she would take horticulture books home and learn about another plant—what conditions it required, how it grew, and what its flowers were like. She wanted to share the best information with her customers.

In the early days, the nursery grew its own fall-blooming, hardy chrysanthemums. Bessie watched over them as if they were her own children. She watered them just right, always checking one more time before the workday ended. She carefully pinched them to encourage more stems and flowers and tagged them so that buyers could be sure of color and variety. When the first cool nights of September arrived, the mums were proudly displayed, bursting into bloom—cheery yellows, deep reds, whites, pinks, and the traditional coppery browns.

The nursery has grown, and space has become a limiting factor. All the flowering annuals and perennials are now brought in from other nurseries, but Bessie's caring hands still give each plant the same individual attention.

Customer Service

Bessie's day begins at 5 a.m.; she arrives at work by 6 (she says that she sleeps in nowadays; she used to get up at 4). Her mornings are spent unloading truckloads of fresh plants, inventorying and restocking her displays, watering where needed, and, of course, helping her customers.

An early customer asks, "Have those peonies you expected this week arrived yet?"

"Yes," says Bessie, "they'll be coming off the truck in a few minutes. You were looking for the ones with the frilly, light-pink flowers, right? I'll have the best ones waiting for you if you stop by when you finish shopping."

Soon the lunch crowd stops by, men and women in business attire. One is looking for just the right plant to brighten the trellis by the patio. "I'd suggest the moonflower vine, because its huge white flowers will open just as you're sitting down to dinner outside," says Bessie.

The Merrifield Garden Center has built a reputation on its customer service, and Bessie loves to work with her customers, many of whom she knows by name. Each customer is treated to her special blend of patience and genuine interest—even if she has only a moment to chat on a busy weekend. She loves it when a customer says, "I always come to you. You help me with the right answers."

Craig J. Regelbrugge/American Association of Nurserymen

Bessie loves to work with her customers, many of whom she knows by name. Each customer is treated to her special blend of patience and genuine interest.

Bessie's customers seek her out, especially during the busy spring and Christmas seasons. She achieved the highest sales of any employee at the nursery during the last two Christmas seasons. "I also got the most tips," she admits sheepishly. "But spring is my favorite time in the nursery. I am so excited seeing all the roses and other flowers come into bloom."

Tanned from working outdoors, Bessie flashes an easy smile when she knows she has made a difference in someone's day. She keeps learning too, by reading and asking questions. "I'm now learning the greenhouse plants and some trees. I want to be able to work all over the nursery."

The booming northern Virginia suburbs of Washington, DC, face a critical labor shortage, and horticultural businesses have been affected. Jobs in horticulture often involve physical labor, long hours during the busy spring and fall seasons, and modest wages. There is stiff competition for good employees. As a result, garden centers and landscape firms have begun to look beyond the traditional employee; retirees, spouses not working outside the home, and immigrants often make good nursery employees.

Bessie found such an employee in Blanca, an immigrant who came to work at the nursery in 1986. Bessie is a hard worker, and she expects the same of others. She quickly seized the opportunity to train Blanca her way.

More than a Job

Bessie's job at the nursery has become a family affair. Her daughter, Toni, now married and with a child of her own, fills in on Bessie's days off, and Bessie takes advantage of this chance to babysit for her granddaughter. Bessie's husband, Vinnie, a regular visitor at the garden center, pitches in each year at the annual fall festival. "We both work a lot of hours," says Bessie, "but enjoy the time we spend together."

Though she admits to being 49, Bessie says that she feels like 20. Bessie makes the most of every day. She enjoys her work and takes pride in doing it well.

Many people working in the field of horticulture share certain common goals and interests—a desire to work outdoors, a yearning to be creative, an affinity for helping others, and the satisfaction of making our world a more beautiful place. Bessie Beuchert is a nurturer—of her family, her customers, and her plants. This nurturing instinct is deeply rooted in her upbringing and has survived in today's hectic world.

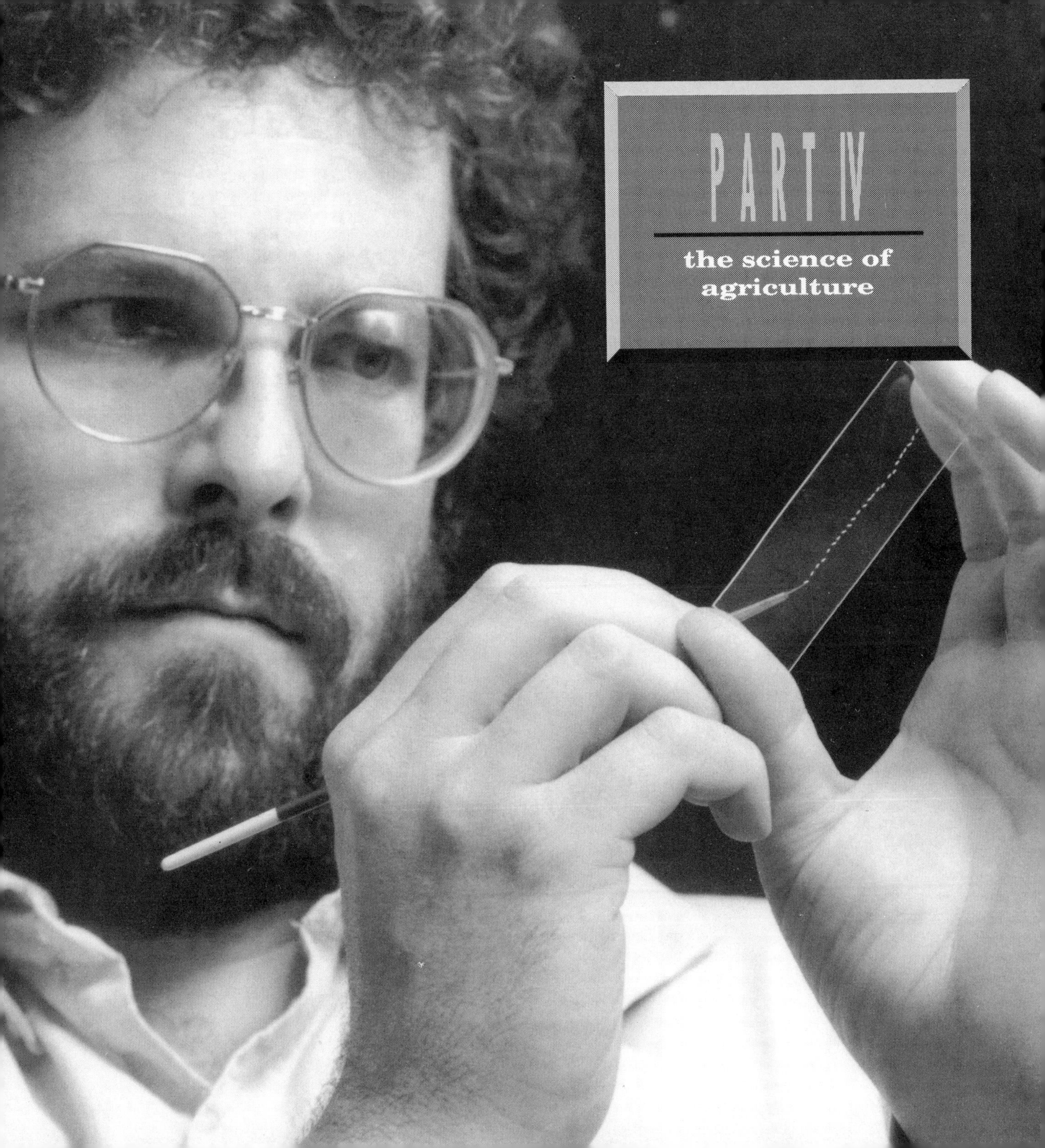
PART IV
the science of agriculture

Mike Gould:

Getting More Value From Crops

Mike Gould owes a lot to his wife's cooking, particularly her pancakes.

"This story goes back to 1983, when we were trying to find uses for crop byproducts, like cornstalks and wheat straw, that a farmer might throw away," says Mike, a chemist and research leader with the Agricultural Research Service at USDA's Northern Regional Research Center in Peoria, IL. "We wanted to increase the farmer's income without increasing investment in that crop."

Mike and a team of scientists discovered that treating the byproducts with hydrogen peroxide made them soft and digestible for cattle, sheep, and other farm animals. The softened cellulose made a flourlike fiber that could be added to feed.

"As we were working on this, I kept wondering if there wasn't some human application for the fiber, some human food value," he says. "But that got put on the back burner while we did animal feeding trials with it."

Late one afternoon, theory took a leap toward reality.

"I went home—it was a Friday—went into the kitchen and made cookies using the fiber. And they were awful," Mike says. "A total disaster. The kitchen smelled like burning wheat straw. I went to bed pretty depressed."

The next morning, Brenda Gould was flipping pancakes. Mike sat down and started eating. As he did, it dawned on him that the reason the cookies failed was because the fiber was probably better suited to something soft like pancakes than something hard like cookies.

by Matthew Bosisio, Public Affairs Specialist, Agricultural Research Service, USDA, Peoria, IL

He began to share that revelation with Brenda when she stopped him.

"She said she uses two cups of flour for pancakes but that this time she used one cup of flour and one of the fiber, just to try it out," Mike says. "I couldn't believe it. I was eating pancakes made with wheat straw and couldn't tell the difference.

"We spent the rest of the day making pancakes, rolls, and blueberry muffins. But when Brenda put it in the pancakes that morning, that was the 'eureka' moment. That's when I knew it would work."

Off and Running

New food uses developed quickly. Mike made a fiber-rich white bread that did not taste gritty or coarse. He made chocolate cake with as much fiber as breakfast cereal. He added the dietary fiber to other foods. Because it replaced a percentage of the flour normally used, it cut the calories of every food item in which it was used.

Soon the product made national headlines. *Business Week* and *U.S. News and World Report* referred to the no-calorie, high-fiber flour as "fluffy cellulose." The *New York Times* called it "piece-of-cake dieting," while *The Washington Post* said Mike's invention "can turn a Twinkie into a high-fiber, low-calorie food—without altering its flavor."

The invention was patented in 1988 and licensed the following year to two commercial manufacturers. Du Pont Co. uses the process to manufacture white oat fiber from oat hulls at a factory in Cambridge, MN. Mt. Pulaski Products, Mt. Pulaski, IL, produces a flour from the filmy outer portion of corncobs. Both companies expect to market their products to firms making bread, cakes, crackers, doughnuts, and other prepared foods.

"These two firms demonstrate what our research is really all about," Mike says. "We developed a product that's now out of the lab and into commercialization, where it will not only provide a product for consumers but also generate jobs and stimulate local economies.

"That type of technology transfer—turning lab research over to industry—is what we are trying to accomplish."

In the Beginning

Growing up in the small town of Xenia, OH, John Michael Gould was insatiably curious. He was a typical boy, by his own account, except for an inclination to collect and dissect dead animals. His house stood on the edge of town, its back windows awash with cornfields.

Mike would take his bike along the quiet roads, pick up small animals, and haul them home for inspection.

"It really grossed out my mom that I did this," he recalls. "I had these little jars of birds' eyes and birds' stomachs in my room. I guess it was a little more than she cared for."

He was also partial to mouse-breeding experiments until one got out of hand, "and we quickly had about 200 mice. When I was young, I didn't really appreciate the need to get them separated right away."

After high school, Mike attended the University of Cincinnati, where he earned a B.S. in biological science in 1971 and an M.S. in cell biology the following year. Two years later, he had a Ph.D. in plant biochemistry from

Michigan State University.

A 1-year postdoctoral position with Cornell University was followed by a similar 2-year position at Purdue University. In 1977, Mike became an assistant professor of biochemistry and biophysics at the University of Notre Dame.

"During all those years, all the work that I did was very basic, very esoteric—research for research's sake," he says. "But I wanted to do something that related to the real world. I had a hankering to do something that would have an effect."

Bruce Fritz/USDA 89BW1028-35

"Fiber-rich breads, waffles, and muffins are just the beginning," says chemist J. Michael Gould. His high-fiber flour substitute made national headlines as a new product that could benefit both farmers and consumers.

In 1981, Mike joined the Agricultural Research Service in Peoria. He was hired to learn how fungi break down lignin, the woody substance that binds plant cell walls. In the ensuing 7 years, he rose from research chemist to research leader, and he now oversees the work of two dozen scientists and support staff and a budget of $2 million.

Along the way, recognition has kept close company. He received an Inventor's Award from the U.S. Department of Commerce in 1986 and a USDA Award for Distinguished Service in 1987. His high-fiber flour substitute earned him the agency's Technology Transfer Award in 1989 for research that has benefited farmers and consumers. The same year, *Research & Development* magazine named the fiber one of the 100 most significant new technologies on the market.

Mike holds three patents from his Agricultural Research Service work, including one on the animal feed research that launched his dietary fiber success. It, too, has been licensed for commercial development. He also has a number of patents pending on new research.

"Before I came here, I considered private industry as a possible career, as most probably do," Mike says. "But I decided that in industry, generally what you do boils down to what's best for the company. But here, in USDA, it all boils down to what's best for the country. And I wanted to do something that was best for the country."

People Power Policy

Although he is a scientist who thinks analytically and theoretically, Mike has a rare grasp on the politics of people and personalities. His management style reflects the philosophy that from people and imagination flow productivity. In short, you increase productivity not by installing new equipment but by making the employees happy.

He does that by praising them, encouraging them, and honoring them for major and minor accomplishments. He gives them support and isolates them from bureaucratic frustrations.

"Mike gives you a lot of room to do things," says Rich Greene, a chemist in Mike's Biopolymer Research group. "A lot comes out of this lab because he's not overburdened by some notion that he needs to remain within the project outline. If research takes you in a direction that's unexpected, then follow it. He lets the research take the researcher rather than the researcher take the research."

Mike's outlook on science might best be defined as creative wonder. Nothing exists that cannot be examined in new ways, with renewed vigor, and with the anticipation of discovery.

"Breakthroughs in science almost always come from people who have visions that are uncluttered by the dogma and theories of science," he says. "Kids do it all the time. They ask why the sky is blue. That is what I always want to do—to ask questions about things we take for granted and discover something different."

James A. Duke:

Duke of the Offbeat Plants

His business card says "Economic Botanist."

"That's what they call you when you work on crops that hardly anyone has ever heard of and that are on the margin of economic importance," explains James A. Duke, a scientist at the Agricultural Research Service's Germplasm Services Laboratory in Beltsville, MD.

What Jim actually works on is alternatives. He explores crops that a farmer could grow in place of conventional crops, such as wheat or corn, or crops that could fill an important void, such as a source for a cancer-curing drug or a tick repellant.

Jim is not a plant breeder; he is a plant finder. He exchanges cuttings and seeds with researchers, seed banks, and breeders around the world and collects them himself from the wild.

"I plug up some of the holes in the germplasm system," he says. "We have curators who collect all the different strains of crops like soybeans and potatoes. But the odd crops—the unusual ones that don't belong anywhere in particular and are maybe on the fringe of the profit margin—that's what I collect."

Plants To Treat AIDS and Other Diseases

For example, about 2 years ago the National Cancer Institute (NCI) came to Jim for assistance because it was interested in St. Johnswort, a weed that has a long history in folk medicine for treating nervous disorders, burns, and urinary infections. Two compounds in the weed have been found to strongly inhibit the AIDS (acquired immune deficiency syndrome) virus.

by J. Kim Kaplan, Public Affairs Specialist, Agricultural Research Service, USDA, Beltsville, MD

Although species of St. Johnswort are native to Europe, western Asia, and North Africa and are naturalized in North America and Australia, none had been systematically collected for inclusion in a germplasm bank.

Since then, Jim has collected five different species of the weed, finding them growing wild along the highway near his home in Fulton, MD. "After a while, you get so you can recognize a species even at 50 miles per hour," he says.

Different species have different levels of the active chemicals, which makes collecting them important to improving the plant's possibilities as a crop.

St. Johnswort is not the only potential AIDS fighter Jim has gone after. A reference in some medicinal plant literature led him to seek out samples of the Moreton Bay chestnut, an evergreen legume that grows in the rain forests and along streambanks in northeastern Australia.

The Moreton Bay chestnut is one of the best sources of castanospermine, a compound that appears to halt reproduction of the AIDS virus. Jim has brought seeds of it from Australia, so it will be available if needed for research studies.

If the compound is useful against AIDS, the plant could be a lucrative alternative crop for a farmer to grow, although it is currently suited only to such areas as Texas, Arizona, Florida, California, and Hawaii.

In 1987, before its anti-AIDS potential was announced, castanospermine was priced at $23 per milligram. "That comes to $9 million per pound, if a pound were salable at the milligram price," he says.

Some Moreton Bay chestnut seeds yield 0.3 percent of the compound,

James Duke, an economic botanist with the Agricultural Research Service in Beltsville, MD, examines an evening primrose. He has studied many unique plants in an effort to find new uses. Of the 2,800 plants in Maryland, he has found published folk medicinal uses for 700.

about 3,000 parts per million, whereas other seeds yield only 2 parts per million. "The difference could be environmental, genetic, or just in the extracting procedure. We need to collect germplasm from different plants that contain the compound, in order to determine the exact cause," he says.

In March of 1989, Jim heard from a friend in New York, one of the "guerilla warriors" against AIDS, who told him they had had some luck using two species of Chinese gourds—*Momoordica* and *Trichosanthes*—as an underground treatment for the disease.

Both of the gourds are listed as official drugs in the Pharmacopeia of the People's Republic of China and have been used in Chinese folk medicine since 300 A.D. Many gourds contain cucurbitacins, which are very active physiologically, according to Jim.

Clinical trials using a highly purified protein from one species of these gourds, *Trichosanthes kirilowii,* have been approved by the U.S. Food and Drug Administration.

Jim delights in finding scientific evidence for plants that have been used in folk medicine. "It proves the wisdom in those old tales," he explains.

He submitted wild-harvested *Huperzia lucidula* recently for alkaloid analysis as a possible treatment for Alzheimer's disease. Plants in the *Huperzia* family have been used as medicine in China for centuries for such diverse ailments as cramps, hemorrhoids, pneumonia, and even wet dreams.

"*H. lucidula* is relatively easy to cultivate compared with most other *Huperzia* species," he says, "so it very well might become a useful, albeit specialized, crop."

He is also trying to obtain spores of a related species from Pakistan that might grow in tissue culture.

A renowned expert on herbs and medicinal plants, Jim developed his passion at an early age. "Even as a child, I was interested in living off the land," he says.

Alternative Food and Energy Crops

As fascinating as that aspect of his job is, his real focus is on alternative food and energy species. He has files on growing almost 1,000 different crops from which someone might make a living.

"You don't have to grow wheat or soybeans. But there isn't a large market for most of these alternative crops, so you need lots of different possibilities."

Take basil, for example. "If a farmer near Omaha wanted to get out of corn, he could make a living with basil," he says. "Each major city can support a basil grower, but probably only one."

Jim recently spent a week in São Tomé, an island off the coast of North Africa, helping the local government decide if farmers there could grow black pepper as a commercial crop.

"I have a file on a firewood tree species that grows very fast and burns well, and could be an important crop for many Third World countries," he says. "And then there is a plant that has a resin in it that could be used as a fuel in diesel engines. If energy costs rise, it could become an economically important crop."

For his native North Carolina, Jim has been collecting varieties of evening primrose as an economically viable alternative to tobacco.

Oil from the evening primrose flower is a major source of gamma-linolenic acid. This fatty acid is a precursor of prostaglandin E_1 and is considered by some to be able to abate the symptoms of several illnesses. It is best known as a treatment for atopic eczema.

"I've exchanged evening primrose seed with people in Israel, Holland, and Canada, so as the demand for the oil increases, we can offer germplasm for making improvements in the crop," he says.

Right now, about 400 acres in North Carolina are being planted in evening primrose, and each year the number grows "about on a par with the growth in demand."

Rain Forest Resources

In his work with alternative crops, Jim has become a strong advocate of preserving the biodiversity of the rain forests, "preferably as they exist in nature.

"We have no idea of what's growing there that has never been tested—a new food crop, a new cure for a disease, a tick repellant, the genes to improve crops we already grow—nobody knows what's out there and we may lose so much of it before we ever learn," he explains.

Jim was recently in Ecuador as part of a team that is trying to put an economic value on crop relatives that grow in the rain forest but are not cultivated.

"Numbers like that help us make the case for preserving the great biodiversity that exists in the rain forests," he says. "Tomatoes, hot peppers, and potatoes originated as wild plants in Latin America, and there are still wild relatives of these crops that haven't been looked at."

While Jim spends a lot of his time on the telephone and updating computer files on crops from jojoba to licorice, he looks forward to the time he actually spends growing some of the germplasm he collects.

Growing in his own backyard garden as well as a greenhouse at his Beltsville laboratory is a wild mountain mint that he collected, which may be the best source of pulegone, the major ingredient in pennyroyal oil. This highly pungent compound has been found to repel fleas and birds and is being looked at as a tick repellant.

"I found the mint as I was walking in the woods because, when I crushed its leaf, the odor of pulegone was so strong," Jim says. "I spend my winter with the computer, but the rest of the year I'm out crushing leaves and sniffing them."

Forest Service Researchers:

Studying Wildlife

Over 90 men and women working for the Forest Service conduct research on wildlife and fish. With 191 million acres of forests and rangelands to manage, Forest Service managers need state-of-the-art information on the fish and wildlife species that live on these public lands. Forest Service researchers at 33 different research laboratories from Alaska to Puerto Rico and from Hawaii to Maine are studying the habitat requirements of fish and wildlife species and how various activities—both natural and human—on the forests and rangelands affect them.

A team of researchers is investigating the interactions among elk, deer, and cattle on the open grassy forestlands of northeastern Oregon. By outfitting the elk, deer, and cattle with radio collars, Jack Ward Thomas and his colleagues can track the movements of the animals 24 hours a day using satellites and nearby radio towers. A microcomputer keeps track of the animals' movements and allows the scientists to study in detail the elk and deer reactions to nearby timber sales or cattle grazing. The results of this study will allow managers to make informed decisions about when, where, and how much timber cutting and grazing should be going on in areas important to the elk and deer herds of the area.

Seven Forest Service researchers are studying the spotted owl in Washington, Oregon, California, Arizona, and New Mexico. One of these researchers, Eric Forsman, began studying this medium-sized owl as a graduate student in the early 1970's and continues his work today as a Forest Service scientist. He has surveyed a wide variety of forests in Oregon and Washington, looking for these owls and learning about their habits, habitat needs, and reactions to nearby timber sales.

Evie Bull tracks the movements of pileated woodpeckers in the ponderosa pine forests of northeastern Oregon. Using radio signals, Evie gets an inside look at the behavior and habitat use of these large woodpeckers. On several western national forests, pileated woodpeckers are "indicator species"—when their numbers decline, it is a sign that other species may also be threatened. Evie's research will help forest biologists learn how to monitor changes in woodpecker populations and how to improve their habitats when necessary.

Every spring and early summer, Dick DeGraaf visits the mixed hardwood and conifer forests of northern New England to study songbird populations. He has compiled what he has learned about the habitat needs of New England's forest birds into a book that land managers use in making decisions about what kinds of forest and age-classes they need to maintain in order to ensure that the full complement of wildlife species have a place to call home.

Hours of turning over rocks, wading in streams, and checking pitfall traps have helped Hartwell Welsh to determine the habitat needs of salamanders and frogs associated with old-growth forests of Northern California and to find out how well these amphibians

USDA Forest Service

Forest Service researchers in Washington, Oregon, California, Arizona, and New Mexico continue to study the movements and habitat needs of the spotted owl.

by Nancy G. Tilghman, Wildlife, Range, and Fish Habitat Research Staff, Forest Service, USDA, Washington, DC

USDA Forest Service

In an effort to maintain the population of the endangered red-cockaded woodpecker in coastal South Carolina, forest biologists installed over 250 artificial nests in trees severely damaged by the 1989 winds of Hurricane Hugo.

tolerate up-stream disturbances. His work has suggested to local land managers that they need to know where local populations of Olympic salamanders, Del Norte salamanders, and tailed frogs occur and give special consideration to these habitats when they are laying out timber sales in nearby forest stands.

Lynn Decker spends her summers wading and snorkeling in streams in the Sierra-Nevada and northern California to learn more about the fish and aquatic insects that live in these mountain streams. She studies streams in areas where a variety of forest management activities are going on upstream and also in areas where no such disturbances occur. Her results will provide managers with much needed information on the cumulative impacts of their activities on fish and other aquatic animals.

Andy Dolloff is studying the streams of the Appalachian Mountains to understand the role of woody debris in providing hiding habitat for several fish species. From his studies, he will develop techniques that can help managers to increase the value of their streams as fish habitats.

USDA Forest Service

Pileated woodpecker research helps forest biologists monitor woodpecker populations and identify improvements needed in their habitats.

Bob Hooper has been studying the red-cockaded woodpeckers in coastal South Carolina for over 15 years. He and his colleagues have learned much about the habitat needs of this endangered woodpecker and the impact that flying squirrels have on local woodpecker populations. Forest biologists in the region have used this information to develop management plans for these old pine forests. In September 1989, Hurricane Hugo hit the forests of coastal South Carolina, leaving much of forest lying flat on the ground. Over 60 percent of the trees woodpeckers use as nest sites were lost. From his understanding of woodpecker biology, Bob knew that the loss of the nest tree would mean the loss of the woodpeckers, so Bob and local forest biologists began to create artificial nest cavities in the trees that had been left standing. They created more than 250 artificial cavities, and woodpeckers are currently using more than 40 percent of these.

John Rinne has conducted research on threatened and endangered fishes of the arid American Southwest for more than a decade. Many of these fishes are uniquely adapted to the extreme conditions of this region, ranging from flood to drought. Because of the general lack of water and the ever-increasing demand for it, John studies the habitat requirements, distribution, and biology of several of these rare fishes. Results of his research on the Apache and Gila trouts are being used to manage and recover these two potential sport fishes. In addition to the Apache trout, John is currently studying the threatened spinedace, spikedace, and loach minnow.

In Space Agriculture, the Work of Carver Continues

Space agriculture. Not your everyday topic of conversation. Yet American, European, and Japanese scientists are conducting research on this topic. Why? Because 15 years or so from now there will probably be long-term manned space missions. People may be living in the Earth-orbiting space station to be built jointly by the United States, the European Space Agency, Canada, and Japan; they may eventually be inhabiting an outpost on the Moon or a base on Mars.

Is it feasible to take along enough food to last the duration of a mission lasting several years? Hardly. Is it feasible to continually resupply such a mission with food from Earth? No, again. So what is the alternative? To grow food in space: space agriculture.

The Life Sciences Division of the National Aeronautics and Space Administration (NASA) initially selected eight crops to be studied for growth in its controlled ecological life support systems (CELSS) program (see Chapter 47). These eight—wheat, rice, peanuts, soybeans, lettuce, sugar beets, white potatoes, and sweet potatoes—and the preparations derived from them could provide a balanced and varied diet for a space inhabitant.

by the Tuskegee University NASA/CELSS Sweet Potato Team (Walter Hill, Phil Loretan, Conrad Bonsi, Desmond Mortley, Carlton Morris, John Lu, Ralphenia Pace, Cyriacus Ogbuehi, P. K. Biswas, Jill Hill, Edwin Martinez, Esther Carlisle, Samuel Adeyeye, and Dana Greene), School of Agriculture and Home Economics, Tuskegee University, Tuskegee, AL

The Sweet Potato and Tuskegee

Some of the criteria for crop selection for CELSS were energy concentration, nutritional composition, ease of processing, proportion and yield of edible plant parts, storage stability, and flexibility of use. Sweet potatoes scored among the highest in all these criteria. Tuskegee University, in east central Alabama, one of the 1890 land-grant institutions celebrating their centennial, was asked by NASA to study the sweet potato.

Beginning with the pioneering work of George Washington Carver, who worked extensively with Alabama farmers on the sweet potato and developed 26 new food uses for it, Tuskegee University has a long history of research with this crop. USDA's Cooperative State Research Service has funded sweet potato research there for many years. In 1986, NASA provided funds to see if sweet potatoes could be grown hydroponically for CELSS. (Hydroponics refers to various technologies for growing plants with or without the physical support of an inert medium, rather than in soil.)

Tuskegee formed a team with diverse expertise in sweet potato research: Conrad Bonsi, plant breeder/pathologist; Walter Hill, soil chemist/plant nutritionist; Phil Loretan, engineer and sweet potato farmer; John Lu, food scientist; Ralphenia Pace, human

Bob Nichols/USDA 90BW0810-35

From left to right, food and nutritional science undergraduate Dana Greene, agricultural engineer Phil Loretan, plant pathologist Conrad Bonsi, project director Walter Hill, and food and nutritional science undergraduate Edwin Martinez are members of the Tuskegee University sweet potato team. The group examines hydroponically grown sweet potato crop suggested for use with NASA's controlled ecological life support system.

nutritionist; Jill Hill, computer systems analyst; P. K. Biswas, horticulturist/plant physiologist; and Carlton Morris, materials specialist.

The Science Story Begins

Initially, the Tuskegee team experimented with hydroponic systems using such media as sand, gravel, sawdust, perlite, and vermiculite, but these media posed potential problems given the mass and volume limitations of space cargo.

Within a year, the team decided to apply the nutrient film technique (NFT) to the sweet potato. This technique involves passing a thin film of nutrient-enriched water solution over the root system of the plants within the growing system, using no solid media. It had previously been used exclusively for aboveground crops. Tomatoes, lettuce, and cucumbers have long been grown commercially using NFT. Other scientists had tried to grow root crops, including the sweet potato, with NFT and aeroponic (nutrient spray) systems, but had obtained limited yields: good foliage but only small roots or none at all.

Long-term manned space missions will need basics such as food and air. Artist Pat Rawlings' view of a future lunar mining operation illustrates the production of liquid oxygen. Ilmenite, a fairly common oxygen-rich component of lunar soil, is shown being processed into liquid oxygen that will be used by the orbiting space station.

In their first attempt using NFT, the team used a commercial system. The result? A sweet potato resembling a carrot shaped like a long, coiled snake.

Walter Hill, Conrad Bonsi, and Phil Loretan had worked with the project in the greenhouse, and they remembered an experiment in which a plant grew with no medium. The plant was held above a nutrient solution by a grid resting on a pot. A small potato formed under that grid close to the side of the pot.

These three scientists, together with the team's materials specialist, Carlton Morris, came up with a design (recently patented) that so far has produced as much as 6.2 pounds (2.8 kilograms) of sweet potatoes per plant, with an average of 3.7 pounds (1.7 kilograms), using the variety of sweet potato known as TI-155, which was developed at Tuskegee. Georgia Jet, another sweet potato variety, bred at the Tifton, GA, Experiment Station, also produces well in NFT. The team's system is now consistently producing sweet potatoes.

"This has been a very efficiently run project," says Dr. William Knott of the Life Sciences Research Office at Kennedy Space Center in Florida. "The Tuskegee team has made enormous progress." Because of the system's success with sweet potatoes, comparative studies are being made with white potatoes and sugar beets.

Questions To Be Answered

In space, plants will be grown in enclosed structures that will have to be protected from radiation and adapted to lower levels of gravity than on Earth —or no gravity at all—not to mention other complicating factors. Therefore, the effort of the second phase of research was to examine the effects of various environmental conditions on sweet potato growth.

To determine the exact needs of the structures, NASA asked specific questions: What is the best artificial lighting system, the best length of the light period, the best temperature, and the best humidity level for growing sweet potatoes? Would sweet potatoes grow if subjected to continuous light rather than the light/dark periods of Earth? How much light is optimum? If energy constraints limited the amount of light available, could sweet potato plants survive and still produce?

New researchers just beginning their scientific careers joined the team and conducted various experiments under greenhouse conditions and in environmental growth chambers. They included postdoctoral research associates Cyriacus Ogbuehi, Desmond Mortley, and Samuel Adeyeye; graduate research assistants Edwin Martinez and Dana Greene; and research technician Esther Carlisle. These young students of plant and soil science, food science, and biology brought tremendous energy and expertise to the team effort.

They conducted experiments to answer questions about the sweet potato's environmental needs, as well as other questions, such as the following: What cultural practices promote growth? How much space should there be between plants? Which varieties of sweet potato grow best in the system? What is the best nutrient solution for sweet potato production? When should it be applied, and should its composition change as the plants grow? What should the pH level of the solution be? Should it be constant or variable? What are the effects of continuous harvesting on sweet potato production in this system?

Sweet Potatoes in the Space Diet

The sweet potato plant has several unique aspects. One is that even a small section of the vines that are regularly produced can easily be cut off and used to start a new plant. Another is that it is a dual vegetable. The tender leaves that form near the vine tip make an excellent green vegetable. People in many African and Asian countries know this and eat them regularly.

Tuskegee food scientists John Lu and Ralphenia Pace have analyzed the hydroponically grown sweet potatoes with those grown conventionally in fields and have found that they compare favorably. As a carbohydrate, sweet potatoes are an excellent energy source; they also provide vitamin A.

The leaf tips are good supplemental sources of protein, iron, and calcium. Ralphenia has subjected the leaf tips to consumer studies and found sweet potato greens are acceptable to Americans. Dana Greene, with the help of a trained taste panel, is evaluating the acceptability of hydroponically grown sweet potatoes—including nonsweet, white-fleshed varieties. The energy and nutrition that come from this crop will be important to a space diet.

Space and Spinoffs

Tuskegee's research is linked to the Biomass Production Chamber (BPC) at the Kennedy Space Center, a three-story production facility that will test the chosen space crops individually and as they interact.

"The Tuskegee Project has already provided much of the baseline information needed for initial testing in the BPC," says Ralph Prince, agricultural engineer at Kennedy and technical monitor from NASA for the Tuskegee project. "Sweet potatoes are in the loop."

Although the main reason for the project relates to space, the research will provide useful information for farmers. Sweet potatoes are the seventh largest food crop in the world. Because it helps to quantify the environmental conditions needed for sweet potato growth, the team's system will serve not only the Nation's space needs but also those of sweet potato farmers here and around the globe. From the work at Tuskegee, scientists will be able to provide better information on how sweet potatoes grow best.

The National Space Program

Space agriculture needs to be put into the perspective of our Nation's space program. The 21st century will probably witness the first human footprint on Mars.

In 1986, the National Commission on Space recommended that the Nation "lead the exploration and development of the space frontier, advancing science, technology, and enterprise, and building institutions and systems that make accessible vast new resources and support human settlements beyond Earth orbit, from the highlands of the Moon to the plains of Mars."

The 1987 Ride Report focused on four possible initiatives in which the United States could maintain space leadership, initiatives that require ever-increasing technological capabilities: mission to planet Earth, exploration of the solar system, outpost on the Moon, and a mission to Mars. Our Nation faces a wide range of possibilities, and we will require advances in such areas as technology, life sciences/CELSS research, robotics, in-orbit assembly, and extraterrestrial systems.

It is difficult to grasp the amount and scope of the work facing the Nation's present and future space scientists and engineers—some of whom are not yet born or are in nursery or elementary school right now. Yet the work of science takes place one step at a time.

Space agriculture is at its threshold. The work at Tuskegee University with sweet potatoes and other food crops continues as an important segment of the NASA/CELSS program. With the team's research, the sweet potato research started by Carver moves into space.

Robert L. Buchanan:

A Scientist Fulfilling His Lifelong Ambition

If there is a hot seat in agricultural research, Robert L. Buchanan is on it. His work is under a microscope just as much as the bacteria that he and his team of scientists analyze.

A microbiologist for USDA's Agricultural Research Service (ARS), Robert is research leader of ARS's Microbial Food Safety Research unit in Philadelphia. His team of 12 scientists searches for answers to the seemingly endless number of questions about food safety.

There are questions from consumers who are worried that microscopic creatures called pathogens are creeping into their food. There are questions from food companies and retail outlets that are trying to keep up with consumer demand for more convenient foods while ensuring that foods are safe. And there are questions from government regulators seeking to anticipate and prevent food safety problems.

Answering these questions is a tall order, but Robert greets every one of them with zeal. "With ARS I have a high concentration of people in my field," he says. "In general, universities can't have more than three or four scientists in one field."

Robert also likes the mix of research and administration. He says his administrative duties as research leader, sometimes unwelcomed by scientists, give him the chance to "build something bigger than just myself."

"Bacteria are so small, yet they have an impact on the whole world," says Robert. "We want to provide sound information so good decisions can be made."

by Bruce Kinzel, Public Affairs Specialist, Agricultural Research Service, USDA, Beltsville, MD

Robert views his work almost like a chess game. For each move he makes to counter the growth of food-poisoning bacteria, the pathogen counters with another. He does not want to lose this game of microscopic chess—but challenges such as some pathogens' ability to grow in refrigerated temperatures make a checkmate difficult.

What led Buchanan into his food safety career?

Oddball Kid

Robert refers to himself as "one of those oddball kids" who since high school knew what he wanted to do in life. When he was a 10th grader in New Jersey, his biology teacher—as part of a class demonstration on how bacteria are used beneficially to produce food—introduced him to microorganisms, explaining their importance and thereby stimulating a lifelong interest.

Keith Weller/USDA 89BW0956-23

Microbiologist James Smith of the Eastern Regional Research Center in Philadelphia, PA, checks growth medium for visual evidence of harmful bacteria.

The next year, he dove into the first of what would become many microbial research projects. While most kids were busy trying to get the keys to the family car, Robert was studying how to optimize penicillin production. It is no surprise that when Robert entered college, he already had his sights set on a biology degree.

Robert enrolled at Rutgers—The State University in New Brunswick, NJ, as a biology major. But, he recalls, "The biology department was very medically oriented. I liked working with applied sciences, so I switched to the College of Agriculture—maybe because I grew up partly in rural Ohio."

Turning Points

Robert's interest in micro-organisms expanded into food safety. In part, that decision was helped by a part-time college job working nights at a local restaurant, where he saw how food was exposed to bacteria. Robert realized he could apply his work in food science to help the food industry prevent undesirable bacterial growth.

After graduating in 1969 from Rutgers with a bachelor's degree in food science, Robert went on to earn his doctorate in food safety from Rutgers in 1974. He accepted a postdoctoral position at the University of Georgia at Athens in 1974. There, he concentrated on mycotoxicology, the study of natural fungal toxins in food. This work helped broaden his knowledge of biochemistry and fungal physiology.

A little more than a year later, Robert left Georgia for Drexel University in Philadelphia. The mix of research and administrative experience he gained there would serve him well at ARS.

In 1981, Robert took a 1-year sabbatical to work with ARS as part of a budding microbiological food safety group at the Eastern Regional Research Center in Philadelphia. He has worked there ever since.

Working Relationships

When Robert's team established a working relationship with USDA's Food Safety and Inspection Service (FSIS) in 1982, they passed an important milestone. This relationship helped coordinate and set priorities for food safety research.

One of the team's first projects concerned the effect of reducing the amount of salt used to cure meat. Salt has been critical for centuries in limiting bacterial growth. As consumers demanded that industry reduce or eliminate salt from meat products, a concern about food safety arose. The team found that by changing other factors that control bacterial growth, such as acidity and storage temperature, they could safely reduce the amount of salt used.

"The way we pick our research topics is a product of our relationship with FSIS," Robert says. "We look at research that we and FSIS believe will contribute most to protecting public health."

Robert says he not only works closely with FSIS, but also with the food industry and the medical community. His team's research helps give industry, the medical community, consumers, and regulatory agencies a head start on addressing new concerns in microbiology.

For example, while many Americans have heard of *Salmonella*, most do not know about it in detail. But knowing all about *Salmonella* is part of Robert's job. He uses every opportunity he has to teach consumers, industry, and regulatory agencies about *Salmonella* and other pathogens.

Industry is very interested in this detailed information about *Salmonella* and other pathogens, because a new product facing regulation may be accepted or rejected based on its food safety potential, Robert says. "The Government's job is to protect con-

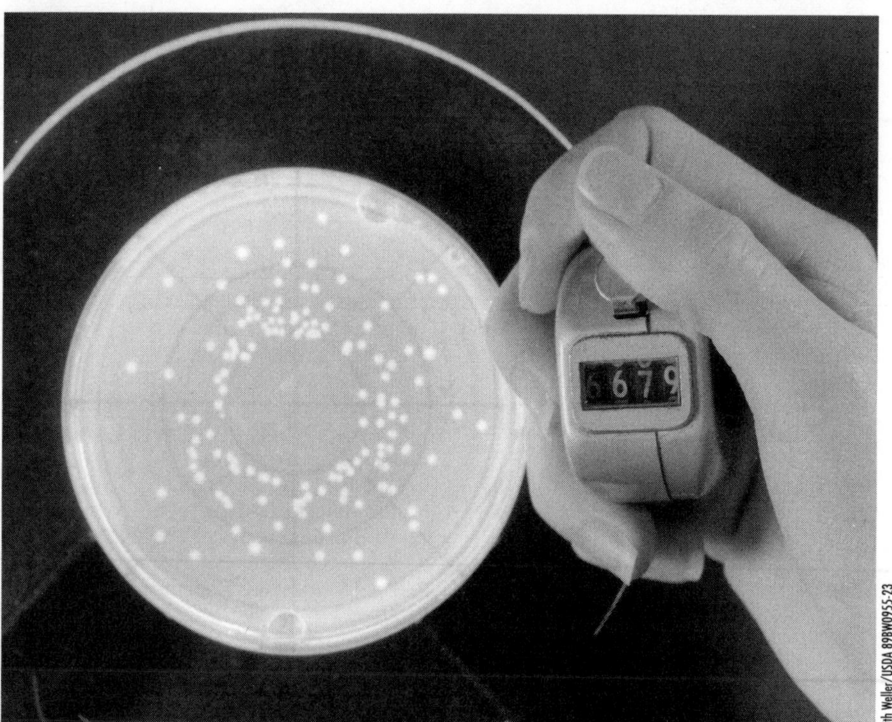

Keith Weller/USDA 89BW0955-23

Fluorescent light illuminating colonies of bacteria in growth medium helps researchers to count organisms that may affect food safety.

sumers' health, and we must do that responsibly with good scientific information."

"We're troubleshooters," he says. "We find solutions to bacterial contamination problems so the food industry, medicine, and regulatory agencies can implement those solutions. It's comparatively easy for us to communicate our technical information to regulatory agencies and industry."

Food Safety: Past, Present, and Future

In the past, microbial food safety research has kept a low profile in the scientific community to avoid public hysteria. But Robert feels it is important to put microbial food safety in the proper perspective, looking closely at who is getting sick and what is making them sick. He notes that consumers share in this responsibility.

Robert says that people tend to be more concerned about the amount and availability of food than they are about microbial contamination. "Because consumers can't see bacteria, they don't normally worry about it," he says. "One of the things consumers have to remember is that the fate of bacterial contamination is usually in their own hands. Proper storage and cooking are crucial."

This observation was heavily supported in a recent trip he made to developing countries to study microbial food contamination. People in these countries do not mind eating poorly handled, contaminated food—as long as they have food.

Technology and better knowledge about health and nutrition are increasing the lifespan of all Americans. Gazing into the microbial crystal ball, Robert sees the aging of the "baby boomers" as a societal trend that will increase the importance of food safety.

USDA 88BW2239-31

Anthony Oyofo treats a laboratory chick with a dose of D*-mannose, a sugar that blocks* Salmonella typhimurium *from invading the bird's intestines. Oyofo discovered the sugar while working in a USDA postdoctoral program.*

This aging will swell the percentage of elderly in the population. Just as the elderly are more vulnerable to all manner of ailments, they are also more susceptible to food-borne illness, so they have a bigger stake in handling food carefully to control *Salmonella* and other food-poisoning bacteria.

Gazing into his crystal ball, Robert sees his own, more personal goal: "I would like to put together a research unit that is internationally recognized as the best in food safety microbiology," he says.

Andy Cockburn:

Diligence and Ingenuity Pay Off in a Genetic Engineering Laboratory

Andy Cockburn will do almost anything to get foreign DNA (deoxyribonucleic acid) into cells.

He has tried blasting it in, shooting it in, and shaking it in. Finally, after 4 years of research, Andy found a technique that works. And it works in a big way.

Andy, a geneticist with USDA's Agricultural Research Service, works at the Insects Affecting Man and Animals Research Laboratory in Gainesville, FL. He began looking for a DNA insertion technique in 1986 with chemist David Carlson. Although Andy's ultimate goal is a genetically engineered mosquito that will not transmit malaria, he began by using housefly eggs as a model.

In that first experiment, David Carlson built a gene gun in his garage out of his grandfather's old .22-caliber pistol. The scientist coated tiny bullets with test dye (to simulate DNA) and tried blasting it into housefly eggs with the gene gun. The eggs were squashed.

So Andy decided to try a variant of microinjection, a genetic engineering technique in which genes are inserted into eggs with a tiny needle. Andy says that the method is based on "punching the smallest hole that you can squeeze material through" so that the egg survives the treatment.

He thought perhaps he could shoot tiny needles—coated with new DNA—into eggs with the gun.

But then he faced the obstacle of finding needles to do the job. He considered fiberglass particles, but none had a small enough diameter.

by Jessica Morrison Silva, Public Affairs Specialist, Agricultural Research Service, USDA, Beltsville, MD

Ceramic Strengtheners Get a New Job

He consulted colleagues at the University of Florida, telling them he needed something very sharp and hard and with a very small diameter. They suggested silicon carbide whiskers—tiny needles that are normally used to give ceramic materials the strength to hold up in such stress-bearing products as car engines.

He coated some of the whiskers with his test dye and tried shooting it in. "The whiskers were so small that they didn't have enough impact to penetrate the eggs," Andy says. "They were a complete flop in that project." Andy put his whiskers up on a shelf in his Gainesville, FL, laboratory and went on to other work.

Barry Fitzgerald/USDA 90BW0018-8

Geneticist Andrew Cockburn arranges housefly embryos for microinjection.

That Nagging Feeling

But he had not given up. He still wanted to develop a technique that could one day genetically engineer mosquitoes.

"I heard through the grapevine that someone in Sweden was using sonication to introduce material into moth eggs," Andy says, "so I started playing around with fly eggs and sonication." He put dye and fly eggs into a sonicator, which shakes material at a very high speed with sound waves.

"I looked at the eggs under a microscope, and all of the ones that had taken up new material were split open. We were shaking them so hard that we were just ripping them apart," says Andy.

But when Andy saw that the eggs that had not taken up dye were still alive, he realized that the shaking in and of itself was not killing the eggs; instead, the dye molecules were punching such large holes into the eggs that they could not survive.

So he reasoned that if he could punch smaller holes, he might be able to slip dye—and eventually DNA—into the eggs without killing them.

Then he remembered the whiskers on his shelf.

He planned to put dye, fly eggs, and the tiny whiskers into saline solution and to sonicate the mixture. But the day he was going to try it out, Gainesville was drenched in one of its summer rain storms, and technician Henry Meier did not want to walk across the parking lot through the rain to the laboratory next door. He suggested to Andy that they try using the Vortex mixer right in their own lab. This ordinary lab device spins material around much more gently than the sonicator. "I laughed and said, 'That's silly, but go ahead,' " says Andy.

The result just a few minutes later: Thousands of dye-injected fly eggs. And one-quarter of them were still alive.

It's Like Being in a Jacuzzi with a What?

Andy describes the technique as "like being in a Jacuzzi with a porcupine. Each time a needle gently hits an egg, a tiny hole results, and that hole allows some of the new material to enter the egg."

Though Andy reproduced the results with a test gene, none of the altered eggs have hatched into flies. But he says that in genetic engineering, tens of thousands of eggs must receive the new gene or genes in order for just one fly to actually show the new characteristics.

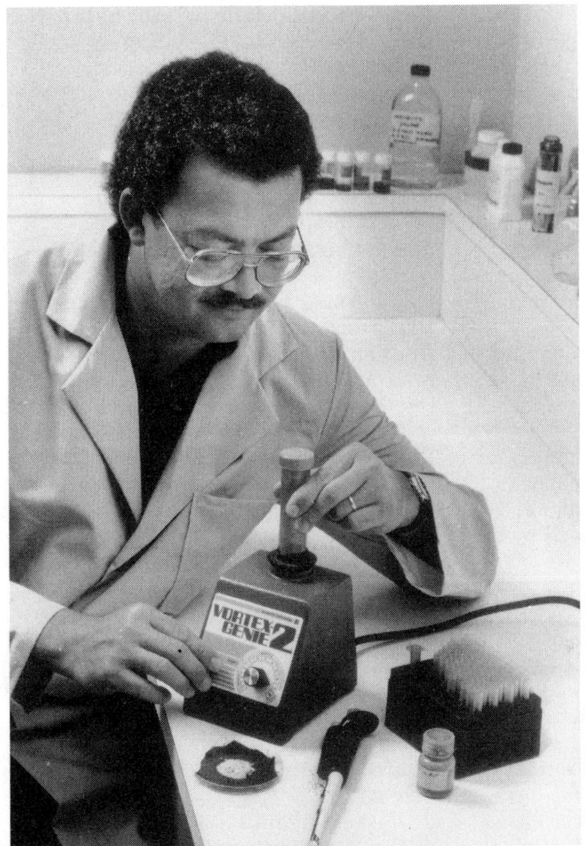

Barry Fitzgerald/USDA 90BW0017-10

Laboratory technician Henry Meier uses a vortex mixer to insert genes into housefly embryos, a method that is much faster than microinjection.

So when scientists use this technique, they should be able to produce one altered fly per hour.

He compares that rate with the efficiency of microinjection, the only other way to transfer genes into fly eggs. With microinjection, a scientist painstakingly inserts genes into eggs—one by one—while watching the procedure under a microscope. In the same few minutes that it takes the vortex mixer to inject thousands of eggs, microinjection injects only two or three. At that rate, microinjection could produce only one altered organism per year—compared with the one per hour with Andy's method.

The Agricultural Research Service has applied for a patent on the method.

After experimenting with his technique on his model fly egg system, Andy transferred material—either a test gene or dye—into eggs of the stable fly, the Caribbean fruit fly, and the nonpest *Drosophila* fruit fly.

He could not, however, transfer material into mosquito eggs, probably because mosquito eggs have harder shells. Nevertheless, he is confident that he can penetrate mosquito eggs by adding more whiskers or reducing the speed of the sonicator—which is still stronger than the Vortex mixer.

Do Not Break That Fragile Spaghetti String

Andy knows he will have to work to get just the right speed to break through the tough mosquito egg shell without destroying the DNA. "DNA is a very large molecule, with a structure of something like a string of spaghetti about a mile long," he says. "It's very fragile in that sense, and if you break DNA at any point, you destroy it."

In fact, sonication is "a classical way of breaking DNA molecules into small pieces," which is why he will be trying a lower speed on the powerful sonicator.

Scientists have been trying for years to genetically engineer these insects and have had success only with *Drosophila* flies. "Insect eggs and plant cells are designed to keep things out—things like viruses, bacteria, and any DNA we might try to insert," Andy says.

He emphasizes that genes that cause beneficial changes—such as malaria resistance—still must be found, but that he has won half of his battle by just finding a way to penetrate eggs.

Keeping the Dream Alive

Even when budget and time limits stopped Andy's work on this method, he has "kept it alive by passing it along to other scientists so they could try it with other organisms." For example, scientists at the University of Florida have successfully transferred dye into citrus tissue, and other groups around the country are trying to "Jacuzzi" genes into rice and *Drosophila* flies.

Meanwhile, Andy continues his other mosquito research, with the help of three graduate students. He says there are many aspects—in addition to perfecting his genetic engineering technique—to his plan for releasing a malaria-resistant mosquito. First, the group must find genes that cause malaria resistance in mosquitoes.

In a second project, the group is looking for quick ways to separate malaria-resistant mosquitoes from normal mosquitoes. For example, one possible method takes advantage of the DDT resistance of some mosquitoes. Andy says, "There are mosquitoes so resistant to DDT that you can line their cage with it and they won't die."

The group hopes to locate the gene that gives mosquitoes DDT resistance and attach it to the gene for malaria resistance. This arrangement ensures that, of the adult mosquitoes grown from genetically treated eggs, only the malaria-resistant ones could survive DDT. Thus, when researchers accumulate enough treated mosquitoes, they could easily remove the normal mosquitoes by dosing the entire batch with DDT. The new mosquitoes with the malaria resistance gene would then be bred in large enough numbers for field use.

If Andy's team succeeds in creating malaria-resistant mosquitoes, field workers could use insecticides to kill as many mosquitoes as possible in an infested area. Then they would replace them with the same number of malaria-resistant ones, which would prevent the natural population of malaria-carrying mosquitoes from recovering. That way, the number of malaria-carrying mosquitoes would be reduced by one-half or three-fourths. The resistant mosquitoes would pass that tendency along to future generations, maintaining the malaria-carrying potential of the entire population at a lower level.

A final project for the group is learning to differentiate the many species of mosquitoes. The group wants to determine which species bite most often and which ones are most likely to transmit disease. "That way, officials could concentrate all of their resources on the problem species, instead of randomly trying to knock back all of the populations," Andy says.

All this work could eventually help military troops stationed in South and Central America and people in tropical and subtropical areas all over the world, and would be equally useful if malaria ever becomes a serious problem again in the United States.

Andy stresses that making his dreams a reality will take years of work. But if his success with his "Jacuzzi" technique—and his perseverance in trying just about anything—continue, the day may come when the worst thing a mosquito can give us is a bad itch.

Claude E. Barton:
APHIS Veterinarian Who Helped Conquer Brucellosis

This is the story of one public veterinarian who chose to pursue an elusive goal for over a quarter of a century: the eradication of brucellosis, a nationwide livestock disease.

The fight against brucellosis requires earning the credibility necessary to change the mindset of livestock producers; arguing beliefs with Federal administrators, Congress, and industry; and establishing and maintaining rapport with many farmers, scientists, and officials at local, State, and regional levels in the United States and in other countries.

This is also the story of a person who strengthened the veterinary medical profession by incorporating a new field of study —epidemiology—and by recognizing that early computers were "friendly" tools.

The Animal and Plant Health Inspection Service (APHIS) supports and protects the Nation's \$70- to \$90-billion livestock and poultry industry. Daily, APHIS veterinarians make a difference in agriculture and sometimes even change history.

Bob Nichols/USDA 90BW1035-3

Claude Barton, an APHIS veterinarian who specializes in epidemiology, was instrumental in the drive to conquer brucellosis, a chronic disease of livestock that causes abortions and reduced milk production in infected animals.

When Claude joined APHIS, the use of epidemiology in veterinary medicine was in its infancy; many veterinarians viewed it as a stepchild to mainstream science.

Epidemiology draws on a number of disciplines, such as statistics, immunology, serology, and pathogenesis. It offers the intellectual challenge of a giant puzzle, which he believed he could help put together.

Epidemiology traces patterns of disease and occurrences in populations. Aiming for the best solution to a problem, the epidemiologist can guess, experiment, and use common sense and intuition as well as the latest technology and scientific data. Claude found the ability to use such a wide range of tools to be invigorating. Perhaps most important, the quiet, undramatic process of describing, analyzing, and solving problems appealed to his nature.

Soon he was on his way to gaining a degree in what he calls "shoe leather epidemiology"—on-the-job-experience that he still uses in making decisions 30 years later.

Epidemiology

In Tennessee in the early 1960's, a young veterinarian named Claude E. Barton, after 7 years of private veterinary practice, accepted the position of Federal station epidemiologist with the Animal Disease Eradication Division (predecessor to APHIS) of USDA's Agricultural Research Service.

by James W. Glosser, Administrator, and Francine S. Linde, Confidential Assistant to the Administrator, Animal and Plant Health Inspection Service, USDA, Washington, DC

He wanted to refresh his professional focus and broaden his knowledge and expertise in animal health. He had been frustrated in private practice with food animals because, he says, "The quality of one's work was frequently determined by the economics of the situation. If the risk was too high, no one would spend money on it."

The Brucellosis Challenge

Brucellosis is a chronic disease of livestock that causes abortions and reduced milk production in infected animals. Historically it has appeared less devastating than other epidemic diseases because it does not kill the animals that contract it. Brucellosis tends to persist for a long time and is often devoid of signs or has signs similar to those of many other diseases that cause abortions. Because it does not cause emergency crises or high mortality rates, it seldom attracts widespread public attention. But it is a contagious disease that is difficult to detect because many infected animals and herds do not have visible signs of infection.

Over the years, brucellosis quietly eats at productivity and profits, causing abortions and reduced milk production and requiring more care and time to ensure livestock health. Contemporary epidemiological and diagnostic methods have been able to confirm the severity of the herd losses that occur over time. Brucellosis has been a major factor in preventing sustained and efficient reproductive performance in cattle, costing untold millions of dollars in losses.

Brucellosis also causes undulant fever in humans, a serious flu-like illness that can linger for weeks, months, or years. In the 1930's, before the discovery of antibiotics, farmworkers, consumers of raw milk, slaughterhouse personnel, and veterinarians who handled cattle were at increased risk of infection compared with the general population.

The human health aspect of the disease created the publicity and attention that finally led Congress in 1954 to appropriate funds for a full-scale brucellosis eradication program.

Claude was familiar with brucellosis. As a private practitioner, he had tested and vaccinated herds on a fee basis for the State and Federal governments. The insidious nature of the disease was a challenge for him, and he began searching for new ways to detect and understand it. It became apparent to him that brucellosis was a community problem and not isolated to a single farm or even to a single herd. For the next 10 years, he fought to convince farmers and producers of this fact.

Bob Nichols/USDA 90BW1035-21

A complement fixation test, one of the better tests to diagnose brucellosis. When Claude Barton joined APHIS in the early 1960's, epidemiology in veterinary medicine was in its infancy. Drawing on a number of disciplines such as statistics, immunology, serology, and pathogenesis, he came up with what he calls "shoe leather epidemiology"—on-the-job experience that he still uses in making decisions 30 years later.

New Approach

Claude identified and promoted a new approach to the problem. Believing that it was not enough to test only the primary infected herd, he demonstrated that the danger could exist in neighboring herds, including those that had very little remote contact. He therefore argued for testing neighboring herds, too, whenever brucellosis-infected herds were found. He worked with individuals, groups, and leaders at all levels to convince them that the "adjacent-herd" approach was an important tool in solving the brucellosis problem.

Ironically, because the brucellosis eradication program started in 1954 had become so successful in reducing the incidence of the disease, it created an optimism that diluted the strength of the program in the late 1960's and early 1970's.

By 1975, when brucellosis began to spread again in the United States, only a few States were free of the disease; approximately 16,000 herds were known to be infected, with between 10 and 20 percent of all neighboring herds infected as well. Claude realized that treating known infected herds without testing neighboring herds for the disease left sources of infection to spread to other herds, possibly to reinfect the original farm owner's herd after eradication.

In 1976 the Accelerated Brucellosis Program was established. As a direct result of Claude's 10 years of perseverance, the new national plan required all States to develop herd plans for testing or quarantining neighboring herds. His insistence on testing neighboring herds was a significant factor in the subsequent decrease of brucellosis. Brucellosis finally was recognized as a community problem rather than a single-animal or a single-herd problem.

He next took a position in APHIS as Tennessee brucellosis program coordinator, also continuing as the brucellosis epidemiologist in that State. According to Billy Johnson, associate deputy administrator of veterinary services at APHIS, Claude's approach "had the greatest single impact in reducing Tennessee's brucellosis infection rate from a high of 0.7 percent [of herds] to the present low rate of 0.01 percent and had a major impact in reducing the national level from 1.1 percent to 0.08 percent."

As brucellosis program coordinator, Claude is largely responsible for the reduction in Tennessee from over 500 brucellosis infected herds in 1976 to only 6 infected herds in 1990. This reduction has saved the United States millions of dollars in indemnity funds in Tennessee alone.

He is now an APHIS regional brucellosis epidemiologist for the southeastern United States. He is past president of the Tennessee Veterinary Medical Association, which in 1979 recognized him as "the outstanding veterinarian for the previous 10 years."

Bob Nichols/USDA 90BW1035-15

The resident herd of Angus-Hereford cattle at the Ellington Agricultural Center in Nashville, TN—just a few of the beneficiaries of Claude Barton's research. The center is headquarters for the Tennessee State Department of Agriculture.

The Computer, a Useful Tool

Claude used the computer as a management tool in Tennessee, which was one of the first pilot States to develop computer applications for controlling brucellosis. He admits to having had fears and misgivings about computers at first, but he quickly realized that the computer could sort data and track the movement of individual cattle and herds as well as store valuable diagnostic information. The computer could summarize data epidemiologically. He did not have misgivings for long.

A Legacy

Claude's dedication to his work is legendary. Communication and personal contact are vital to him. He has trained APHIS computer personnel and brucellosis program field personnel and has been a technical advisor on computer applications in the national brucellosis program. He has helped design computer programs and traveled all over the country to conduct training courses and seminars in applied epidemiology, serology, immunology, technical know-how, and regulatory agency work and responsibility. He has created links of communication with academics, private veterinarians, and the cattle industry.

With good teamwork and a dedicated and well-trained support staff, he continues to set an example. "There must be stability in the staff and program at the grass roots," he says. "Otherwise, the program cannot be successful at any level." He is particularly pleased with the work of two of his most recent protégées, Colleen Erbel, who now serves in Claude's original position in Tennessee, and Sherrilyn Wainwright of Jackson, MS.

"These two women were the best available candidates for APHIS positions as area veterinary epidemiologists," Claude says, "the most enthusiastic, the most trainable. They are motivated to try harder." With such recruits, he is confident in the legacy that he will leave when he retires in a few years. He says, "If we expect our vision, values, and beliefs to outlive our careers, then we must be willing, even eager, to accept the role of mentor, teacher, and colleague to future generations."

The great progress in eradicating brucellosis during the past 10 years has influenced the livestock industry to adopt a rapid completion plan for brucellosis eradication, designed to totally eradicate the disease from U.S. livestock by 1995. "This plan is very achievable if given adequate support by all concerned participants," he says.

What will Claude Barton do once brucellosis has been totally eradicated? "Veterinary medicine," he says, "is like mountain climbing; there is always a new challenge out there. The dynamics of modern U.S. animal agriculture create new disease problems every day. The value and flexibility of epidemiological methods in meeting these challenges have been proven many times over. No doubt, there will be plenty of mountains to climb after we fade from the scene."

Why did Claude became a veterinarian in the first place? "There was nothing really spectacular about it," he says. "In grade school through early college years, I was fascinated by any subject related to the biological sciences. My interest in medicine evolved as part of the process. I grew up on a small farm in west Florida that had several species of livestock. My first experience 'doctoring' animals was as a teenager treating farm animals for screwworm infestation then rampant in the area. I guess becoming a veterinarian was just the culmination of these interests and boyhood experiences."

He has been married to the former Barbara Ann Johnson for 37 years. They have three daughters and three grandchildren. "My grandchildren are my number one hobby," he says. "Number two is growing roses and fruit trees in the backyard. Third is listening to music, especially classical and old-time fiddle music. And occasionally I indulge in hunting and fishing."

Regional Research Centers:

The First Half Century, 1940-1990

In 1928, Alexander Fleming, a Scots bacteriologist at a London hospital, found a mold killing the bacteria in one of his growth cultures. In 1943, Mary Kathryn Hunt, a research assistant at USDA's Northern Regional Research Laboratory in Peoria, IL, unearthed a moldy cantaloupe from the discarded produce at a local market. Fleming's mold (a strain of *Penicillium notatum)* produced a substance he named penicillin. Hunt's mold (a strain of *Penicillium chrysogenum)* also produced penicillin. The difference between the two strains: Fleming's penicillin could not be mass-produced; Hunt's could.

Although Fleming did not pursue penicillin's potential as an antibiotic, scientists experimenting with penicillin at Oxford University in the 1930's were more persistent. By 1941, their years of trial and error had paid off with small but promising successes. What the Oxford scientists still needed was a way to mass-produce penicillin. England's facilities were then vulnerable to bombing attacks, so two British scientists came to the United States to get help and were referred to USDA's Northern Regional Research Laboratory.

Four USDA Laboratories Born in 1940

The Northern Regional Research laboratory at Peoria was one of four opened in 1940. The others are at Philadelphia, PA; New Orleans, LA; and Albany, CA. The Agricultural Adjustment Act of 1938 charged the Secretary of Agriculture with establishing the regional laboratories to develop new uses for farm commodities, especially surpluses. Part of the Agricultural Research Service (ARS) since 1953, the four laboratories are now known as regional research centers.

The Peoria center houses the ARS Culture Collection, which is a collection of micro-organisms used for industrial processes such as fermenting drugs. Today, the collection contains over 80,000 strains, which are available to researchers worldwide. In 1941, the collection was much smaller, but scientists in the laboratory's Fermentation Division were already producing industrial chemicals from some of the molds.

With help from the University of Wisconsin and the Carnegie Institute, the Peoria fermentation specialists invented an industrial method for mass-producing penicillin. For their technique, they needed a mold suitable for industrial production. None available was sturdy enough, which is why Moldy Mary, as she came to be known, was digging through the garbage in 1943. Her cantaloupe mold—NRRL 1951 B25 in the ARS Culture Collection—has been the source of most of the world's penicillin ever since.

Andrew Moyer, the USDA scientist who led the penicillin research and developed the key techniques, is a member of the American Inventors Hall of Fame, alongside the Wright brothers and Henry Ford, among others. Moyer received two patents on the process,

USDA Agricultural Research Service

Andrew Moyer developed the industrial process for mass-producing penicillin. Research at the Northern Regional Research Center opened the era of antibiotics in medicine.

by Ruth Coy, Writer, Agricultural Research Service, USDA, Beltsville, MD

which were licensed to drug and chemical companies that had helped with the research.

Developing a means for mass-producing penicillin may not be everyone's idea of agricultural research, but microorganisms are mostly products of the soil and can be cultivated and harvested like crops. More importantly, the fermentation media used to produce penicillin and other antibiotics contain vast tonnages of carbohydrates and proteins derived from agricultural commodities such as corn and soybeans.

Like the method for mass-producing penicillin, other successes of the regional research centers have deeply affected the quality of life for people the world over and have benefited American agriculture. Many conveniences people take for granted owe much to work done at the regional research centers in the past 50 years. Among the most familiar: year-round orange juice, instant potato flakes, wrinkle-free cotton shirts, and high-quality frozen foods.

Tim McCabe/USDA 1285X1458-16

Engineers at the Eastern Regional Research Center process potatoes into instant potato flakes.

Frozen Concentrated Orange Juice

Fifty years ago, orange juice was either canned (and tasted like the can), concentrated (and, when reconstituted, tasted like water), or fresh (but only in season), and Florida was producing surplus oranges. This was an ideal project for one of the regional laboratories.

As it happens, the person who came up with the solution was not a USDA scientist. Louis G. MacDowell was director of research at the Florida Citrus Commission. In 1946, he figured out that adding a little fresh juice, or cutback, to concentrated juice would restore the flavor and aroma lost during the concentration process.

Of course, solving a problem often takes more than thinking up the solution. It also usually takes more than one scientist working alone. MacDowell and his colleagues knew that USDA scientists at Winter Haven, FL, had the knowledge and tools to help refine the new process. At the time, the Winter Haven laboratory was a field station of what is now the ARS Southern Regional Research Center in New Orleans.

Working together, the Citrus Commission and USDA researchers developed the process and also discovered that the concentrate could be easily frozen. A new industry was born that has profited orange growers in billions of dollars over the years and has given people a reliable year-round source of a highly nutritious food.

Instant Potato Flakes

Much of the food processing research at the regional research centers has been similar to the development of frozen orange juice concentrate. Take a surplus; find a way to stretch its usefulness; invent a new convenience food.

Consider the potato. More potatoes are processed each year than any other fruit or vegetable. In the United States alone, some 20 billion pounds of potatoes a year are commercially processed into chips, fries, hash browns, instant potatoes, canned potatoes, and other snack and convenience forms.

But in the late 1950's, people were eating fewer potatoes, and farmers had large surpluses of cull potatoes with low market value. A team of chemical engineers at the Eastern Regional Research Center in Philadelphia developed the key steps needed to process potatoes into instant potato flakes.

The development of instant potato flakes helped revitalize the potato industry, now worth $2 billion a year, and opened a new era in high-quality, low-weight, shelf-stable foods. Potato flakes are also used as the main ingredient in reconstituted products such as extruded potato chips, and the key steps are used to make frozen french fries, which account for nearly half the potatoes sold to processors.

High-Quality Frozen Foods

Although we prize frozen foods mostly for their convenience, they are generally high in nutrient quality; have long-term storability; are safe to eat; and have good flavor, texture, and color. The reliability of these qualities today owes much to research carried out at the Western Regional Research Center in Albany from 1948 into the 1970's.

When the Albany center began its research on quality problems in 1948, commercially frozen foods had already been on the market for 20 years, but the industry could not explain many aspects of flavor deterioration, color change, nutrient loss, and bacterial contamination during processing and storage. The laboratory's studies for the next 25 years evaluated effects of prefreezing treatments and freezing and storage methods.

The results: Procedures for blanching vegetables; enzyme tests to evaluate these procedures; changes in freezing methods, including individual quick-freezing methods; comparisons of efficiency for different packaging methods; and data on how fluctuating temperatures affect frozen foods. The research on fluctuating temperatures resulted in the food industry's "Mark of Zero" campaign. This alerted processors and distributors to the importance of keeping temperatures below 0°F throughout processing, storage, and distribution.

Textiles and Hides

When most people see a wrinkled shirt, they see bent and crumpled fabric that needs ironing, but a textile chemist sees broken and rearranged chemical bonds. Applying heat under pressure (the hot iron) "mends" the bonds and restores the smooth finish.

But most people do not like to iron clothes, so in the 1940's and 1950's, the textile industry invented synthetic fibers that make up into easy-care fabrics, enticing consumers away from cotton fabrics. The market loss was devastating to cotton growers and ginners.

In the 1950's, scientists at the Southern Regional Research Center worked to counteract this loss. They developed treatments and processes that give cotton and cotton-blend fabrics the wrinkle-resistant and permanent-press qualities of fabrics made wholly from synthetic fibers. This technology was adopted worldwide and is the basis for the permanent-press cotton and cotton-blend garments that have been marketed for the past 35 years. The technology contributed substantially to preserving cotton's share of the textile fiber market. It also gave consumers the comfort of cotton with most of the convenience of synthetics.

Textile researchers at New Orleans have devised many other finishing processes that build on cotton's versatility and make it usable in unprecedented ways. For instance, they have developed chemical treatments that make cotton fabric flame retardant. These treatments are used in making protective clothing for military and

Jack Dykinga/USDA 0885X887-35a

At the Southern Regional Research Center, technician Anastasia Hammond distills formaldehyde from cotton samples.

civilian use. Flame-retardant cotton garments prepared with this technology are used by U.S. astronauts.

Similar research on wool was done for several years at the Albany center, which came up with treatments for flame- and mothproofing wool blends and for shrinkproofing wool. Most ARS studies on wool now take place at Philadelphia in the Hides, Leather, and Wool Research unit.

The Philadelphia center's work on hides has resulted in a new tanning agent that enhances leather's softness. The tanning agent helps the leather resist perspiration, repeated wetting and drying, and washing in hot soapy water. The leather industry has widely adopted this tanning agent to produce leathers for work shoes, golf gloves, garments, shoe uppers and linings, and jungle boots for the military. Center scientists have also developed several techniques and processes to minimize worker and environmental exposure to some of the noxious chemicals used in tanning.

Industrial and Medical Products

We usually think of agriculture as the source of food and fiber, but many commodities can also be used in industry. These products make us less dependent on imports (especially of petroleum), eliminate wastes, and increase demand for agricultural commodities.

The regional centers have developed many plant and animal products for industrial use. Among them are lubricants, plasticizers, adhesives, and resins made from soybeans; cocoa butter substitutes from cottonseed oil and tallow; and superslurper, a highly absorbent material made from cornstarch. Other industrial products resulting from center research include food additives, medicines, personal care products, and soaps and other cleansers.

Center scientists have also found microorganisms and developed techniques used in making riboflavin (vitamin B_2), vitamin B_{12}, several antibiotics, dextran (a blood plasma extender/substitute), xanthan gum (a thickening and texturizing agent for processed foods that has several industrial uses), beta-carotene, biocontrol agents, and hundreds of equally useful products.

In addition to work involving convenience foods, textiles and hides, and industrial chemicals, the centers also devote much research to ensuring food safety and minimizing the impact of commodity storage and processing on the environment. Some of the work at the centers has been basic research, including development of analytical methods widely used by scientists elsewhere and by regulatory agencies, such as USDA's Food Safety and Inspection Service.

The Next 50 Years

The work of the regional research centers will continue to evolve to meet changing needs. Right now, center scientists are concentrating on developing nonfood uses for crops while addressing environmental problems. Some of the projects they are working on include a practical motor fuel from vegetable oils, biodegradable plastics, encapsulated pesticides that will allow greater precision and lower inputs, and fermentation products, such as alternatives to road salts.

Most center accomplishments have been and will be small additions to our lives—a way to heat-transfer prints (such as slogans and pictures) to cotton T-shirts, a method for preserving apple cider longer, a way to extract sugars from surplus products.

Small though the individual accomplishments may seem, added together they greatly expand agricultural markets and make daily living easier for people everywhere.

Scientists Who Make a Difference

Some researchers stay locked in their laboratories, looking for clues that will unlock the mysteries of science. But those who make a real difference see not only the pieces of the puzzle before them but also the connection between these pieces and other aspects of life. These are the real leaders.

Five scientists exemplify this breadth of vision. They are but five of the 12,500 scientists in the land-grant university agricultural research system, scientists working in cooperation with USDA's Cooperative State Research Service. These scientists work in some of the high-priority areas that were identified in USDA's National Initiative for Research on Agriculture, Food, and Environment. The initiative calls for Federal support of competitive grants to fund agricultural research in critical food, fiber, and environmental areas.

Arthur Kelman: Explaining Bacteria That Attack Food Plants

University of Wisconsin plant pathologist Arthur Kelman, a member of the National Academy of Science, was the first chairman of the Board on Basic Biology and chaired the committee that drafted an influential report on introducing recombinant-DNA-engineered organisms into the environment. The report led to the establishment of rational policies to regulate biotechnology. Arthur has dedicated his scientific career to the study of bacteria that cause diseases in plants—to the study of simple phenomena that have eluded explanation.

One of the bacteria that he has spent years studying is *Pseudomonas solanacearum,* a scourge in warm climates for its attacks on a variety of plants, including tomatoes, potatoes, peanuts, and bananas. Time-consuming and costly methods are required to keep many pathogenic bacteria alive for study, but Arthur discovered that scientists could keep *Pseudomonas* alive and virulent for study simply by storing it in water. This technique has been used now for more than 40 years.

Arthur also has an interest in *Erwinia* bacteria, which devour such plants as potatoes. Not many scientists like to handle slimy and smelly rotting materials, but Arthur thrives on dissecting the mystery of why and how *Erwinia* works.

Scientists had assumed that bacteria in the soil were the major source of *Erwinia* contamination. Arthur discovered, however, that potato tubers, before they were planted, generally were contaminated with *Erwinia.* The *Erwinia* bacteria isolated from tubers were of two related groups, the so-called subspecies *atroseptica* and *carotovora.* At one point, Arthur thought that he was able to tell the two subspecies apart by the characteristic odor of cultures. He became so excited about this possibility that he spent an entire weekend smelling plates of *Erwinia.*

Although many people have rather routine lives, some have the nerve and dash to be different, and their lives can be exciting. Arthur and the other scientists described in this chapter are noted not only for their contributions to agricultural science but also for their courage to stand out from the crowd.

Ron Sederoff: Bringing Biotechnology to the Forest

Ron Sederoff, of North Carolina State University, is another agricultural scientist forging his own way. Once, Sederoff was speaking to a university advisory committee on pine tissue culture. As an invited guest from the genetics department, he had been talking about the research potential in forest biotechnology.

It was a gray day and a difficult afternoon of talks before a group that was made up mostly of wood products industry representatives who supported the university's program. The program had been working on improved tree seedlings and plantlets for 7 years, but it was slow going. The plantlets were more resistant to rust than the seedlings, but they grew more slowly. The research team needed to learn more about roots.

Ron paused and bowed his head and said very quietly, "I intend to be the first to isolate a gene from pine."

"What did you say?" somebody in the crowd called out.

Ron raised his voice a little and announced, "I intend to be the first to isolate a gene from pine," and he abruptly sat down. The break period that day was punctuated with excited talk about Ron's pronouncement. The group was clearly impressed.

About a year later, Ron and his colleagues had taken molecular genetics in pine trees a major step forward. They had proven that methods for

---

by Patricia Brazeel Lewis, Public Affairs Consultant, New Jersey Agricultural Experiment Station, Rutgers—The State University of New Jersey, New Brunswick, NJ

(Also contributing to this chapter were Ellis Cowling, North Carolina State University; Deane C. Arny, University of Wisconsin-Madison; Regina Broadway, Mississippi State University; Barbara Cooper, Purdue University; and Cathey Wolpert, University of California-Davis.)

identifying, isolating, and splicing genes from pine trees would work. Ron and his colleagues Anne-Marie Stomp, W. S. Chilton, and L. W. Moore demonstrated that foreign genes could be transferred into cells and tissues of pines using the crown gall bacterium, *Agrobacterium tumefaciens*. Although simple in themselves, these experiments implied that genetic engineering of pine trees was possible.

Ron and other men and women who work indoors, wear white lab coats, and study molecules in test tubes are part of a new breed of forest biologists. They study genes and grow trees in test tubes from pieces of plant tissue barely visible to the naked eye, and they are as comfortable with molecules, which are invisible without magnification, as they are with whole trees.

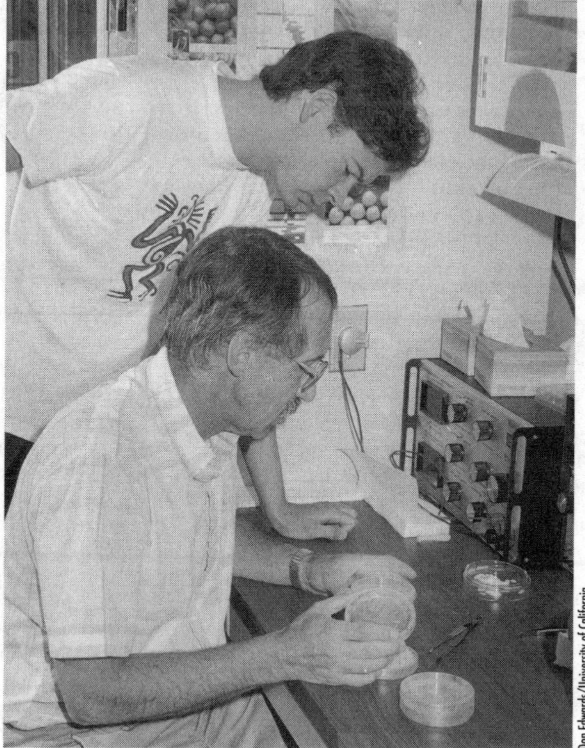

Don Edwards/University of California

Frederick Bliss (seated) and graduate student Mark Lewis discuss plant transformation procedures.

Frederick Bliss: Breeding Better Beans

For scientists like Frederick Bliss of the University of California-Davis, the scientific quest began in childhood. As a child on a Nebraska farm, Bliss learned from his grandfather, a German immigrant, about the skills and concern that go into budding and grafting fruit trees.

As an internationally known plant geneticist and horticulturist, Fred has focused on the genetics, breeding, biochemistry, and quality of legumes. He and his associates have investigated the genetic regulation of seed protein synthesis and the improvement of nitrogen fixation. These advances continue to be translated into practical applications, such as the development of new bean varieties with more protein (of improved quality), an enhanced ability to fix nitrogen, and resistance to insects that attack seeds in storage.

Like most scientists, Fred admits that knowledge sometimes is uncovered by accident. Clues pop up and a whole new picture emerges. It was like that with the new bean varieties that Fred and his colleagues hope will soon be released to farmers.

For 20 years, he had been studying seed proteins in common beans to increase protein and improve their nutritional content. In 1988, scientists at CIAT (Centro Internacional de Agricultura Tropical) reported finding wild beans that were resistant to the bruchid weevil, a pest that causes untold damage to stored beans in Africa and Latin America. Fred and his research team found that the resistance in these wild beans to the bruchid weevil was caused by one of the interesting proteins, arecelin, they had been studying.

Knowing that the protein was not present in cultivated bean species, Fred and his team believed that adding arecelin to other species would provide protection against insect damage and increase the food available to subsistence farmers. They set out to produce a modified version of the bean variety Sanilac that contains the arecelin gene, and tests show that the modified versions are resisting the bean weevil.

"This is one of the reasons research is so rewarding," Fred remarks. "The breeding of new plant varieties is challenging and pushes our creativity to the limits."

John Waldrop: Catfish Are Good for Consumers, Farmers, and the Environment

If creativity is sparked by new ideas, then John Waldrop is a very creative person. Whether working as an agricultural economist or a volunteer chef, John focuses on catfish.

As a researcher at Mississippi State University's Agricultural and Forestry

Experiment Station, John is interested in the conservation of natural resources. He became interested in the aquaculture industry when he learned that catfish production can help avoid erosion and runoff problems and that producers can make use of heavy clay soils that are often unproductive for row crops. The freshwater ponds used in catfish farming also help restore wildlife habitat.

"The catfish industry fills a need," he declares. "It's right in line with society's demand for food that is healthy, pure, safe, and pollution free. Even the ingredients in catfish feed are environmentally safe."

When John is not trying to evaluate the economics of new technology for commercial catfish production, he is cooking catfish.

As part of an earlier catfish education program, he gained acclaim as a chef by cooking the dish for people representing all of the continental United States and 24 foreign countries.

Once the dish of common folk, the catfish has made its way to the finest restaurants from coast to coast. The secret of its rise in popularity is simple: availability, economics, easy preparation, and good taste.

All researchers know that if a product does not taste good, consumers will not eat it—no matter how nutritious or economical it is. But as John has helped to prove, catfish does taste good. The mild flavor now comes in many forms, and catfish dishes can suit even the most discriminating diner.

John is not an advocate. He stresses that his job is to evaluate the economic viability of an aquaculture enterprise. "I can tell you how to be efficient and what the economic consequences of your actions may be," he says, "but I can't tell you whether to try raising catfish."

Philip Nelson: Can-Do Attitude

Some idealistic college graduates set out to change the world, but few actually do. Purdue University's Philip Nelson did. He changed the food processing industry.

Food processing is in Philip's blood. It is what he knows and what he likes. Philip grew up in Indiana, where his family grew tomatoes and owned a processing plant.

Everything had to be done in a few short weeks, and often processors had to guess on the need for can size. If too many processors guessed the same, the market became glutted. Philip started thinking about how to solve those problems and he studied them while a student at Purdue.

Because of consolidation in the food processing industry, the Nelson family business closed, and he went back to graduate school.

He says he does not recall any real obstacles along the way, but he does remember dropping a beaker of acid in a chemistry lab right after he started graduate school. "It ruined the only pair of shoes I had, and I wanted to quit school. But my wife and others encouraged me to forget obstacles and move on," he remembers.

Now Philip keeps a crumpled piece of paper in his desk that says, "Failure is not the falling down, but the staying down."

Philip has been determined. He has never forgotten those can size problems, and his determination has revolutionized the processing industry. By focusing on the development of a big can—a large tank—that could partially process tomatoes, hold them, and then process the product that the market wanted throughout the rest of the year, Philip advanced the cause of aseptic processing.

Aseptic processing uses high temperatures over short periods for sterilization. The product is sterilized outside the container and cooled, then the container is sterilized, and the two are brought together in a sterile environment. In traditional canning methods, food is cooked and processed right in the container.

With Philip's bulk storage system, no chemical additive or refrigeration is required for storage, and acidic fruits and vegetables can be stored indefinitely.

In addition to the holding tanks that range from 40,000 to 250,000 gallons, Philip has developed a 20,000-gallon rail car that requires no refrigeration.

The bulk storage system he invented is used by processors worldwide, from Japan to Morocco. The citrus industry also has adopted it for storing fresh orange juice.

The railcar allows tomatoes that are grown and made into paste in California to be shipped to the Midwest for making catsup.

Philip says, "Being able to give a part of yourself to someone else is important."

One of the ways Philip gives of himself is through working with students and passing on the "excitement of science." "The satisfaction," he says, "is in knowing that scientists can have an impact on human well-being."

That is something that Philip shares with the other scientists in this chapter—making the world a little better and a little more understandable.

PART V

education: the future of agriculture

Ag in the Classroom:

Teachers Plus Students Plus Volunteers Add Up to Agricultural Literacy

Every year the playgrounds of San Francisco's inner-city schools resound with laughter and learning as students meet farmers and farm animals in California's Farm Day in the City.

Across New York State, suburban, inner-city, and rural children are learning about New York's apple, horticulture, and dairy industries while improving their map reading and geography skills.

In Kansas, Missouri, and South Dakota, thousands of school children who attend State fairs do more than look at the animals and eat cotton candy—they learn through an "Ag-citing" experience that takes them through the exhibits on a search for answers to questions about agriculture.

In Nebraska, Massachusetts, South Carolina, and Alabama, elementary and secondary school teachers are attending training workshops on how agriculture can help students understand more about their world.

These activities are but the tip of the iceberg of the Ag in the Classroom program. Ag in the Classroom is happening in all 50 States plus Guam and the Virgin Islands. And because they saw the benefits of the U.S. program, the Canadians have set up their own Ag in the Classroom network.

Ag in the Classroom is a national voluntary program coordinated by USDA; participants are educators and people in agriculture and government across the country. The national Ag in the Classroom program began in 1981, but many farm organizations, particularly women's groups, had worked with schools before then.

Since 1981, Ag in the Classroom has increased and improved what is taught about agriculture in American schools. Today, as students in kindergarten through twelfth grade study science, language arts, social studies, or math, they often also learn about agriculture. They learn that agriculture is not just cows, sows, and plows, but that it is a sophisticated business—America's largest industry—and that there are many exciting and challenging careers for them in agriculture.

Ag in the Classroom is a grass roots movement. It is people—teachers, farmers, artists, writers, curriculum specialists, agribusiness people, and volunteers—who make the program work. Here are the stories of just a few of the dedicated and creative people in the Ag in the Classroom network.

by Shirley Traxler, Director, Ag in the Classroom, USDA, Washington, DC

Ag in the Classroom in California

It is a long way from San Francisco's Haight-Ashbury district to California's rich Central Valley, but teacher Elmer Eckart has helped shorten the distance for his urban students.

"Every year, I start by asking students some basic questions like 'Where does milk come from?'" Elmer says. "And every year, their first reaction is, 'It comes from the grocery store.'"

Elmer teaches fourth and fifth grade students at Grattan Elementary School. He first learned about Ag in the Classroom when the California Farm Bureau sponsored Farm Day in the City at eight San Francisco schools. Although Elmer had grown up in the city, he was intrigued by the possibilities of using agriculture to teach other subjects.

In 1984, Elmer was part of the pilot class that helped create California's innovative Summer Agricultural Institute (SAI). Each year, 30 educators with little or no agricultural background participate in an intensive 5-day workshop that introduces them to all aspects of the food and fiber system. SAI includes tours, lectures, and even an overnight farm stay to give participants some real "hands-on" experience.

Mark Linder, executive director of the California foundation for Ag in the Classroom, says, "Teacher training is essential. We cannot expect our friends in the city to understand us if they've never even visited Grandpa's farm."

For Elmer, perhaps the most valuable aspect of SAI is the network of teachers who have graduated from the program. "Each year, the alumni (there are more than 180) get together at least once." For teachers, who spend much of their professional lives with limited time to meet and talk with other adults, these meetings prove invaluable. "No one is as honest as another teacher," Elmer says. "People constantly say, 'Ag in the Classroom really works.'"

Integrating Agriculture into the Curriculum

A key to the success of Ag in the Classroom is that it does not ask teachers to teach agriculture as a separate subject. "Teachers have so much material to cover that they can't add anything else," says Elizabeth Wolanyk, State contact for New York. "Curriculum materials must integrate agriculture into what teachers already need to teach."

Elizabeth grew up on a farm in western New York and majored in agriculture at Cornell. She was one of the first women to become an agriculture production teacher in New York.

Today, she works with the New York State College of Agriculture and Life Sciences at Cornell, helping to develop the Ag in the Classroom curriculum and training teachers in how to use the materials.

"One of the things I realized when I was teaching is that there are many opportunities to integrate agriculture into other subjects. In history, for example, the development of this country is directly related to the development of agriculture," Elizabeth points out. "Often teachers don't make the connection with agriculture for their students because they're not aware of it themselves."

The New York Ag in the Classroom program offers teachers in grades 3 through 6 a looseleaf notebook filled with activities they can use in their classrooms. The notebooks—one for each grade level—are tied to the State curriculum objectives for each grade and offer teachers specific suggestions on how a lesson on agriculture can teach a particular objective in subjects including math, science, social studies, and language arts.

Each teacher notebook comes with a supply of student workbooks. New York City teacher Irma Graf has found that the workbooks incorporate fun and learning. Irma notes, "Students enjoy the lessons so much they don't realize they're learning about math."

But Ag in the Classroom's goal is not just to teach students more math, science, and history; it is also designed to help students recognize how important the food and fiber system is to their lives. A comment by one of Irma's students reflects the success of the New York Ag in the Classroom curriculum materials. One sixth-grader noted, "New Yorkers live in apartment buildings and don't care [about food sources]. But now I care where food comes from."

Dave Hansen/Minnesota Extention Servicve

Kirsten Anderson, a student at Emmet D. Williams School in Roseville, MN, reviews the latest edition of Minnesota Agriculture *magazine. Education is primarily a State and local responsibility, and each State's approach to Ag in the Classroom reflects its own needs and resources.*

Agriculture and Economics

Many programs began by developing materials for fourth grade, because that is when most students are introduced to the study of their State's history and geography, subjects that agriculture naturally enhances. But States have found that agriculture is a natural part of many other important subject areas as well.

One example is an Arkansas program on teaching the economics of the food and fiber system. "The program," says Phil Besonen, associate director of the Moore Center for Economic Education at the University of Arkansas and State Ag in the Classroom contact, "helps students learn more about two vital, yet seldom taught, subjects—agriculture and economics.

"It's currently possible for young people to graduate from high school with little understanding of or appreciation for the economics of the system that provides them with the bountiful harvest of food, clothing, and other life essentials," Phil says. "This program gives teachers 122 separate lessons that incorporate agricultural economics into other curriculum areas."

An Innovative Magazine

Education is primarily a State and local responsibility, and each State's approach to Ag in the Classroom is based on its own needs and resources. States are responsible for organizing, funding, and publicizing their programs; developing materials; and training teachers. This diversity has led to a number of innovative ways to help students learn about agriculture. *Minnesota Agriculture* magazine *(AgMag* for short) is distributed free four times a year to over 1,200 public and nonpublic schools in the State, reaching approximately 70,000 students.

AgMag gives real meaning to the term "public-private partnership"—nearly 60 organizations support the development, printing, and distribution of the magazine.

Education writer Jan Hoppe has written every issue of *AgMag*. She draws on her experience as a former teacher and on her agricultural roots. "I grew up on a dairy farm and spent many years in 4-H," she says.

As she writes the magazine, Hoppe says she tries to "visualize a particular kid." Keeping an individual child in mind helps her think about such educational concerns as reading levels and appropriate vocabulary. She adds, "I also keep in mind what kids think is cool and what's dumb. And—very important—I focus on what they think is funny."

Humor is part of every *AgMag*. From riddles (Why did the farmer name the pig "Ink"? Because it kept running out of the pen) to contests (How many animal sayings can you recall?), humor helps keep student interest high.

Interstate Cooperation

Although each State Ag in the Classroom program is organized to meet local needs, States in a given region do work together. For instance, the New England States and New York have established the New England/New York Ag in the Classroom consortium. According to Chairman Gerald Fuller of the University of Vermont, "We plan to cooperate in many activities, such as training teachers and developing materials."

The consortium has developed a poster that shows the many aspects of America's food and fiber system. Artist and sheep farmer Jefferson Cotton has worked with the consortium to develop the poster. "The border of the poster features commodities and products of our region," Jefferson says. "Students can begin their exploration of agriculture by looking at things they recognize."

The poster depicts the flow of food and fiber products from the farm through processing and marketing into the city. "It also helps students understand other processes essential to agriculture—soil and water conservation, waste management, and transportation," says Chaitanya York, State contact for Ag in the Classroom in Maine.

Teaching Beyond the Classroom

In many States, Ag in the Classroom reaches beyond the classroom. Some projects involve and educate children who attend State fairs. Loreen McMillan, a Kansas State Board of Education staff member, says these exhibits are a way to "help parents and students use the State fair as the big classroom it is."

In Kansas, students are invited to take part in an Ag-citing experience. When they arrive at the Ag in the Classroom booth, they are handed agricultural activity sheets containing questions such as, "How do you tell the difference between a pumpkin and a squash?" Posters around the exhibit in the Pride of Kansas Building provide the answers (a pumpkin has a five-sided stem).

"We contact all the exhibitors to enlist their help in developing the questions," explains Becky Koch, Kansas State Ag in the Classroom contact. "We want students to learn something—but we don't want them to feel as if they're taking a test." Each student who brings back a completed worksheet receives a prize donated by an exhibitor. Even this part of the exhibit is educational: To receive a prize, students reach into a big bucket of Kansas wheat.

The Role of Volunteers

Volunteers play a vital role in Ag in the Classroom. Whether it is developing materials or training teachers, volunteers have made it possible for the Ag in the Classroom program to reach out to many thousands of students and teachers.

In Montana, Betty Jo Malone exemplifies the impact that volunteers can have. As State contact for Agriculture in Montana Schools (AMS), she is part of a program that involves hundreds of volunteers across the State.

The Montana treasure chest has been one of the State's most ambitious projects. Sturdy wooden boxes (built by Kiwanis and FFA volunteers) contain farm commodities, miniature farm machinery, and lesson plans. A treasure chest has been delivered to every school in the State that enrolls more than 20 students.

AMS is entirely a volunteer effort. Today, AMS is producing five videotapes to add to the treasure chests. Most of the work—from scripting through distribution—will be handled by volunteers. Malone says that makes it easier to ask for—and receive—grants to support the project's work. "Funders know they're getting a great return on their money," she says.

David Phillips, program advisor for elementary and secondary education at the U.S. Department of Education, is a charter member of the task force that was named in 1981 to guide the Ag in the Classroom program. He says, "Agriculture is not simply farming. It's the supermarket, the equipment factory, the trucking system, the overseas shipping industry, the scientists' laboratory, the houses we live in, and much more. It has an affect on the air we breathe, the ground we walk on, the water we drink, and the food we eat. Ag in the Classroom is giving thousands of students an opportunity to learn about this vital industry and the role it plays in their lives."

Discover New Worlds in the Agricultural Future

"I would rather dream dreams about the future than read histories of the past."

—Thomas Jefferson

Weightless farmers? Cosmic cows? How long can any concept be considered farfetched when the world's information base is doubling every 6 to 7 years? Over the next 20 years the rates of technological and social change will be phenomenal.

The food, agriculture, and natural resources system is the largest industry in the United States, employing about 24 percent of all workers and projected to generate 25 percent of the gross national product by the year 2000. This industry is definitely at the forefront of the new and emerging technologies that are fueling the rapid changes in society.

Agriculture put this Nation on the road to its present prosperity, and agriculture will carry that prosperity into the 21st century. U.S. agriculture offers excellent and varied career opportunities to people who want to participate in meeting the challenges of change and in reaping the benefits of a new agricultural revolution.

Revolution

U.S. agriculture is experiencing a revolution. In terms of production, business, science, education, consumers, and community, the agricultural world of the future will be very different from what it is today. The basic purpose of agriculture will still be the production of high-quality food and fiber products at economical prices, but the tools, methods, and hardware used to accomplish this mission will be very different, very scientific, and very sophisticated.

by Susan Forte, National USDA Agriscience Ambassador, University of Florida, Gainesville, FL

The mission of agriculture also is becoming broader and more diverse, encompassing improving the environment, managing resources, marketing internationally, and producing nonfood products—such as plastics, fuels, rubber, ink, medicines, and newspapers—from food crops.

Bob Nichols/USDA 90BW0806-24

Susan Forte (left) explains the advantages of producing plastics with ethanol—a byproduct of corn—to Tom Farrish (right), agricultural science teacher at Ransom Middle School, Cantonment, FL.

Biotechnology

Leading the way into the future is biotechnology. Biotechnology is not new; people have used biological systems for profit and comfort ever since someone noticed that one bull consistently sired bigger calves, that some vegetables were bigger and tastier than others, or that sugar fermented with grain and water yielded a very different sort of beverage.

Powerful biological tools have emerged in the last 2 decades. These tools are helping scientists to delve into the world of the gene, to better understand biological systems and to manipulate them more skillfully than ever before. In the 1980's, computers drove technology forward; in the 1990's, the driver will be genetics.

Agricultural scientists are applying the tools of biotechnology in the development of biological controls for insects, using a variety of micro-organisms—such as bacteria, viruses, fungi, and protozoa—as insect fighters. In addition, many micro-organisms modified by genetic engineering hold great potential for decomposing residual chemicals, such as polychlorinated biphenyls (PCB's), that pollute soil and ground water. For example, researchers have genetically altered a microbe that naturally breaks down 2,4-D, an herbicide that once was widely used and that today is often found heavily concentrated in waste dumps; the genetic variant is better suited to degrading the chemical, consuming six times as much as the parent organism.

Agriscientists are taking genes from certain plants and transferring them into crops. For example, a gene from

Peranthium, a South African plant that has no known insect predators and produces its own natural insecticides, has been genetically engineered into wheat and corn. Genetic engineering is being used to mass-produce bovine somatotropin, a natural hormone that can stimulate a 10- to 15-percent increase in a cow's milk output. The sterile grass carp has been engineered to eat water weeds that clog canals and lakes, minimizing the need for chemical control.

The farmers of the future will be in the biology business, and a diverse business it will be. Salt-tolerant tomatoes, freeze-resistant citrus and strawberries, drought-resistant corn, cloned cattle, and ultralean pork all are examples of biotechnology at work in agriculture. Biotechnology could add $5 billion a year to the value of the world's major crops by 1997, rising to $20 billion a year by 2010.

Beyond Food and Fiber

Crop plants are the United States' most important annually renewable source of wealth. Today, with the Nation's capability of producing quantities of the major crops well in excess of domestic needs, and with an export market that often is inadequate to absorb the excess, diversification into new crops is imperative. U.S. farmers have had great success with such former new crops as soybeans, sunflowers, and safflowers. What new crops are being developed today?

Crambe, guayule, grain amaranth, jojoba, canola, and kenaf are among the crops that appear most promising. Crambe produces an oil suitable for industrial lubricants. Guayule is a source of domestic natural rubber. Grain amaranth seeds are rich in the amino acid lysine, which is found in relatively low levels in many other grains. Jojoba seed oil is a liquid wax used today mostly in the cosmetics industry. Low-cholesterol canola oil is an excellent example of a planned effort in new crop development that paid high dividends: Coordinated research programs, including genetic engineering, improved the crop and made Canada the world leader in export of canola oil. Kenaf has good potential as a fiber crop for paper pulp. (Other promising new fiber crops are bamboo, sorghum, eucalyptus, and crotalaria.)

Other potential new crops, including annual canarygrass, yellow mustard, oriental mustard, coriander, flatpea, and birdfeed sunflower, are useful for food condiments and birdfeed. Crown vetch controls weeds, requires no mowing, and makes a beautiful ground cover, especially for roadsides; it is particularly valued for preventing soil erosion.

Ethanol from corn has established a substantial niche as an alternative source of energy. Other energy crops under investigation, which could eventually compete with petroleum, include Jerusalem artichoke, seaweeds, high-sugar sorghum, and cattails.

Diversity

The key to the future health of the agriculture industry is diversity. Farmers will need to use the knowledge of scientists and businesspeople. No

Bob Nichols/USDA 90BW0806-15

Tom Farrish and seventh-grade students—Johanna Robinson, Amanda DeLaney, and Julie Gallop—discuss progress of the corn that the students planted, signs of healthy growth, and detection of disease and insect damage.

longer defined solely as food producers, they will be growing industrial lubricants on the lower 40 acres and raising ink, paper, and fast food containers on the upper 40. In the dairy barn the farmer might be producing tissue plasminogen activator (TPA), a human hormone that is used to treat heart attack victims. And on the back 40? Perhaps insulin, interferon, interluken, or even hemoglobin.

Space Agriculture

And what of those cosmic cows? What does the future hold for agriculture beyond "Spaceship Earth"? Consider this: Food is the most important fuel in space; without it, astronauts cannot function or perform their missions.

The National Aeronautics and Space Administration's Controlled Ecological Life Support System Program is exploring ways to develop the life-support system technology necessary to allow people to live on a self-sustained space station, a Moon base, or even an outpost on Mars (see Chapter 40). The Controlled Ecological Life Support System will be a complete system of food production, waste recycling, and crew housing. Current research is concentrating on the actual plant, or biomass, production; later research will concentrate on resource recovery, waste management, and living requirements.

The idea of space agriculture has crystallized. Agriscientists are growing food crops experimentally in lunar soil and studying foliage plants for their ability to absorb impurities from air and water in closed living systems; the National Aeronautics and Space Administration is evaluating a recently completed experiment examining the development of chicken embryos in zero gravity.

Futurists predict space colonies with space farms, where agricultural productivity will be 10 to 40 times greater than on Earth. Plants will be growing in 1-foot-deep nonorganic lunar soil. Light, temperature, soil moisture, nutrient levels, and stress will be monitored constantly by computers managed by "agrinauts." "Spacestock" will include chickens, rabbits, turkeys, some cattle and sheep, and fish. Aquaculture will be a major animal protein source in space. Many of these cosmic creatures will photosynthesize their own food through algae in their skin or plant chloroplasts engineered into their cells. And "agrobots" will be everywhere, measuring fertilizer, shearing sheep, picking fruit, harvesting microbes, transplanting seedlings, and conducting experiments (many of these agrobots already exist today).

Space Agriculture Spinoffs

The most exciting aspect of space agriculture is its beneficial agribusiness spinoffs—technology transfers for agriculture on Earth. Privatizing and commercializing space research and development provide new agricultural technologies. "Space-age spinoffs" include the following:

- The application of commercial expertise to land remote sensing by EOSAT, the Earth Observation Satellite company
- Thermal analysis of agribusiness structures (such as poultry houses), vegetable cooling, and nursery containers by NASTRAN (National Aeronautics and Space Administration Structural Analysis System)
- Aerial color infrared (ACIR), which provides maps for crop inventories
- Microwave vacuum drying (MIVAC), a rapid, efficient method of drying agricultural crops, provided through McDonnell Douglas Space Research
- A version of soil and rock analyzing instruments developed for the Viking lander spacecraft on Mars that is now used for detecting and analyzing metal and mineral elements
- Soil surveying, wetland surveys, urban expansion studies, and poultry plant noise control with aerospace materials . . . .

The list continues. Space agriculture is a reality, right here on Earth.

The future world of agriculture will be exciting, dynamic, and diverse, transcending all areas of production, business, science, education, consumers, and community. Perhaps the greatest diversity in future agriculture will lie in the richness and variety of career opportunities in such areas as biotechnology, new crop development, and space agriculture.

Cosmic cows, zero-gravity strawberries, agrobots, salt-tolerant tomatoes, natural pesticides, genetically engineered microbes, animals that photosynthesize their own food . . . What new foods will we be eating and what new products will we be using by the year 2000? The goal of this decade's agriscientists must be to make use of the opportunity of a lifetime. The world is moving, and anyone who wants to participate in the future must get on. One thing is certain: The shot of U.S. agriculture will be heard and felt throughout this world—and even in those beyond.

FFA Goes High-Tech

"Hayseed, pumpkin, turnip, squash,
Future Farmers we are by gosh."

— *Future Farmer Yell,*
FFA Manual, *circa 1930*

Once that chant was appropriate, because once, the Future Farmers of America was a farm boy club. Those days are gone.

The organization that once ushered young men into careers in farming has undergone some serious soul searching and repositioning for the next century. From that process came a new look and a new approach—one that puts more emphasis on future than it does on farmer.

This change has taken place because today's FFA membership is increasingly urban and headed for promising careers in agriculture—but not necessarily on the farm. Today the largest FFA chapters are in Philadelphia, Chicago, and other metropolitan areas. About 80 percent of FFA members today pursue education after high school, disproving the old notion that the vocational agriculture classroom was best left to students with limited interests or intellect.

"FFA is highly geared to agriscience and agribusiness now," says Danny Grellner, a 20-year-old FFA member from Kingfisher, OK. "The scope of FFA is broadening beyond production agriculture."

Yet production agriculture has been FFA's base ever since it was established in 1928 as a grassroots way to bring high school farm students together for leadership training, judging contests, and fellowship as an integral part of agricultural education in high schools.

by Michael Wilson, Managing Editor,* Prairie Farmer, *Decatur, IL

The organization swelled in numbers, peaking at over half a million by the late 1970's. It opened its doors to women in 1969, more recently to junior high school students. Now members range in age from 12 to 21.

But U.S. farm numbers have steadily dropped, and FFA membership declined by over 100,000 in the last 12 years.

However, USDA has predicted an annual shortage of 4,000 college graduates for nearly 50,000 new agriculture-related jobs throughout the 1990's. And that is one reason FFA has launched an urgent campaign to broaden its base. The organization now embraces sciences, marketing, and computers—and any urban student interested in those subjects.

The New Look

Changes have come fast. Two years ago the national organization began calling itself only by its acronym, FFA, discreetly avoiding the notion that it still serves only students destined for farming careers.

In recent national FFA conventions, student leaders grappled with fundamental changes in their organization's structure. Besides the name change, members have tinkered with the most time-honored symbols, emblems, and ceremonial wording, in an effort to update the look and feel of the organization.

The tinkering has had a dramatic effect on grassroots training. In tiny Clinton, MO, for example, 15 personal computers—1 on each desk—make the vocational agriculture classroom look like a NASA flight center. The computers are used daily to teach agricultural business management and marketing, as well as agricultural business sales and economics.

Future Farmers of America

Leadership training—including how to speak in public and preside over meetings—prepares FFA members for success in a wide range of civic and agricultural positions.

"Five years ago my enrollment was declining dramatically in the traditional crop and livestock classes," says Dan Wallace, Clinton's agricultural instructor. "We decided to go ahead with two new classes, and in 3 years enrollment doubled." In 1990 Clinton tore up its old vocational agriculture shop and replaced it with an animal science laboratory. Enrollment shot up from 65 to 212 students.

The new approach appeals to urban students. In the Tulsa, OK, FFA chapter, membership zoomed from 35 to 200 students in 3 years.

Urban and rural students alike enjoy the broad leadership training and community service activities. The Building

Our American Communities (BOAC) program lets FFA chapters boost rural economies through fixup, cleanup, or makeover projects, saving local governments thousands of tax dollars.

FFA's Computers in Agriculture award program provides prizes for young people who adapt new technology. The agriscience recognition program offers members a chance to develop projects that showcase science skills in topics related to agriculture. FFA's new agricultural sales contest incorporates both leadership skills and an understanding of agricultural marketing.

"Agribusiness has a crying need for well-trained, motivated sales and marketing people. We think this contest can be an excellent source of those individuals," says Charlie Scholes of Vicon, one of many agribusiness firms to support FFA through the organization's fundraising arm, the National FFA Foundation.

Despite the changes, many still can not get over the cows-and-plows image that FFA is trying so hard to dispel. Danny Grellner expects to change that perception.

"Once you get past the part where people think you're just teaching kids how to plow or raise cattle—and they see the leadership or other aspects—it changes their entire perspective on FFA."

Unlocking Plant Breeding Secrets

Mark McCully's vision of the future includes agricultural career fields so unbelievable that a job description cannot yet be written.

"There will be an increase in genetics in both plant and animal science, finding better ways for crop production, pest control, and erosion control," says the Varna, IL, FFA member. "There's going to be a lot more opportunities in science and technology in the future—new jobs in areas we can't even imagine."

Mark, an agricultural economics and business major at Illinois Valley Community College, tested his science interests and intellect in FFA's new agriscience student recognition program 2 years ago. Born and reared on a grain and cattle farm, he developed a project to help plant breeders ensure corn pollination during the growing season.

Mark says male corn plants in some hybrids will shed pollen about 5 days before the female plants can accept it. Traditionally, seedsmen will plant the male inbreds 5 days after the female inbreds and then hope that the two plants pollinate.

"If heavy rains or some other weather condition delays planting of the male seed by more than 6 or 7 days, a severe reduction in pollination could occur," Mark explains.

After 2 years of research, Mark discovered a way to delay pollination by using the growth regulator ethephon. He discovered it would delay growth of the male plant if applied in the right proportion about 5 days before tassel emergence—the critical point when pollination occurs.

The pollination delay research will help make the seed industry more stable, explains Mark. "Almost all my judges commented on the fact that they liked this project because it showed that I identified a problem, researched it, and came up with a solution that can now be applied to solve that problem."

Mark had help from Mid-County High School science instructor Eric Rittenhouse, agricultural instructor Vernon Watt, and local agribusinessman Lynn Griffith, of Griffith Seed Co., McNabb, IL. "The project Mark is pursuing could provide some very beneficial information to the hybrid seed corn industry," says Griffith.

Mark likes the new hi-tech look of FFA and agricultural education.

"Implementing science is just going to make the FFA program a lot stronger and increase enrollment and participation," Mark says. "Future instructors are going to have to specialize further in science. Curricula will have to be changed to deal with science as it relates to agriculture. If high school agriculture can be made into a science credit, that will be a big step in increasing enrollment in agricultural courses.

"FFA needed to change. All we're doing is adapting to the times. We should have done it sooner."

Leader for the Next Century

Danny Grellner was 18 years old when he put his laser concentration and velvet voice to the ultimate test—a prepared speech before 22,000 FFA members at the annual National FFA convention in Kansas City, MO.

"I was shaking walking up to the stage," he says. "But after the first word, a calm came over me. I didn't want to leave, to tell you the truth."

The Kingfisher, OK, youth spoke eloquently about biotechnology, international trade, farm policy, and free enterprise—and came away with the top prize. That was 2 years ago. The affable Danny still gives all credit to his FFA leadership training.

"We can provide leadership training no other organization can," he says enthusiastically. "Surveys show that students enrolled in agriculture and

FFA who go to college end up ranked as the top agricultural students. I think that's a tribute to FFA leadership training."

In Oklahoma, nine contests, plus extemporaneous and prepared public speaking, offer a multitude of ways for students to learn to lead. "We've probably touched 4,000 high school agricultural students in Oklahoma with our public speaking contests alone," Danny says.

As State FFA president, Danny witnessed dramatic changes in FFA classrooms and attitudes. "People think agriculture is limited to the farm. It's the same thing we've put up with for 20 years," he says. Oklahoma agricultural education authorities revamped the curriculum in 1988. "Ag teachers are being retrained to go beyond production agriculture. Now we're telling people that if they don't want to farm that's fine, there are other areas.

"We don't want to disassociate ourselves from production agriculture," he cautions. "We're walking a tightrope. We've got to make sure changes are made for the right reasons."

Danny, who majors in agricultural economics and international agriculture at Oklahoma State University, hopes to launch his career in an overseas position in agribusiness. He grew up on a beef and wheat farm and, like many FFA members, wrestled with the decision of whether to return to his roots. "I considered going back to the farm, but I'd like to first get a job and get some financial security," he explains. "Eventually I'd like to bring my kids up on a farm because of the rural values."

Danny is considering a run at national FFA office. If elected he will become one of six elite national officers selected from around the country. National officers become the voice of agricultural education and FFA. If he makes it, Danny will have a year-long chance to test his leadership skills.

"The organization is going through so much change. I want to be a part of it," he says.

Fixing up Hometown America

Each year thousands of FFA members work together to make their hometowns better places to live. An FFA program called Building Our American Communities (BOAC) lets them organize local projects to help develop rural economies, beautify neighborhoods, and improve the quality of life in smalltown America. It is estimated that the labor donated by FFA members in BOAC projects, sponsored by the RJR Nabisco Foundation, is worth about $9.5 million annually.

The FFA chapter in Raton, NM, is one such group that has made a big impact on its community. The chapter went to work on a mining reclamation project supervised by the Mining and Mineral Division of the State's Natural Resources Department. The project began in May 1989 in Sugarite State Park, where the Raton chapter had previously built picnic tables.

Elizabeth Morgan, 18, one of three FFA member project leaders, says 28 students dug seed basins, built rock dams, terraced steep slopes, and built a diversion channel to change the flow of a small stream. Five students worked as administrative assistants, helping with bookkeeping, photography, and research and documenting the chapter's efforts.

Elizabeth won the national achievement in volunteerism award in 1988 for her work with earlier Raton BOAC projects. She spearheaded a project to build a wildlife rehabilitation center and greenhouse operation. The wildlife center, now licensed by the U.S. Fish and Wildlife Service, was developed by Raton FFA to help injured animals and to teach grade school students about wildlife. The high school's wildlife biology class now has 90 students per year, explains Ray Chelewski, Raton FFA adviser and agricultural instructor.

"We've had mountain lions, deer, eagles, and other birds recuperating from injuries," says Ray.

"It's neat for me to sit back and watch the community and the kids put something together that they feel is important," says Ray. "The program works on community involvement."

Ray sees in the chapter's community service a bonding between students and citizens. "Even if the students leave the community, they'll have a lasting impression and a positive attitude about being here," he says.

Students like Elizabeth gain more than a positive attitude. For her efforts, she earned a $24,000 scholarship from the RJR Nabisco Foundation and is now an agricultural communications major at Mississippi State University.

"My involvement in FFA and BOAC played a direct part in getting the scholarship," she says. "Working with BOAC gave me incredible opportunities. It's based on cooperation: working with people and yet being a leader. It deals with citizenship—something people need all of their lives."

High School Agriculture Teachers: People Builders

Once, young people from America's farms would go to school to get their book learning and then be out in the field to sow oats, cut hay, do thrashing, or pitch hay from spring until fall. The American agricultural education system was one of apprenticeship—work, watch your parents, and learn how.

In the 1920's, however, an organized system of educating farm boys began to take shape: vocational agriculture.

The education system had three parts: Teach students about agriculture (such as planting corn) in the high school classroom; give them hands-on or laboratory experiences with projects (grow your own 5 acres of corn); and recognize their efforts and help them grow personally as agricultural leaders (through FFA). Although "vocational" has been dropped from the name, 12,000 agriculture teachers today still use the basic three-part framework for agricultural education in 7,000 high schools.

From the beginning, high school agriculture teachers have been the key to successful agricultural education. Their hard work and dedication make the future come alive for hundreds of thousands of teenagers every year. They push and encourage young people to explore, study, get involved in agriculture, be a part of the community and the school, strive for higher goals, be leaders, be proud of their professions, and learn to work together. They are an important part of the agricultural leadership in rural communities.

by Jack Pitzer, Senior Editor, and Andrew Markwart, Managing Editor,* FFA New Horizons *Magazine, Alexandria, VA

Changes in High School Agriculture

Significant changes have taken place in high school agriculture, including the addition of girls as students and women as agriculture teachers.

Cathy Hively is a 26-year-old teacher in Chancellorville, VA, near Fredericksburg and 60 miles south of Washington, DC. She is new to the job and faces her 62 students in five classes each day with energy and enthusiasm—it is hard work, but she is up to the task.

She confesses that part of her strength comes from having been a student of vocational agriculture in high school and from serving as a State president in FFA. She also traveled in Japan and Germany as part of an FFA exchange program.

Cathy's biggest challenge is to provide exciting and meaningful training for her agriculture students. She teaches classes in "applied science and technology" and "agricultural business," and she supervises a group of students who attend classes half the day and also work in related agricultural jobs. Many of her students are seeking work experiences to mesh with their career goals. One student wants to be an agricultural journalist, so Hively is helping that student find a relevant job near school.

In all parts of the Nation, the content and presentation of agricultural education have changed drastically, and the future promises more change.

The number of job opportunities for actual farmers is low, but there is a great need for young people with agricultural education in as many as 200 related career fields, such as livestock marketer, meat cutter, researcher, communicator, salesperson, machinery technician, horticulturist, golf course caretaker, forester, zookeeper, veterinarian assistant, county Extension agent, teacher, food processor, and cotton marketer.

Andrew Markwart/Future Farmers of America

Patrick Hiser, high school instructor in Vero Beach, FL, examines locally grown grapefruit with student Wesley Davis.

Different from the Traditional Program

As with so many cities in the United States, the metropolitan area of Madison, WI, is slowly creeping outward. What once were small, independent farming communities on the outskirts of the city have now taken the shape of suburbs. The nearby town of Verona has gone through that transition, and the agriculture classes at Verona High School have also changed.

"Ours is a lot different from the traditional program," explains agriculture instructor and FFA advisor Ferron

Havens. "It has to be, or we wouldn't be in business. This program would have died years ago if we had stuck with the 4-year production agriculture program."

Verona's agriculture program and FFA are far from dead. This year 150 of the school's 730 students enrolled in agriculture classes, and 100 joined FFA.

Three main ingredients are responsible for the continuing success of Verona's program—good instructors, exciting classes, and a growing seventh and eighth grade exploratory program.

Ferron and 35-year teaching veteran Farres Harrison are well liked by the student body because of their ability to relate to young people and keep classes interesting.

One reason the courses are fresh and interesting is that the class selection is continually being updated by the two instructors. "We try to change the curriculum to meet the needs of the students and the industry," says Ferron, "In the next 2 years, you'll see a course here in biotechnology, and we're revamping our whole agribusiness management class into a business and marketing class."

The junior high program, which now includes seventh and eighth grade classes, is presented with a strong hands-on emphasis and a "high entertainment factor." During the 9-week course, nine different topics are explored—the total agricultural industry, horticulture, companion animals, conservation, forestry, products and marketing, agronomy and soils, mechanics, and livestock production.

Each day, the students encounter a new topic through an activity in which they can be involved. For example, when welding is introduced, Farres gives the students a quick introduction to welding, and a few minutes later they have welding rods in their hands. "They get hold of an electrode, strike an arc, and they're scared to death," he says. "But at least when you talk about welding, they know what you're talking about and can visualize that experience. They don't think of agriculture as just farming. They've got to see agriculture as a total, vast area of employment and career opportunities for them. If we can't accomplish that, we haven't done anything at all."

Today's agriculture teachers are emphasizing the science of agriculture. It is important to the future of the industry, and is another way to attract into agriculture the teens who did not grow up on farms.

Fast-Growing Plants

There is a little green and yellow plant causing quite a stir in Wisconsin agriculture classrooms—and around the world. It is the FastPlant, a member of the cabbage family whose growth cycle has been accelerated to the point that it flowers only 14 days after it has been planted.

Students in the Beaver Dam, WI, agriscience department have been experimenting with the FastPlants for 4 years. Instructor David Laatsch attended a 1987 summer workshop for biology teachers that featured FastPlants. David quickly saw the possibility of using these plants to teach agriscience and introduced them to his class in the fall of 1987. The next summer, David put on a 1-week workshop for agriculture and other science teachers. The popularity of the plants has spread across the State from there.

The plant was developed by Dr. Paul Williams, a plant pathologist at the University of Wisconsin. He wanted to be able to test certain disease-resistant varieties in a short time.

Within a test group, he selected the top 10 percent that flowered early and bred those together. After a number of generations (12 crosses) of crossing the top ten growers, he had plants that were blooming and running a full life cycle in just 36 days.

This was the birth of FastPlants—the plant's life cycle, which would normally take 2 years, now takes 1 month, and research is accelerated dramatically.

David says his students use the plants to study plant growth, plant physiology, and genetics. "The part I like about it is the 'wow factor,'" says David. "'Wow, they grew this much' or 'Wow, they've got blossoms on them and last Friday they didn't.' They are seeing it all happen right here in class."

The students also conduct their own experiments, treating the plants with different levels of herbicides, oil, and road salts to test their tolerance to such chemicals. They also can test how the plants are affected by different amounts of light, colors of light, or whatever interests the student. The experiments are made to be displayed in the showcase in front of the agriscience classroom.

FastPlants are one of the many innovative tools David uses. His classes have been science oriented since he began in Beaver Dam in 1976. Because David's courses are part of the science department, his classroom has been moved out of the vocational area of the school into a new addition being built onto the science department.

The system of agricultural education is only as strong as the men and women who teach, encourage, and lead students to the careers waiting for them in American agriculture.

Jeffrey Berry:

Campus Leader Credits 4-H

"I could be viewed as an idealist," says Jeffrey Berry, "But because of 4-H, I know that people can learn to live together. I have seen ideals working, and I know they can work!"

A junior at Centre College, a liberal arts college in Danville, KY, 4-H alumnus Berry is a campus leader. He credits 4-H with much of his success.

Jeffrey is one of 5.1 million 4-H members nationwide involved in educational projects and activities of the Cooperative Extension Systems' program for youth. Like Jeffrey, more than one million 4-H'ers live in central cities with populations of more than 50,000, and more than half a million more live in the suburbs. As Jeffrey indicates, they find differences between themselves and the 4-H'ers who live in rural areas and small towns. However, as he also explains, basic self-enhancement is common to all youth involved in 4-H.

William Mesner/University of Kentucky

Jeffrey Berry credits the 4-H program for experiences that opened broader horizons. As a full-scholarship student at Centre College in Danville, KY, he is able to develop leadership skills and to pursue his ambitions.

Serving the Community

Berry says he thinks often of one 4-H theme, "from yourself to your world," in his busy daily life. The 4-H program helped him develop his own potential, but he especially likes its emphasis on serving the community.

As a full-scholarship student at Centre College, working part time at two or three different jobs, Jeffrey still accepts many leadership responsibilities. Currently he is secretary of Centre's Student Congress and also secretary of the Black Student Union. Last year he cochaired the campuswide committee to improve relations among all groups in the Centre community. Jeffrey believes that many of his skills at bringing people together came from his 4-H experiences.

Growing up in urban Louisville, KY, Jeffrey first got involved in 4-H speech activities. In his first year he was a runner-up in the State competition in Lexington. The trip to Lexington was his first outside Louisville and the first of many 4-H experiences that opened broader horizons.

During his first summer in 4-H he participated in the Citizenship Washington Focus program, through which about 180 Kentucky 4-H'ers each year spend a week in Washington, DC, visiting congressional representatives, lobbyists, and Government agencies, and learning firsthand about citizenship and citizen participation in government.

"I'll never forget how excited I was," he remembers. "When Mike Caldwell (the 4-H county agent in Louisville) drove his van up to my home to pick me up, I forgot to put on my shoes! I got to Washington still wearing my bedroom slippers!" Jeffrey's intense

by Charlotte G. Baer, Publications Editor, Cooperative Extension Service, University of Kentucky, Lexington, KY

experience in this program made him aware of the wider world beyond his neighborhood, and what it could mean to him.

After visiting Washington, Berry got involved in 4-H community pride program activities through his club in Louisville's West Central District, an inner-city neighborhood. This program helps 4-H'ers explore all aspects of their community and encourages them to ask themselves what they can do about problems and how they can have a positive effect on their communities. In 1989, almost 21,000 Kentucky 4-H'ers participated in community pride projects ranging from beautifying public spaces to working with senior citizens and helping low-income families.

Jeffrey also continued in 4-H speech contests. He was a State runner-up for 3 years, and in his fourth year he was the State winner.

An Urban 4-H'er Meets Rural Kentucky

In his first year at 4-H camp, Jeffrey met campers from all over Kentucky. Jeffrey and the other Louisville youngsters got to meet and make friends with their rural and small town counterparts. "I remember being amazed," Jeffrey laughs, "that some 4-H'ers had animal clubs. We didn't have anything like that in my part of Louisville."

Each camper found a way to shine and something to contribute. That first summer, he recalls, a camp theme was "The Sixties." Jeffrey's group, the Shining Stars, made several presentations about civil rights events, and Jeffrey delivered Martin Luther King's "I Have a Dream" speech.

William Mesner/University of Kentucky

Berry doesn't know what is in his future; there could be a job teaching, graduate school, or a position in public service. He knows that Kentucky's 4-H program helped him develop his own potential.

Berry became a counselor at the Conrad Feltner 4-H camp, on a wooded lakefront site 200 miles from his home. "I had so much fun seeing the children grow and seeing them be stimulated by so many new experiences," he says. "Sharing their joy and excitement made me know that was something I wanted to do with my life." At Centre College today he is a double major in elementary education and government.

Going to camp from an urban setting, Jeffrey was fascinated by the natural environment and enjoyed learning to be comfortable outdoors. He fondly remembers the new experiences of hiking in a cave, swimming in the lake, and trying archery. "And before long," he recalls, "there I was, leading a nature hike. I couldn't believe it!"

The 4-H program enabled Jeffrey to try many new activities. One that he especially enjoyed was narrating the State fashion show. He liked it so much that he is developing a similar fashion show for Centre College students this year.

Overcoming Poverty

The youngest of five children, raised by a single mother in Louisville's West Central District, Berry has gone through some hard times. When he was a junior in high school his mother died. His brother and sisters took over the bills and the apartment and kept the family together so that he could finish high school.

Because of his experiences, Jeffrey thinks he sometimes has a greater understanding of other people's perspectives. He has thought deeply about the things that really matter, and he cares about his ideals: "I'm not willing to settle for less than the best," he affirms. "I want to fight for my idealism. I want to be a positive role model for my peers and for young people and to bring them a message of hope."

Jeffrey Berry does not know exactly what he will be doing 10 years from now, but he sees teaching, graduate school, and public service in his future. He is sure to be a leader wherever he goes, drawing on so many skills developed in Kentucky's 4-H program.

Jimmy Cheek:

Teacher of the Year

Bunny Stafford/University of Florida

Professor Jimmy Cheek's classroom has been called a boot camp in communication skills. Cheek says students who can communicate clearly have a competitive edge in the workplace.

In Professor Jimmy Cheek's class, no one hides behind a book.

At first, his students may be shy or just plain terrified, but by the time they are through with Jimmy's oral communications course, his pupils are polished speakers, ready to meet the business world head on.

by Susan O'Reilly, Managing Editor, IMPACT Magazine, Institute of Food and Agricultural Sciences, University of Florida, Gainesville, FL

Obviously, Jimmy is a man who knows how to communicate. In his 15 years at the University of Florida, he has won over the most critical student audiences with classes that prepare a novice for the high expectations of the business world.

He was named the 1989 University of Florida College of Agriculture Teacher of the Year—an honor his students applaud. "A class is only as good as the teacher teaching it, and this class ranks high on my list of great classes," says Scot Weis, one of Jimmy's former students.

Two years ago, Jimmy developed his most talked-about class, "Oral Communications in the Agricultural Professions," when he saw a need going unmet in the university system.

A Real World Skill

"Ask employers to name one of the major deficiencies of students fresh out of college and they'll say, 'Communication,'" reports Jimmy. "Students can't write well and they can't speak well."

Jimmy's class is a boot camp in communication skills. Tomorrow's scientists, executives, and growers stifle their jitters to practice speeches in front of their peers.

They learn how to deliver a speech without sounding as if they are reading from cue cards. They divide into groups to conduct mock business meetings, complete with parliamentary procedure. They try out job interview skills in videotaped skits that are critiqued by the class.

In short, Jimmy's class could be subtitled "Business Basics for the Real World." As agriculture becomes increasingly sophisticated, Jimmy says students who can clearly communicate have a competitive edge in the workplace.

Jimmy also puts students through their paces with exercises that teach them how to prepare charts, posters, and graphics to accompany a formal business presentation. He instills in his students confidence that they can each become a smooth public speaker and find a niche in their chosen professional field.

"I remember hating the idea of giving oral presentations and feeling very intimidated by the situation," says Kimberly Wehinger, a former student now in the University of Florida's College of Veterinary Medicine. "However, after a few weeks, my fears subsided and I began to enjoy the class."

Jimmy fosters a classroom climate that encourages students to open up and overcome their inhibitions about public speaking. He knows everyone's name and background. To break the ice, he instructs students to pair up for interviews so they can introduce one another to the rest of the class.

"The atmosphere needs to be open, and students need to feel free to ask questions; it needs to be friendly and warm, not adversarial," says Jimmy.

Sometimes, students are fooled into thinking Jimmy's course will be as easygoing as his Texas-bred manners. They quickly learn differently.

"The original reason you signed up for the course was to get a fairly easy two or three hours of 'A,'" says former student Weis. "Then the class turns into something you did not expect and you find yourself challenged."

The Challenge of Teaching

Jimmy has thought of teaching as a challenge and a calling ever since he was a vocational agriculture student in high school. After his apprenticeship as a student teacher in the small rural town of Mart, TX, Jimmy was convinced that teaching would be his career.

He earned a bachelor's degree in agricultural education at Texas A&M University. Although he enjoyed economics, he loved teaching so much that he gave up a chance to study agricultural economics in graduate school at the University of Missouri.

He remembers with a smile the day he won his first job teaching vocational agriculture to high school students in Beaumont, TX. Fortunately, he displayed that job-winning determination and confidence that he now teaches to his students.

"When I talked to the principal, Mr. Kennedy, I said, 'This is a job that I would like and I think I would do a good job at it. What else can I do? Who else can I talk to about this position because I'm fit for it and it's fit for me.'" Two weeks later, he had the job.

In Beaumont, Jimmy earned a master's degree in guidance and counseling at Lamar University. Later, he returned to Texas A&M on a graduate fellowship to pursue a Ph.D. degree with an emphasis on agricultural education.

Since he arrived at the University of Florida 15 years ago, Jimmy's only regret is that more students have not followed his example and become agricultural education teachers.

"We need to let people know there are jobs in agricultural teaching and Extension that pay well," he says. "This is a career with an exciting potential and a lot of demand for our graduates."

At the University of Florida, Jimmy nurtures the careers of aspiring teachers and county Extension agents, counseling a quarter of the students in the Department of Agricultural and Extension Education at the university's Institute of Food and Agricultural Sciences (IFAS).

Long after they graduate, many students still call upon Jimmy for advice—a testimony to his character as well as to his teaching ability.

"Teachers touch the future through their students," he says. "Thus, with excellent teaching, our future will be bright, and we will continue to solve the increasing problems society faces."

Plan Your Education for a Career in Agriculture

There may have been a time when it was fairly easy to prepare for a career in agriculture in the United States. "Agriculture" meant farming, and farming was more an art than a science. Sons and daughters shared the chores on the farm and learned from their parents and neighbors; then they either took over their families' farms or moved on to a new territory to start afresh.

Times have changed, and the farmer as artist has merged with the farmer as scientist and businessperson to pursue the complex, varied, and dynamic endeavor that is modern American agriculture. Sons and daughters still learn many things from their parents, and productive farmers remain the base on which all agriculture is built, but a substantial amount of formal education is required to be successful and to cope with the rapid changes taking place.

Today's and tomorrow's agricultural professionals are not only farmers but also scientists, engineers, educators, managers, market and sales representatives, communicators, and diversified production specialists. Each of these careers requires a liberal education in mathematics, science, and communication skills in addition to a foundation in the technical area of choice. And as U.S. agriculture continues its partnership in the world agricultural network, it is also necessary to know foreign languages and to understand other cultures, customs, and peoples.

by Keith Wharton, Acting Dean, and Jean M. Underwood, Coordinator of Career Services, College of Agriculture, University of Minnesota, St. Paul, MN

University of Minnesota

Ed Zottola, Department of Food Science and Nutrition, University of Minnesota, discusses research techniques with students.

Bright Opportunities in Agriculture

One dramatic change in agriculture has been the decline in the number of people needed to produce crops and livestock. However, while demand for people in this area has decreased, opportunities have increased in the businesses that support the production and processing of food and fiber. Biotechnology and the changing international marketplace are two powerful forces that have changed employment opportunities in agriculture.

Opportunities for people prepared in agriculture will increase in coming years. A July 1986 USDA report, "Employment Opportunities for College Graduates in the Food and Agricultural Sciences," predicted a 10-percent shortage, annually through 1990, of graduates with food and agricultural expertise. The most significant shortages were projected for the scientific and business specialities associated with agriculture.

These predictions were correct: During the past 2-3 years, agricultural employers have found fewer graduates to fill available positions. Placement offices in colleges of agriculture report an increase in the number of opportunities for internships and full-time positions, but fewer available students. For example, recruiting activity for full-time positions has increased 44 percent since 1985 at the University of Minnesota, and recruiting for internships has increased 90 percent. By all indications, this highly favorable job market for college of agriculture graduates should continue.

Education: Preparation for a Dynamic and Changing Future

Colleges and schools of agriculture across the United States are responding vigorously to demands for a better education for agricultural professionals—at the undergraduate and graduate levels. Curricula have been revised during the 1980's. National, regional, and local curriculum projects have been assisted by grants from the USDA Higher Education Program and from numerous corporations and foundations. One national project emphasized an integrated systems approach to agriculture and issues of values and ethics; some regional projects looked at revitalizing the curriculum to meet the demands of the 21st century.

"The career opportunities in agriculture are skyrocketing," says Aaron Goy, a district manager for Ciba-Geigy Corporation. "But agriculture is a highly complex endeavor, involving issues and questions that are crucial to society. We recruit students who have a degree in agriculture because we know that they will have faced these issues in their schooling and experiences and will be prepared to help us deal with them in a positive and responsible way."

Students considering and preparing for careers in agriculture must realize one important fact: Opportunities will come only to those who are adequately prepared in both coursework and experience for the jobs that are available. There is a bright outlook for career opportunities in agriculture, but competition will be keen and employers will be selective. There will be no place for the person who avoids rigorous coursework or who tries to just get by in the quality of work or experience.

Says J. Scott Early, a regional sales manager for the Wayne Feeds Division of Continental Grain Company:

"We look for students who have a degree in agriculture because that demonstrates to us their commitment to and preparation for a career in agriculture. In addition, we look for graduates with good communication skills and the ability to project themselves in a manner that would make them successful in working with people. Also, we want graduates who understand that they have to continue to learn in order to keep ahead of the many changes that will occur in their lifetimes."

Adaptability, a commitment to lifelong learning, and effective communication skills will be three of the most important characteristics of the agricultural professional of the future. Situations and businesses will change rapidly, and the people who succeed will be those who can respond positively to the opportunities that these changes will bring. Those who wring their hands and long for the perceived stability of the good old days will be left behind.

University of Minnesota

Times have changed, and Rob King (left), management information systems instructor, knows that students need all the knowledge they can get in order to succeed in agricultural business and industry careers.

Career Planning: Key to Educational Planning

One important way in which a student can prepare for a career in agriculture is to adopt a "portfolio" approach to education planning. Instead of thinking about preparing for a specific job, such as agronomist or animal scientist, the student should think about himself or herself as a whole person, with the wide range of skills, interests, and abilities that every person has. The student should develop these abilities and experiences into a portfolio to offer to prospective employers. For example, a student might plan to be able to say at graduation something like this:

I have just graduated from college with a bachelor of science degree in agriculture. I have a good background in production agriculture courses, particularly in the plant sciences. I have a solid base of coursework in mathematics and science, as well as some courses in business, marketing, and economics. I completed internships with two agricultural companies—one large, the other small—during the summers while I was in college. I speak Spanish well, although not fluently yet, and I understand something of Hispanic culture through coursework and through the experiences I had on a 3-month study-travel project in Uruguay. I have good speaking, writing, and presentation skills, and I have participated actively in several student and community organizations, holding leadership positions in some of them. I know that I will have to continue learning in order to be successful, and I know how to do that.

This student will be employable. Confidence, self-knowledge, skills for life, and an attitude that embraces growth and development will serve this graduate throughout the coming years.

University of Minnesota

Activities beyond the conventional classroom play an important part in the educational experience. Dale Dahl (standing) advises student chapter members of the National Agricultural Marketing Association.

Where To Study

The choice of where to study agriculture is as broad as the field of agriculture itself. The colleges that have agricultural curricula reflect the diversity that is found in today's agriculture. Colleges of agriculture are found in every State, in rural communities as well as major metropolitan areas. There are large, public institutions as well as small, private colleges.

Values play an important role in the choice of college. The student should consider taking risks, stretching, trying new environments. Sometimes what feels the most comfortable may not provide the best opportunities. The student must consider such variables as location, cost, majors offered, reputation of the institution, placement record of graduates, study-travel options, and research specialties of the faculty.

For more information about colleges that offer an agricultural curriculum, you may contact—

Food and Agricultural Careers for Tomorrow (FACT)
127 Agricultural Administration Building
West Lafayette, IN 47907

Historically Black Land-Grant Institutions—the First 100 Years

The Emancipation Proclamation of 1863 was the "light at the end of the tunnel" leading to educational institutions for Negroes in the Southern States. It raised the hopes and aspirations of the Negro and aroused the curiosity, interest, and sympathy of the Nation for the uplift of some 400,000 citizens who were former slaves.

Early Days

In the years immediately following the Emancipation Proclamation, three main forces were responsible for the creation and growth of Negro institutions that were either founded as such or later became land-grant institutions under the Second Morrill Act of 1890. These three forces were the Negroes themselves, religious organizations, and State legislatures.

The Negro citizens of the South played a major role in the founding of educational institutions accessible to them. Lincoln University in Jefferson City, MO, is a product of those enlisted men and officers of the 62nd and 65th Missouri Colored Volunteers who dreamed of a school for colored children and provided funds for its founding. Other examples of Negro involvement include the founding of what is now Fort Valley State College, Alabama A&M University, and North Carolina A&T University. A coalition of ex-slaves and former slave masters led to the chartering of Tuskegee University by the State of Alabama.

The University of Maryland Eastern Shore, founded by the Methodist Episcopal Church, stands as a memorial to the influence of religious organizations on the growth of black land-grant institutions. The remaining 1890 institutions were established by State or territorial legislatures.

In their early years, these institutions had two things in common: They were all designated as schools for colored people, and they were all chartered as normal schools for the training of colored teachers, because there was a shortage of trained teachers to expand educational opportunities for colored children.

by B. D. Mayberry, Director, Carver Research Foundation, Tuskegee University, Tuskegee, AL

New Farmers of America calf show (circa 1935).

The Morrill Act of 1862

The Morrill Act of 1862 provided for the establishment of at least one land-grant institution in each State. In States having legal separation of the races, the legislation was sufficiently flexible to allow for the establishment of a second land-grant institution accessible to Negroes. Only Mississippi took advantage of this provision and established Alcorn State University in 1871 for Negroes and designated it as a "land-grant" school.

In Virginia, 1862 land-grant funds were extended to the Negro by way of Hampton University, a private institution. Several other institutions for Negroes received 1862 land-grant funds, but they were not designated as land-grant schools before 1890.

The Morrill Act of 1890

The Morrill Act of 1890 was passed specifically to provide further endowment of the 1862 institutions. A provision was included, however, indicating that institutions that were practicing racial discrimination in admission would not be eligible to receive the 1890 funds. This provision was circumvented by establishing separate land-grant schools for the Negro. Each Southern State either established a new school for this purpose or took over an existing public or private Negro school and designated it as a land-grant institution. The historically black or land-grant institutions are listed in table 1.

The Land-Grant Mission

The basic land-grant mission, which has come to apply to both 1862 and 1890 institutions, includes instruction, research, and Extension.

Instruction. The 1890 institutions were under the same legislative mandate to provide instruction in agriculture, home economics, and mechanical industries as were the 1862 institutions, and they were already heavily involved in teacher training. This was continued as agricultural and other land-grant courses were phased in and became very significant by the turn of the century.

Instruction in agriculture, home economics, mechanical industries, and general education was continued until 1917, when the Smith-Hughes Act was passed, providing for the training of vocational teachers for the public schools. At this point, the 1890 institutions accepted the responsibility of training Negro vocational teachers. This continued until the Smith-Hughes program was folded into the Vocational Education Act of 1963 and later into the Carl D. Perkins Act of 1984.

Research. Research was included in the founding mission of the 1890 institutions, but research resources were not made available to most of these institutions. The Hatch Act of 1887 and the Second Morrill Act of 1890 provided for agricultural research to be conducted in each State, usually on the campus of the 1862 school. An exception to this pattern was the branch experiment station established at Prairie View, TX, under provisions of the Hatch Act of 1887.

The State of Alabama established an experiment station at Tuskegee University in 1897, staffed it with George Washington Carver, and provided it with an annual appropriation of $1,500. With this, Dr. Carver completely revolutionized agriculture in the deep South, by showing what could be done with soybeans, peanuts, and other alternative crops, and by doing research and training in such areas as soil conservation and crop rotation. In addition, he developed many commercial products from the peanut and the sweet potato.

Research support at the other 1890 institutions during the first half of this century was too little to make a significant difference.

George Washington Carver, innovator in research and extension.

Extension. Outreach activities in the 1890 institutions predate the formal National Extension System, established under the Smith-Lever Act of 1914, by almost 40 years. Outreach efforts by Alabama A&M University date back to 1875, when William H. Council, the principal, published a farmers' newsletter to facilitate technology transfer. Tuskegee University initiated outreach activities in 1881, established an Extension department in 1889, and organized an annual farmers conference in 1892—which still operates after 98 years.

In 1896, Dr. Carver made weekend visits to the country in a wagon with demonstration tools, which evolved to become the Nation's first "movable school." This concept spread across the Nation, and to Africa, Europe, and the Middle East.

T. M. Campbell was employed at Tuskegee University on November 12, 1906 to become the first Negro Cooperative Extension Agent in the United States. About one month later, John B. Pierce of Hampton University was employed in a similar position in Virginia. Campbell coordinated and supervised Negro Extension in the southern section of the Southern States and Pierce coordinated Negro Extension in the northern half of the Southern States.

The Smith-Lever Act

Beginning in 1914 under the Smith-Lever Act, Negro Extension programs were operated by the 1890 institutions in each of the Southern States, under the supervision and administration of the 1862 institutions. T. M. Campbell and John B. Pierce continued to work as coordinators, motivators, and facilitators within the Negro Extension program. In 1918 they were promoted to

Federal Field Agents for Negro Extension.

The 1890 institutions developed and executed a long list of special, and in many cases unique, approaches to reaching and serving the unreached. Examples include the "movable school" and such annual events as the "Ham and Egg Show" (a demonstration project on producing and processing swine and poultry), which was initiated by Negro County Agent Otis S. O'Neal at Fort Valley State College, GA, in 1916 and continued for more than 50 years. Other special activities included summer camps, judging contests, and talent shows open to Negro boys and girls. This Negro Extension System continued until the Civil Rights era of the mid-1960's, when it was reorganized, integrated, and in many cases discontinued, purportedly in the interest of eliminating racial discrimination.

Table 1. Founding Dates and Sponsors of Historically Black Land-Grant Institutions

Founding date	Name and State	Sponsor
1866	Lincoln University, Missouri	Civil War Negro Infantry Men
1871	Alcorn University, Mississippi	State Legislature
1872	South Carolina State University	State Legislature
1873	University of Arkansas, Pine Bluff	State Legislature
1875	Alabama A&M University	Group of Ex-Slaves
1876	Prairie View A&M University, Texas	State Legislature
1880	Southern University, Louisiana	State Legislature
1881	Tuskegee University, Alabama	State Legislature
1882	Virginia State University	State Legislature
1886	Kentucky State University	State Legislature
1886	University of Maryland Eastern Shore	Methodist Episcopal Church
1887	Florida A&M University	State Legislature
1891	Delaware State College	State Legislature
1891	North Carolina A&T University	Citizens Group
1891	West Virginia State College*	State Legislature
1895	Fort Valley State College, Georgia	Citizens Group
1897	Langston University, Oklahoma	Territorial Legislature
1912	Tennessee State University	State Legislature

*Voluntarily dropped "1890" designation in 1957

The Breakthrough in Federal Support

The breakthrough in Federal support of agricultural programs at 1890 institutions came following the Civil Rights Act of 1964. Starting in 1967, under the authority of Public Law 89-106, the Secretary of Agriculture allocated $283,000 of discretionary funds to be divided among the 1890 institutions for research.

In fiscal year 1972, while still under the grant mechanism of PL 89-106, the Secretary of Agriculture used discretionary funds for Extension as well as research; the funds for that year amounted to $8,600,000 for research and $4,000,000 for Extension. By 1972, Tuskegee was included, but not as a land-grant institution (see table 2).

Starting in 1977, the 1890 institutions' programs in research and Extension were funded directly under Public Law 95-113, requiring functional coordination with the respective 1862 institutions. By 1977, the annual appropriation for 1890 schools had reached $13,352,000 for research, and $8,400,000 for Extension, based on a formula, or percentage, of 1862 funding. These funding levels for programs continued to increase, so that in 1990, the centennial year, $25,300,000 is allocated for research and $24,000,000 for Extension.

In 1984, the U.S. Congress authorized a $50,000,000 grant to improve research facilities at the 1890 institutions, and in 1986, $50,000,00 was authorized for improving Extension facilities.

USDA/1890 Initiative

In the last quarter century, to make up for years of past discrimination, USDA has aggressively and forcefully supported the growth and development of the 1890 land-grant institutions. This began with the "breakthrough" in Federal formula funding of agricultural programs under the grant mechanism of Public Law 89-106 in 1967 and continued with the many efforts sponsored under legislative authority of the 1977 Farm Bill, Public Law 95-113.

USDA sponsored a symposium in Nashville, TN, April 24-26, 1988, which was cosponsored by the 1890 institutions and Tuskegee University and hosted by Tennessee State University. The goal of this symposium was to

Table 2. Federal Formula Funds for Research and Extension at 1890 Institutions and Tuskegee, 1967–1990

FY	Purpose	Research	Extension	Total
1967	Programs	283,000	- 0 -	283,000
1968	Programs	283,000	- 0 -	283,000
1969	Programs	283,000	- 0 -	283,000
1970	Programs	283,000	- 0 -	283,000
1971	Programs	283,000	- 0 -	283,000
1972	Programs	8,600,000	4,000,000	12,600,000
1973	Programs	10,883,000	6,000,000	16,883,000
1974	Programs	10,883,000	6,000,000	16,883,000
1975	Programs	11,824,000	6,450,000	18,274,000
1976	Programs	12,706,000	7,823,000	20,529,000
Interim	Programs*	3,176,000	195,572	3,371,572
1977	Programs	13,352,000	8,400,000	21,752,000
1978	Programs	14,153,000	8,833,000	22,986,000
1979	Programs	16,360,000	10,115,000	26,475,000
1980	Programs	17,785,000	10,453,000	28,238,000
1981	Programs	19,270,000	11,250,000	30,520,000
1982	Programs	21,492,000	12,241,000	33,733,000
1983	Programs	22,394,000	16,241,000	38,635,000
1984	Programs	22,844,000	17,241,000	40,085,000
1984	Facilities**	50,000,000	- 0 -	50,000,000
1985	Programs	22,474,000	17,741,000	41,215,000
1986	Programs	22,329,681	16,877,000	39,206,681
1986	Facilities**	- 0 -	50,000,000	50,000,000
1987	Programs	22,329,681	16,877,000	39,206,681
1988	Programs	23,333,000	18,291,000	41,624,000
1989	Programs	24,300,000	18,300,000	42,600,000
1990	Programs***	25,300,000	24,000,000	49,300,000
Totals		$398,486,362	$287,328,572	$685,531,934

* Federal fiscal year changed from July to October

** Congressional 5-year authorization

*** USDA funding proposal for the 1890 Initiative (January 1989)

enhance communication among the 1890 institutions, Tuskegee University, and USDA agencies in order to achieve and maintain active partnerships to strengthen the agricultural enterprise.

The symposium was attended by decisionmakers from USDA and the 1890 institutions. Secretary of Agriculture Richard Lyng expressed his personal commitment to enhancing and strengthening the relationship between the historically black land-grant institutions and USDA. He also emphasized the need to encourage minorities and women to pursue education and careers in agriculture. Participants discussed how to attract more minority students into agriculture and strengthen links between the 1890 institutions and USDA.

A task force consisting of presidents of the 1890 institutions and career agency heads was established to provide oversight and assistance in carrying out symposium recommendations. A task force working group, with representatives from each USDA agency chosen for their particular skills, was established to help implement the 17 symposium recommendations.

The most publicized recommendation concerned the establishment of a USDA Liaison Office on each 1890 campus. By February 1990, each 1890 campus had a liaison office established, with at least one liaison officer based in it. The duties of these liaison officers are tailored to the specific needs and circumstances of the institutions they serve. Yet in every case their value is immeasurable as a link between the specific 1890 institution and the Federal Government, especially USDA.

USDA has a full-time staffer in the Deputy Secretary's office to provide oversight, motivation, and supervision in implementing programs arising out of the Nashville symposium, as well as other initiatives taken by the Secretary and Deputy Secretary.

Model Program on Hydroponics and Aquaculture

At the University of Maryland Eastern Shore (UMES), administrators and faculty search for ways to apply basic research for the good of the local community and rural economy, both through the classroom and through the county Extension Service.

The mandate of the university's 1890 Land Grant Experiment Station is to address the problems and concerns of small-scale agricultural producers. Thus, university researchers must address a host of concerns from a largely rural population.

Two projects, one on hydroponics and one on aquaculture, have used small-scale production models to make research easier and to teach the results of that research on all levels—to farmers, county Extension agents, college students, and even high school and elementary students.

Hydroponic Model

In 1987, Mortimer Neufville, dean and 1890 research director at UMES, initiated a project to determine the best technology for growing alternative crops hydroponically. The research station established a large-scale production unit and collected technical information on basil, red leaf lettuce, and watercress.

The research focused on nutrient management and disease control, and demonstrated the underlying principles of hydroponics. These principles include plant management, plant scheduling and marketing, plant growth and development, yield per square foot,

by Thomas S. Handwerker, Assistant Professor, Department of Agriculture, University of Maryland Eastern Shore, Princess Anne, MD

Bob Nichols/USDA 90BW0804-24

Mortimer Neufville, Dean and 1890 research director at the University of Maryland Eastern Shore, with students Bi Jay Upapayay from Nepal, Ngale Kingsley from Cameroon, and Radhika Narayana from India. Bi Jay and Ngale are undergraduate students in the Agricultural Sciences program, and Radhika is a graduate student in the Marine Estuarine and Environmental Sciences program. They are harvesting sweet basil, one of the crops they grew in a closed loop, recirculating hydroponic system.

potential insect and disease problems, nutrient uptake, specific effects of pH (acidity), effects of nutrient deficiencies, and optimum combination of nutrients for the hydroponic solution. The model was also used to demonstrate these findings and production techniques in training county Extension agents, grower cooperators, and UMES undergraduate and graduate students.

The next step was to produce small "table-top" working units based on the knowledge gained during the research conducted with the original production unit. During this phase of the project, local growers visited the research facilities and discussed building small-scale production units.

Researchers found the experimental results of the hydroponic research project very promising, as were the initial estimates of economic return and market acceptance of hydroponically grown crops. The results of this research were published in the article, "Hydroponics—Space Age Agriculture," in *Agricultural Education* in 1989.

Despite the system's promise, it still required good management practices and a substantial investment, which many small-scale producers hesitate to make.

Bob Nichols/USDA 90BW0809-35

A portable hydroponic teaching model developed as a small-scale agricultural project. Local farmers may borrow the model to learn how a hyrdoponic system works.

Extension agents working with Jean Scott of Wicomico County, MD, conducted several workshops with growers to demonstrate hydroponic management techniques and to provide educational materials for small demonstration projects.

During these discussions, we saw that growers needed almost daily exposure to these production systems to fully understand how they worked. We loaned the small hydroponic models to the growers so each could produce a crop and evaluate the technology.

Each system cost approximately $80 to build, required about 3 by 4 feet of tabletop space, and used a 5-gallon plastic pail as a nutrient reservoir. Growers could operate the borrowed models as commercial facilities and produce 7 heads of lettuce per week (or similar amounts of another crop) on a 6-week production schedule. One grower actually used this produce to establish a market that could be expanded to a commercial scale.

What came back to the research program was a group of experienced growers: a group that understood hydroponic production methods. The growers had hands-on experience with the day-to-day routine of planting, harvesting, and cleaning the system, so they could concentrate on marketing the products they were able to grow. It was exciting for the researchers and Extension agents to see growers making changes in the model design and to evaluate these new configurations.

Growers shared information with each other, and some of them even built their own models when they returned the original for another grower to use. Growers were able to experiment with new technology, discuss results of trials conducted by the UMES Experiment Station, and then develop commercial facilities. The hydroponic units are now provided by the UMES Experiment Station through the local county Extension offices and used for educational exhibits and demonstrations.

High School Students Try Out the Models

UMES conducted a 5-day workshop for the Maryland vocational agriculture program in which high school teachers came to UMES and built hydroponic models for classroom use. Bob Keenan, a vocational agriculture teacher and supervisor in Baltimore, has helped introduce the hydroponic production units into both the shop and the agriscience curriculum. Agriculture students have also demonstrated these models in science classes.

Some of these high school students who are interested in agriscience have developed new prototypes, and these are being evaluated at UMES. Models are even being introduced into Baltimore's elementary school classrooms. These hydroponic models are being used as tools for teaching experimental methods.

The expertise of the growers and students working with the UMES Agricultural Experiment Station has increased. They help identify specific research problems that address local production technologies and keep abreast of current research projects.

Aquaculture, Benign for the Environment

Another research project—the development of a recirculating aquaculture production technology—used similar methods for transferring the experimental results to county Extension agents, growers, and students at all levels. The aquaculture models, also built for less than $80 each, were developed for research in fish nutrition and biofiltration mechanics.

The UMES aquaculture project was funded by private company support and by a matching industrial development grant under the Maryland Industrial Partnership program. The research objective was to design, build, and operate a pilot plant model of a recirculating fish production system that would combine mechanical and biological filters to clean the water. The biofiltration method uses various stones and other materials on which beneficial bacteria, which help remove fish waste, could grow. The cleaned, recirculated water minimizes effluent discharge and decreases environmental impact in the Chesapeake region.

The research project began in 1988 and has evaluated several different engineering technologies, expanding into the areas of effluent management, nutrition, and alternative species.

The pilot plant was evaluated for its economic feasibility, and the biological filtration system it used was so effective that it led to the first commercial indoor aquaculture facility on the Delmarva Peninsula. As with the hydroponic system, smaller, experimental units had to be built first to test various treatment techniques at the UMES experiment station.

The aquaculture models were presented in two vocational agriculture teacher workshops. High school and college curriculum materials outlined the principles and applications of the research results from the UMES model.

These aquaculture models, like the hydroponic models, are being redesigned by students who recognize new opportunities in agriscience as they experiment to discover more effective materials or tank configurations.

The visitors center at NASA Wallops Island (VA) has also visited the research facility to get design information for constructing a "biosphere" operated by students from grades 7 through 10 growing space tomatoes using the hydroponic models.

Integrating Systems

These efforts to present our research efforts are leading to even greater participation by growers, teachers, and students. The research staff is planning a demonstration model that uses both the hydroponic model and the aquaculture model to explore the integration of plant and animal production systems.

Agricultural Extension agents view the models as a way for growers to gain practical experience in producing and operating commercial systems. Teachers view the models as ways to demonstrate concepts and principles they are discussing in class. We recognize them as the tools we use to teach the results of our research efforts to the clientele we serve.

A Science Career, Working "The Land"

I go to work each day where millions each year go to play. I'm a plant scientist with the unique opportunity of working at the Walt Disney World vacation resort. My workplace and laboratory are in EPCOT Center's agricultural show, "The Land." After completing my doctorate in agronomy and crop physiology in summer 1989, I assumed the position of plant nutritionist here.

Mary Schon examines a pepper fruit with a common nutritional disorder, blossom end rot. The plant is in a research plot being tested with calcium and boron sprayed on the fruit to alleviate the problem.

Why "The Land"?

How did a farmer's daughter from Iowa end up as plant nutritionist at EPCOT Center? My interests in plants and agriculture may seem natural after growing up on a farm, but as the oldest daughter in a family of 10 children, most of my responsibilities centered around the traditional female roles inside the house rather than tending to crops or livestock outside. I always loved school, especially math and science classes, and dreamed of being a teacher, but no one in the family had ever earned a college degree. I didn't consider college an option until I was an upperclassman in high school.

Then, I was lucky enough to have a biology teacher who involved me in a science club and in doing science fair projects. That was my first taste of the excitement of science and research. Since then several science teachers have been my role models and have kept my interests in science and education alive.

Educational Decisions

I completed a B.A. degree in biology at Mount Marty College in Yankton, SD, in 1976 and taught high school biology for a year before working as a laboratory technician in the Agronomy Department at Iowa State University in Ames. I was again doing research in this position, so when I was offered a research assistantship in biology at the University of South Dakota (USD), I accepted with the thought that getting a master's degree would open more doors for my future.

At USD, I worked with plant science research and its agricultural implications, but when I graduated in 1981 I was still relatively unaware of the career possibilities in agriculture. Instead, I used my advanced degree to attain an administrative position as registrar at a private college.

I spent 4 years working outside the world of science before I heard about the National Needs Fellowships being offered by USDA, which had become aware of the acute shortage of young people going into science. To entice prospective students into graduate programs, USDA was offering fellowships that made it financially possible for people like me to leave the security of a job to return to school for doctoral training in the sciences.

I had always been interested in education, and missed doing research, so I considered going back to school so I could possibly become a college professor. In 1985, I applied for and received one of the USDA fellowships offered by the Interdisciplinary Plant Biochemistry and Physiology Group at the University of Missouri-Columbia (UMC).

by Mary Schon, Plant Nutritionist, "The Land," Walt Disney World, Lake Buena Vista, FL

Career Decisions

Throughout my 4 years at UMC, the importance of several concepts was stressed: getting a strong foundation in the basic sciences, using an interdisciplinary approach to problem solving, conducting creative and far-sighted research, and communicating science both among peers and to the public. Therefore, when I was finishing my dissertation and starting my job search, the position of plant nutritionist at "The Land" seemed particularly attractive to me.

At "The Land," an interdisciplinary approach to problem solving is part of the daily routine; it has to be if the team of scientists is to keep the show looking its best 365 days a year. Research interests also tend toward the interactive approach, such as looking at plant nutrition as a possible means to increase plant resistance to insects and pathogens. "The Land" is a great promotional tool for agriculture and strives to educate the public, especially the young, about exciting career opportunities in agricultural sciences.

American youth need to be aware that agriculture is more than farming, that there are many career opportunities for both men and women. The importance of good teachers and role models in science cannot be overstated, and a great need exists for hands-on experiences in science from a very early age. We are working at "The Land" to encourage curiosity and pass on the excitement of research and discovery in agriculture. We hope this will help increase the number of young people entering agriscience in the future.

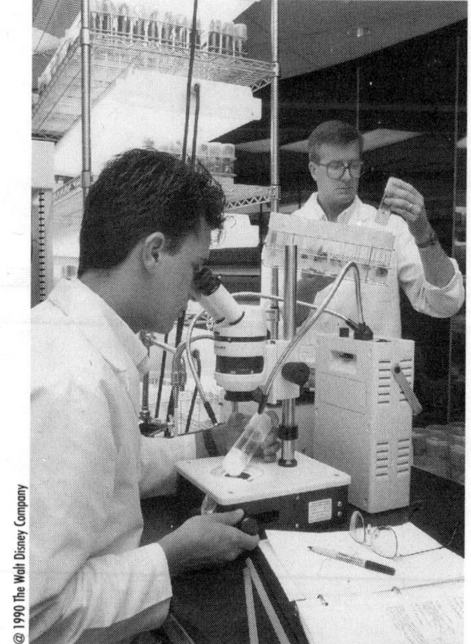

Biotechnology student intern Meluyd Nabavi (left), Seminole Community College, and David Forehand (right), Auburn University, work in the Biotechnology Laboratory, where they develop techniques to produce disease-free banana, vanilla, and pineapple seedlings for "The Land" greenhouses through the use of tissue culture.

My Role as Plant Nutritionist

As nutritionist, my job is to fine-tune the nutrient solutions delivered to the roots of more than 30 crops grown at "The Land." One of my initial challenges was to attempt to turn the yellow, stunted rice growing in the Tropical Greenhouse into lush, green, "show quality" plants.

Leaf tissue analyses revealed that the rice was deficient in iron and manganese, two micronutrients necessary for plant growth. Ample amounts of the nutrients were being delivered to the plant roots by drip irrigation, but apparently these minerals were having problems getting into the plants. Phosphorus had accumulated in the sand where the rice grew, making it difficult for iron to be taken up by plant roots. Flushing the sand with fresh water helped, but did not alleviate the problem.

Iron and manganese are most readily absorbed by plant roots under acidic growing conditions, so I increased the acidity of the nutrient solution and was able to increase iron and manganese in the rice leaves. In fact, now that conditions for nutrient uptake are optimal, I deliver only a fraction of the nutrients that were originally provided to the plant roots and still raise lush, green rice plants with full seed heads.

I also carry out research aimed at solving plant nutritional disorders and improving overall plant quality and yield. The most prevalent nutritional disorders at "The Land"—blossom end rot on tomatoes and peppers and tip burn on lettuce and cabbage—are all associated with calcium or boron distribution problems. I am especially interested in these problems, since my dissertation research at UMC involved boron and its functions in plants.

The challenges at "The Land" are exciting and endless. I work with a team of scientists—entomologists, plant pathologists, horticulturalists, plant biotechnologists, agricultural engineers, and aquaculturists—who maintain and improve the greenhouse-grown plant life and the fish production facility that showcase the diversity and the potential of agriculture around the world. Through up-to-date technology and behind-the-scenes research, the staff's major goal is to promote agriculture and educate the public about its prospects for the future.

Horticulture student intern Tim Cozort, Southwest Missouri State University, plants kohlrabi next to the sugarcane in the Tropics House while guests on the "Listen to the Land" boat ride look on.

Educational Programs at "The Land"

Several educational programs are under way at "The Land," either on a daily basis for our guests at EPCOT Center or as special events:

"Listen to the Land" Boat Tour. A winding canal carries millions of visitors each year on a guided "Listen to the Land" boat tour through the four greenhouses, the aquacell, and the biotechnology laboratory that make up the show. This journey is quite an education for most of the general public. Many who seldom think of plants as sources of food, fiber, fuel, and forage are amazed by the agricultural diversity displayed in our greenhouses. The boat tour is also an initial exposure for many to such concepts as intercropping, hydroponics, integrated pest management (IPM), and biotechnology.

In the **Tropic Greenhouse**, the Florida sun warms the glass-domed area where tall coconut palms are intercropped with shorter shade-tolerant cacao trees, cantaloupe and winged beans grow on trellises, papaya and banana trees stand laden with fruit, and 12-foot-tall sugarcane and heading rice plants line the canal. The tour guide notes that rice is one of the three most important food crops in the world, and points out the uses of our less well-known crops such as cassava roots for tapioca and cacao seeds for chocolate and cocoa. The guests discover that vanilla is a member of the orchid family and that pineapples grow on the ground rather than in trees.

As the boat enters the dimly lit **Aquacell**, aquaculture—cultivation of fish—is presented as the fastest-growing segment of the food production industry. Guests observe channel catfish, the leading aquaculture product of the United States. As the boat passes circular tanks full of tilapia, the tour guide explains that the tilapia grows fast, feeds efficiently, and reproduces readily in captivity, thereby making its cultivation optimal for fast turnover of a delicious, high-protein food.

In the **Desert House**, guests see bountiful plant life growing in what was once thought of as a harsh, dry environment. Drip irrigation tubes lie under flowering rows of cotton plants, and the guide points out that water and all the nutrients necessary for plant growth are delivered, via computer control, to plant roots below the surface of the sand. The guide reinforces the idea that if people work with their environment and "listen to the land," there is hope for expanding food production on this planet.

Intensive food production is practiced in our **Production House**, where hydroponics (plant growth without soil) and vertical growth are used to produce large amounts of food in a limited amount of space. Peppers, cherry tomatoes, and foot-long cucumbers hang on plants. Leaf lettuce floats on polystyrene beds while the plant roots dangle in aerated raceways of nutrient solution. The tour guide notes that all the things that soil provides to plant roots—support, water, nutrients, and oxygen—are provided by alternative means in hydroponic systems, allowing humans to increase food production in a world with an ever-increasing population.

Insects and diseases destroy millions of acres of food crops yearly, and would cause severe damage in Florida greenhouses without a well-developed IPM program. At "The Land," guests are introduced to the concept of biological pest control—lady bugs and tiny predatory wasps are released into the greenhouses to control aphids and leaf miners, two major insect pests. Guests are told how insects and pathogens can be kept under control with minimal use of pesticides—definitely the way of the future in a world becoming much more keenly aware of our impact on the environment.

The **Creative House** is "The Land's" concept of agriculture in the future. Plant roots dangle down the inside of long hanging canisters and are misted periodically with nutrient solution; shoots flower and fruit in full view of guests. The tour guide describes the process as "aeroponics." Children and their parents observe three-foot-long roots on squash plants that pass by the boat on a conveyor belt returning them to the mist box. Guests see wheat and soybeans growing in a simulated lunar soil, and observe plants thriving in a hydroponic system identical to the one being tested by NASA to produce food and recycle oxygen and water for astronauts in space.

At this point, guests are brought back to the reality and amazement of present-day science by viewing the **Biotechnology Laboratory**, jointly sponsored by USDA's Agricultural Research Service and Kraft General Foods. Monitors along the canal illustrate the proliferation of roots and shoots of plantlets developed through tissue culture, and guests actually observe scientists at work in a brightly lit lab. The guide explains that some of the plants grown at "The Land"—cassava, banana, pineapple—are not produced from seed, but are reproduced from individual cells of a parent plant, thereby allowing us to provide disease-free seedlings for our greenhouses.

As the boat slows and comes to a halt, the millions of guests each year who experience the boat ride through "The Land" are left with one very important thought: Agriculture has almost limitless potential if scientists, producers, and consumers alike "listen to the land" and use its resources wisely.

Harvest Tours. In addition to the millions who take the "Listen to the Land" tour each year, more than 50,000 people annually take a 50-minute walking tour through the greenhouses, guided by a member of the agriculture staff. The Harvest Tour, as it is called, is designed for anyone—home gardeners to university professors—who wants a closer look at what "The Land" has to offer. Since the number in a tour is kept under 12, guests have ample opportunity to ask questions to get a better understanding of the practices used at "The Land" and to find out about behind-the-scenes research. Special tours are prearranged for groups such as FFA, 4-H, class field trips, and university scientists.

College Student Internship Program. A college internship program at "The Land" started with two students in 1982 and has developed into a program that provides internships to 12 to 15 college students every 6 months. Upperclass students with majors ranging from horticulture or agronomy to microbiology or fisheries are selected from colleges and universities around the country.

Students are an integral part of the workforce at "The Land" and are involved in all aspects of plant propagation, irrigation, and harvesting, and in overall maintenance of the show. Their training is supplemented by giving Harvest Tours daily, by weekly classes taught by the agriculture staff, and by several field trips that acquaint them with the agricultural diversity of Florida.

Earth Shuttle Tours. Earth Shuttle, a Boston-based company that provides field trips to students and teachers around the country, has made "The Land" part of the educational package of its central Florida field trip. An estimated 25,000 3rd- to 12th-grade students will tour "The Land" in 1990 alone. Walking tours provided by "The Land" staff are specially designed to accommodate the students' age and interests.

These educational programs at "The Land" generate interest and excitement about agriscience among the young people who experience them, and they introduce the wide range of opportunities that are available to people considering careers in agriculture.

PART VI

government serving agriculture

Velitchko Velev and Bessie Berry:

Keeping Meat and Poultry Safe, from Plant to Plate

Each year, the Food Safety and Inspection Service (FSIS) assures the U.S. public of the wholesomeness of meat and poultry from about 120 million livestock and 5.9 billion chickens and other poultry, as well as 150 million pounds of beef stew, chicken pot pie, and other processed products.

The FSIS food safety team includes 7,700 inspectors in the 6,700 meat and poultry plants that sell products in interstate and foreign commerce.

Inspection and other regulatory activities ensure that the food industry has done its job of producing and selling safe, accurately labeled meat and poultry. But the job of ensuring the safety of food is not complete when products leave the plant; the food still must be handled safely through sale and preparation.

Velitchko Velev, a supervisor of FSIS inspectors, is a key player on the FSIS food safety team. Another key player is Bessie Jones Berry, an expert on safe food handling.

Inspection includes checking for drug and chemical residues in animal tissue. Residues can result from the improper use of pesticides and animal drugs as well as industrial and environmental accidents.

Lester Shepard/USDA 89BW1302-26

Veterinarian from Bulgaria

Velitchko Velev, a naturalized American citizen, is a veterinary medical officer who supervises more than 20 Federal inspectors. He encounters tough situations in his job, but those challenges pale in comparison with those he overcame to reach the United States and then to practice his profession in his new home. He fled communism, survived a refugee camp, and learned a new language.

Velitchko was born in Russe, the fourth largest city in Bulgaria, and graduated from the Veterinary Institute in Sofia. "In high school, I was interested in any subject that dealt with animals and plants," he says. "After I graduated, it was a matter of deciding whether to concentrate on biology or another natural science. I decided on veterinary medicine because it is one of the most multidisciplinary of the sciences."

After earning his doctorate in veterinary medicine, Velitchko worked as a veterinarian for Bulgaria's agriculture department for 10 years. He escaped from Bulgaria to Istanbul, Turkey, in 1967. After a year in Turkey

Velitchko Velev, Supervisory Veterinary Medical Officer, Food safety and Inspection Service, USDA

by Herb Gantz and Irene Goins, Public Affairs Specialists, Food Safety and Inspection Service, USDA, Washington, DC

and more time in a refugee camp in Italy, he finally reached the United States in 1968.

Settling in the United States. Reaching the United States was not Velitchko's last challenge. "It was tough getting started because I did not know the English language, and I could not work in my profession," he recalls.

Before he could practice veterinary medicine in this country, he had to be certified by the American Veterinary Medical Association (AVMA). He settled in Chicago, near the AVMA headquarters, and studied English for 2 years. "During this time, I assisted in a veterinary clinic," he says. "I could help with the animals because the medicine used in treating them is in Latin. And animals, of course, don't care what language you speak."

Velitchko was certified by the AVMA in 1970, which opened the door for a job with the USDA as a veterinarian. He was a veterinary medical officer for 4 years before becoming a supervisor at Monfort, Inc., a cattle slaughter operation in Garden City, KS. The plant where Velitchko works prepares large "primal cuts," such as chucks or loins of beef, which are vacuum-packed and distributed to other companies to be further processed into steaks and other beef products.

Velitchko attributes much of his success in this country to his coworkers: "My friends at work helped me overcome the language barrier. They were very patient," he says. "Veterinary medicine is universal, and I did not have any trouble learning the U.S. inspection procedures."

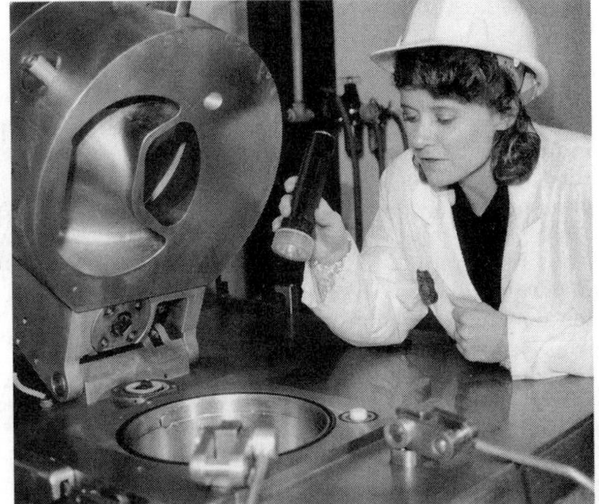

USDA 90BW0043-3

Canned chili and soups are made in highly technical processing operations. Food technologists check several safety factors in the food processing facility, including the equipment, to make sure it is clean before production begins.

As a supervisory veterinary medical officer, Velitchko ensures that inspectors carry out their responsibilities, which include making sure the facility and equipment are clean and checking all carcasses and organs for disease and other abnormalities. He makes the final decision on whether a carcass or organ should be condemned. He also conducts in-plant testing, such as the STOP (swab test on premises), to ensure that food animals are free from illegal antibiotic residues.

Velitchko believes that although it is FSIS' responsibility to regulate industry, industry realizes the importance of consumer trust. "Plant managers are doing more to ensure that their products are safe. Some, for instance, con-

Lester Shepard/USDA 89BW1301-11

The first step to producing safe products is starting with healthy animals. At the plant, inspectors examine live animals for disease and other conditions, ensuring that only healthy animals are used for food.

duct testing on their own. Also, new technology used in the plants and packing houses today results in the production of safer and better products." He believes that Government and industry must work together to produce the safe products that consumers demand.

An American citizen since 1974, Velitchko is proud to be part of the Federal public service: "I take pleasure in knowing that we provide a service that American consumers appreciate," he says. "They rely on the Federal Government, and that's the way it should be."

Food Safety Merchandiser from Oklahoma

There are many different jobs in USDA, but none is more challenging than "merchandiser" of food safety, which is how Bessie Jones Berry, a home economist on the FSIS Meat and Poultry Hotline, describes herself. Bessie also sees herself as a consultant, helping consumers with varied food safety questions.

The Hotline. The hotline is a nationwide, toll-free service that consumers, media, and anyone else can call for advice about how to handle foods properly to avoid foodborne illnesses. Last year, 64,000 consumers called the hotline about proper handling of meat and poultry, how to tell whether food is safe to eat, and how to better understand label information.

"The FSIS hotline is important because it helps consumers identify critical areas where something can go wrong once they bring food home from the grocer, such as thawing, cooking, and handling leftovers," explains

Bessie Jones Berry, Home Economist, Food Safety and Inspection Service, USDA

Bessie. "In other words, the hotline is called by people who need help in deciding that what they do is not only safe but prevents a potential outbreak of food poisoning."

"I've watched the hotline quadruple in size since I came on board just 4 years ago," Bessie says. She also has seen the questions grow more complex—ranging from safe handling and preparation of foods to what medications are used in food animals, what animals and birds are fed, and how foods are grown for safety.

Bessie is a supervisor and also serves as a research and product complaint manager. "One of the goals of the FSIS hotline is to ensure that callers get the answers they need on the spot," she says. "If necessary, they are called back with more information later in the day. That's where my research duties come into play."

These research duties include collecting information from scientists and other specialists in USDA, other Federal agencies, industry, colleges and universities, various health organizations—any expert source Bessie needs to contact.

As product complaint manager, Bessie gives serious and immediate attention to complaints about meat and poultry products, which account for about 1 percent of hotline calls. "These complaints cannot be taken lightly, since someone's health could be endangered," Bessie stresses. "Complaints may refer to foreign matter in a product, off-taste or odor, or an appearance problem."

Bessie's seemingly endless duties also include developing the work schedule for those who staff the hotline, and she also answers calls herself. "No one on the staff is exempt," she says.

Bessie has been able to pass on what she has learned through the years to her fellow workers and to consumers who call in. "Some people take their work home *from* the office," she says. "I like to think that I bring my home and my life's experiences *to* the office. That's what makes this job so rewarding."

Acquiring the Knowledge. Bessie is a native of Guthrie, OK. Driven by the inspiration she received from her high school home economics teacher, Ilma Thompson, Bessie knew that she wanted to be just like her when she grew up.

Her journey to Washington and the FSIS hotline was challenging. "I followed my family around the country

Lester Shepard/USDA 888BW1924-4

The FSIS Meat and Poultry Hotline is a nationwide, toll-free service that consumers, media, and anyone else can call for advice about how to handle foods properly to avoid foodborne illness. Home economists answered approximately 64,000 calls last year.

and attended five different colleges before settling in Washington and graduating with a B.S. degree in home economics from the University of Maryland in 1967," Bessie said.

At first, she wanted to follow in Mrs. Thompson's footsteps by teaching food and nutrition courses in public schools. That teaching experience encouraged her to return to college for her master's degree, which she received in 1982 from Howard University in Washington, DC. "As part of my graduate work, I served an internship at the White House Office of Consumer Affairs," she says. "That was a most rewarding experience, which I shall never forget."

Although Bessie has completed her formal training, her roots remain deep in the academic process. Her work with the hotline has taken her in the past 2 years to 1890 land-grant universities—in Prairie View, TX, and Baton Rouge, LA—where she has helped recruit candidates for positions in FSIS and elsewhere in USDA. "I really feel good when I can influence someone to come work with us," she says.

The Future. And what about the future? "For one thing, I'm looking forward to seeing my grandchild grow up," she says proudly. "But I'm also looking forward to the challenges that lie ahead in my work, not only with the hotline but also with the exciting new directions FSIS is taking as it prepares to enter the 21st century. I plan to stay and see it all happen."

Mattie Sharpless:

Setting Goals for a World-Class Agricultural Career

There have been a lot of firsts in Mattie Sharpless' career in USDA's Foreign Agricultural Service (FAS)—for instance, first and only woman or minority to serve in the senior foreign service and first woman or minority to serve as an FAS assistant administrator. But to Mattie, "first" does not mean much unless it also means "best."

"I don't think my rank has made any difference to me," she says. "I've always viewed myself as a person. The fact that I'm the first to have done this may make a difference to others, but I never looked at myself that way. I have always set goals at a level I think I can attain in both my professional and my personal life. When I approach one goal, I set another one."

Teaching Was Her First Goal

Mattie's first goal was not a career in agriculture. Born and raised in a rural farming region of North Carolina, she set out to teach business education. However, after graduating from North Carolina College at Durham, NC, in 1965, she found that the job market was glutted with teachers. Faced with few job prospects, she was recruited by USDA to come to Washington, DC.

"About 13 of us classmates landed here in Washington, mostly in clerical and administrative jobs, despite the fact that we all had 4-year degrees and all were teachers," Mattie said. "Later, some of my colleagues switched into teaching in Washington. I had just gotten fingerprinted when I was offered a teaching position in North Carolina. But I thought that once I had been fingerprinted, I was here forever."

---

by Sally Klusaritz, Public Affairs Specialist, Foreign Agricultural Service, USDA, Washington, DC

FAS Job Leads to Second Goal

Mattie's next goal was to work in a foreign country, so she researched USDA agencies and discovered FAS. FAS represents U.S. agricultural interests overseas, reports on agricultural production and trade in foreign countries, promotes exports of U.S. farm products, and works to improve world trading conditions. FAS operates worldwide, with personnel located in U.S. embassies and consulates in about 80 countries.

"After just a few months in FAS, I was asked to go to Geneva, Switzerland, to work with the U.S. delegation for the General Agreement on Tariffs and Trade multilateral trade negotiations," she recalls. "A year later, I was asked, 'Since you're doing such a great job, why don't you go to Paris to work in our office at the Organization for Economic Cooperation and Development?' I had no interest in staying in Europe because I was lonely and missed my family. But I told myself, 'It's just for 2 years, and you can live anywhere for 2 years.' So I took advantage of the opportunity and moved to Paris."

More Education for the Next Level

After 4 1/2 years in Paris, Sharpless set her next goal—moving from the clerical and administrative side of FAS to the professional side. She decided to go to graduate school in the United States.

"FAS wanted me to go to school in the Washington area and work part time, with FAS paying my way," she says, "but I decided to pay my own way so I could have the flexibility to decide what I wanted to do after I received my degree. So I put my belongings in storage, paid my own way, lived on campus at North Carolina Central University in Durham, and got my master's degree in business administration, minoring in economics. Then I came back to FAS and went into trade policy work. Since then I've been gradually climbing the career ladder."

Richard Norwitz/USDA 90BW1154

"Setting goals is the way to climb the career ladder," says Mattie Sharpless, assistant administrator in USDA's Foreign Agricultural Service.

Appointment to Brussels

Mattie's next goal was to be appointed assistant agricultural attaché at a foreign post, her first appointment as a foreign service officer. After graduate school and 4 years in Washington, DC, she achieved that goal when she was named assistant agricultural attaché at the U.S. Mission to the European Community in Brussels, Belgium.

"That was a very challenging job because it was an opportunity to learn about European agricultural policy as well as keep abreast of U.S. policies," Sharpless recalls.

In 1979 she returned to FAS headquarters and for 4 years headed up the group that dealt with Western European agricultural affairs. Then she was sent to Bern, Switzerland, for 3 years.

"That was my first 'head of office' post, where I supervised two foreign-national employees," Mattie says. "It's a challenge when you're on your own and don't have anyone to turn to for guidance. It's also a challenge to be responsible for market development activities that can help create new export opportunities for U.S. producers."

Agricultural Counselor Role Overseas

In 1986 she transferred from Bern to Rome, Italy, where she supervised a staff of nine for 3 years. As the head of a large staff at an important post, she conducted a wide array of activities.

"As the agricultural counselor, you are the personal representative of the Secretary of Agriculture," she says. "You report directly to the Ambassador and, through the Ambassador, to the Secretary of Agriculture. You must keep abreast of all U.S. agricultural policies and programs. You also are expected to know your host country's policies and whether they adhere to international trade rules and regulations. You monitor the country's policies and practices to make sure there are no trade barriers that would impede U.S. agricultural exports. At the same time, our primary goal is to expand the sale of U.S. agricultural products, so you carry out market development activities that are most appropriate to that market."

Heading FAS Overseas Staff

After 3 years in Italy, Mattie returned to Washington, DC, to serve as deputy assistant administrator for international trade policy. After 1 year in that position, in 1989, she was appointed to her current post as assistant administrator for foreign agricultural affairs.

In this demanding position, Mattie is responsible for managing about 270 people at more than 80 embassies and consulates around the world. The staff reports on about 110 countries.

Mattie is also the chairperson of the FAS recruitment committee. In that role, she travels to college campuses around the country to explain the goals and missions of the agency.

"We recruit good, qualified people for FAS," she says. "We explain the different types of careers in the Agency in both the civil service and the Foreign Service. Many potential employees come to FAS because they've heard about it, either from Peace Corps or other foreign agencies," she explains. "They come to the agency with a keen interest in joining the Foreign Service. Many young people today think there's more glamour in the Foreign Service than there is. When I first joined the agency and started traveling abroad, security problems, such as terrorism, weren't so prominent. Today, there is a lot of day-to-day stress in living in foreign countries."

She adds that "life overseas is interesting because you have an opportunity to live in foreign countries, to learn foreign languages and different cultures, and to travel. But at the same time, it can be lonely, especially for a single person. It takes a strong person to be in the Foreign Service, because it's very stressful to literally pack up every 2 to 4 years and move from one country to another."

Career Opportunities at USDA

Despite some of the drawbacks of life overseas, Sharpless is positive about advising young people on careers at FAS and USDA: "USDA has many agencies with different goals and missions. There are so many types of jobs that you can have in USDA."

At FAS, for example, "you can work with producers and trade associations, negotiate agreements with foreign countries under credit guarantee or food aid programs, or help U.S. trade associations develop programs to sell U.S. agricultural products. The trade policy area keeps you going from world capital to world capital to try to resolve bilateral and multilateral trade problems. You can be a diplomat right here in Washington, DC."

Time To Set the Next Goal

"I'm a person who does a lot of soul searching," says Mattie. "Before I make a personal or career move, I look at all sides of an issue and analyze the pros and cons of my decision. People tell me I'm too organized, but I just have a way of looking long term to see what the next step should be. It's about time for me to begin thinking about going overseas again, so I have to decide what my next goal should be and set out to achieve it."

Robert Johnson:

Successful Small Farmer Using Extension Service

Robert Johnson is an 80-year-old successful black small farmer. He has lived and farmed all his adult life in Hinds County, MS, in the small rural community of Edwards, 20 miles west of Jackson, the State capital.

Robert and his late wife, Ella, were able to rear 14 children on the farm and to give each of them the opportunity to go to college.

"You raise 14 children by putting them to work on the farm," says Robert. He believes that work—particularly, hard work—keeps children out of trouble and in school.

Robert owns and operates a 57-acre farm. He now farms 15 acres, primarily by himself—including 3 or 4 acres of cotton and a few acres of produce (mostly peanuts, watermelons, peas, butter beans, and some leafy vegetables). He also raises some hogs and chickens. To cultivate his crops, he has a small, old two-row tractor and two horses. The tractor is used to break the ground, and the horses are used to cultivate. From the glow and expression on his face when he talks about his horses, it is apparent that Robert enjoys plowing with them.

When Robert was a child in 1920, blacks owned 15 million acres of farmland, compared with today's figure of about 1.7 million acres. The number of black farm operators has also dwindled significantly, from a peak of 926,000 in 1920 to the present 23,000. In only 5 years, from 1982 to 1987, farmland operated by black farmers dropped from 3.5 million acres to 2.6 million acres. Robert fears that if this trend continues, by the year 2000 there will be no black farmers or black farmland owners in the United States.

by Samuel L. Donald, Director, and Robert E. Sanders, Staff Writer, Division of Agriculture, Research, Extension, and Applied Sciences, Alcorn State University, Lorman, MS

Robert Sanders/Alcorn State University

Robert Johnson is 80 years old and operates a 57-acre farm in Edwards, MS. With over 60 years of farming experience under his belt, he believes that "success is making a balanced living out of whatever you are doing in life."

With more than 60 years of farming experience under his belt, Robert is intimately aware of the many obstacles that can hinder the progress of the black small farmer in the South. However, despite the many obstacles that clutter the road to progress, Robert's success proves that the essentials of a successful family farm are the same in almost any social environment. "If you don't have knowledge and good management skills, you aren't going to get anywhere," he says.

Getting Help from Extension

One reason for Robert's success is that he learned the required knowledge and management skills by doing. Another reason is that he faithfully attended production workshops sponsored by the local county Extension office. It was there that he first came in contact with Alcorn State University's Cooperative Extension Program (ACEP) through Lamar Yates, an ACEP agricultural program assistant who participated in the workshops. In these workshops, Robert received valuable information on such topics as cotton, grain, soybeans, and weed control, as well as further sources of information and assistance.

When Robert was faced with the common but plaguing problem of highly erosive soil on his farm, he sought the assistance of the Hinds County Soil and Water Conservation District. He implemented the district's practical recommendations so receptively and fruitfully that it honored him with a merit award for resource conservation. He was further recognized as the conservation farmer of the year for Hinds County.

ACEP's mission is to conduct continuing and adult education programs that serve people who are disadvantaged and who have limited resources, especially small farmers in Mississippi. The program has particular interest in small farmers (those with gross agricultural sales of less than $40,000 annually). ACEP considers Robert a role model for small farmers in southwest Mississippi.

ACEP focuses most of its educational programs on people living in southwest Mississippi. The staff works closely with Alcorn State University's teaching and research personnel, especially those in agriculture and home economics, to design and implement its programs. ACEP especially uses the findings of researchers to provide thousands of small farmers with the latest and most reliable information. The major program areas are agriculture and natural resources, home economics, community and economic development, and youth development.

Education

Robert has only a fourth-grade education. Nevertheless, he and Ella instilled in their 14 children the value of an education. "An education," says Robert, "is more valuable than gold. You may lose your gold but not your education." All of the Johnson children have graduated from college, 13 of them from Alcorn State University, and most of them have continued their education, earning graduate and professional degrees. They are teachers of English, mathematics, biology, and industrial arts; principals and assistant principals in elementary and high schools; and government and university employees.

In addition to helping his own children, Robert has helped others go to college. He believes that one must help other children when one can. For his efforts in education he received the Mississippi NAACP's Robert Smith family award and the Alcorn State University alumni's Parent Distinguished Service Award.

Robert believes that people should have common sense as well as an education. "A person without common sense," he says, "is a foolish person and never amounts to anything. An education on a foolish person is a wasted education."

Success

What about success? Robert believes that he has been successful because of what he has been taught. He also believes that it is important for a person to pass on what he or she knows: "You can't teach what you don't know, and you have to be willing to change."

For Robert, success as a small farmer means more than yield per acre or size of litter per sow or gallons of milk per cow or how much money is made. He believes that "success is making a balanced living out of whatever you are doing. Whatever you do in life, you must put your life into it. Life is what you make it."

Robert's father was a preacher, and Robert, also a religious man, has been a Sunday school superintendent for more than 40 years. He loves life and people, especially children.

Robert Sanders/Alcorn State University

All 14 of Robert Johnson's children graduated from college. He believes that you must help children understand the importance of an education. "You may lose your gold, but not your education," he says.

Volunteers, the Heartbeat of the Forest Service

The number of volunteers in the National Forests is double the number of paid Forest Service employees.

According to William (Bill) Rice, Deputy Chief of Administration for the Forest Service, "We have 35,000 paid employees in the Forest Service and 68,000 people who volunteered last year."

"Volunteers are the heartbeat of the Forest Service," says Rice. "We can't get our work done without them."

What motivates people to volunteer with the Forest Service, year after year, in ever-increasing numbers? Here is what volunteers tell the Forest Service:

- I learn new job skills.
- I have fun, fun, fun.
- I love the outdoors and want to do my part to keep it beautiful.
- I want to do something for the environment that will guarantee a good future for my children's children.
- I like physical activity.
- I enjoy working in beautiful surroundings.
- I like to meet new people.
- I like to share my knowledge.
- I love the fellowship.
- I learn about the outdoors.
- It's a challenge.
- It gives me variety and change from my regular job.

What is a typical volunteer like today? Volunteers in the Forest Service range from 8 to 80 years old. The biggest group of individual volunteers in 1989 was white males, 30 to 50 years old, living in or near rural areas. Boy Scout troops, churches, and environmental organizations are the biggest contributors to group volunteer projects. Older Americans are usually attracted to volunteer assignments as campground hosts.

More and more people are expected to volunteer for service in the national forests during the next decade. In the 1990's, often referred to as the decade of environmentalism, Forest Service personnel hope that volunteers will include minorities, women, and urban people of various ethnic backgrounds.

Volunteers in the National Forests mean double the energy, double the accomplishments, and double the fun. Factors motivating volunteers are love of the outdoors, meeting people, and doing something for the environment that will guarantee a good future for their children's children.

USDA Forest Service

by Ann Matejko, Public Affairs Officer, Forest Service, USDA, Washington, DC

The volunteer work force added 68,000 people to the Forest Service staff. Thanks to them, many fences are built and repaired. Trees are planted and pruned. Many office tasks and some not so glamorous jobs are completed just for the reward of volunteering.

USDA Forest Service

"The Forest Service actively tries to attract diverse volunteers, just as we strive for diversity in our paid work force," says Rice. "Diversity will increase as the word spreads about what a fun, rewarding, and unusual experience volunteer work on environmental projects can be. The rewards are such that volunteering will sell itself."

Some volunteers enjoy their experiences so much that they return year after year or become full-time employees.

What kind of projects do volunteers do? Most volunteers request recreation and outdoor projects; in fact, 70 percent of volunteer projects are in recreation. Volunteers can help with almost any Forest Service project, including office work with the computer, photography, and typing.

The following are some of the most popular volunteer projects in 1990:

- Repairing fences
- Building and maintaining trails
- Picking up litter
- Planting trees
- Building and installing nesting boxes
- Search and rescue
- Building and installing picnic tables
- Reinforcing streambanks
- Digging latrines
- Raking and cleaning campgrounds
- Planting seeds for erosion control
- Painting and building signs
- Answering phones and greeting visitors
- Sorting, labeling, or contributing to photo files
- Washing and waxing Government vehicles
- Building barrier-free campsites, docks, and trails
- Providing snacks and meals for volunteers and employees

Volunteers are so important to the Forest Service's work force and to other land management agencies that the agencies sometimes compete with each other for recruits. Realizing that cooperation, rather than competition, would benefit everyone, a national interagency volunteer conference, attended by 270 people from 10 agencies, was held recently in Salt Lake City, UT.

"One of the values of the conference," said Don Hansen, the Forest Service volunteer program manager who conceived and organized the conference, "is the sharing of the multitudes of programs that each agency has, and what makes the programs work." The 10 agencies agreed to cooperate in seeking volunteers.

A last word for volunteers? Rice says the Forest Service cannot thank volunteers enough. A handshake, a tee shirt, or a pin is a small thank you for everything that the agency, the Nation, and the environment receive in return.

"At all levels, the Forest Service has renewed its management commitment to double the number of volunteers in the next 2 years," concludes Rice.

Washington State Livestock Master Volunteers:

Farmers Teaching Farmers

The coastal and mountainous areas of northwest Washington State enjoy a rich blend of human settlements: cities, commercial agricultural enterprises, and thousands of small part-time farms. Cooperative Extension agents and specialists keep trying to find new ways to reach and teach the diverse farmers who live and work there.

One way, proven successful, is to recruit volunteers, who will give their precious time and skills to help their neighbors improve their livestock production, as well as their stewardship of land and water.

So Many Small Farms, So Little Time

In recent decades, large commercial farms continued to use the results of university research, but small family farms received less attention. In the 1970's, many small farms were operated by former city-dwellers, part of a back-to-the-land movement. The newcomers, or "pilgrims," needed very basic information.

I could not meet the demand for basic information, while serving commercial livestock producers and the large 4-H youth program. Five telephone lines were busy every day. Callers typically requested all sorts of information—from pasture seed mixes, to sheep nutrition, to rabbit-hutch plans, to egg sales regulations. I was swamped, a "green" and desperate (but enthusiastic) county agent with no professional relief in sight.

A similar problem existed during the early days of Extension work in Washington, when each agent served more than 300 farms. To meet the demand, "cooperator" farmers were recruited and trained. In return for this special university training, the volunteers taught new techniques and conducted on-site crop and livestock demonstrations in their own neighborhoods.

So I decided to look for nonprofessional relief. I worked out a way to reach the small family farms with the help of specially trained volunteer producers who would work as teachers in their own communities. Because a thorough search found no current volunteer programs in livestock education, I based the plan on both the earliest county agent work and the modern "Master Gardener" program in the Seattle area. Thus, the Livestock Master program was launched in 1983.

Livestock Masters in Action

Through the Livestock Master program, one family reaps the benefits of lengthy, knowledgeable, one-on-one visits by Frank Ashcroft, a concerned, retired producer. The family had moved onto 10 acres after years of planning and saving—it was their dream come true. The outbuildings needed repair and the pastures had returned to "nature," but, with hard work and time, they believed that they could raise and

Perry Rech/USDA 90BW1054-27

Volunteers in the Livestock Master Program share precious commodities of time and skills with producers, as well as young people in such programs as 4-H and FFA.

by Michael R. Hackett, Snohomish County Livestock Agent, Washington State University Cooperative Extension, Everett, WA

market livestock. They had everything going for them but experience. They needed help with their many questions: What breed of beef cattle should they raise? Were the fences adequate? Were the buildings useful?

In the past, the typical county Extension agent's response to these questions would have been to mail a bulletin or two, which could have been more dangerous to the family (and the environment) than no response at all. Now, though the county Extension agent cannot make a farm visit, the agent sends a trained and certified Washington State University Livestock Master, who is retired and loves to visit and plan with new family producers.

Generally, Livestock Masters inspire management changes on neighboring farms by making visible improvements on their own farms. Sometimes this starts a ripple effect—the neighbors themselves become Livestock Masters. Many Livestock Masters have taken under their wing one or two struggling families, whom they "bring along" with them as they make practical changes to their own livestock enterprises.

Livestock Masters, who work either in the office or at home, field hundreds of basic questions by telephone every week. Calls are directed to those volunteers who live within local calling distance whenever possible. Adrienne Buyagawan and Bill Dickey have logged hundreds of hours at the office; Gene Fusch, Jerry Bailey, and Ann Muchoney have taken dozens of calls a month from their home phones. The program is working, and paying off in unexpected ways.

Recent public consumer concerns about farm animal welfare, food safety, health foods, and water quality are answered by Livestock Masters who choose to specialize in these areas. They do a more effective job of informing the public than the agent who is trained in animal science only. Steve Marsh assembled an educational slide program on water quality; Gisele Massengill supervised a very successful petting farm at the County Fair. The petting farm showed 33,000 Seattle-area city folks that most animal producers really do love and properly care for animals.

Jack Estes, a beef producer, taught other producers the absolute necessity of using antibiotics to treat serious illnesses, and that grass-fed, "natural" beef can command a premium price today.

Perry Rech/USDA 90BW1052-29

Attending a livestock show like this one in Snohomish County, WA, is just another day at the office for Michael Hackett, originator of the Livestock Master program, and Shirlee Park, coordinator.

The Benefits of Becoming a Livestock Master

What motivates the volunteers? Do they all have super-generous natures? Maybe, but there are some real benefits, including the intensive 12 weeks of instruction, continuing direct access to the county agents and their resources, and association with people who share their love of producing farm animals for income. As a result of their work, some volunteers have found jobs, been admitted to graduate degree programs, or received special county and State committee assignments.

Shirlee Park, Livestock Master program coordinator and assistant to the agent, began her Extension career as a volunteer Livestock Master. Her enthusiasm, motivation, and volunteer management skills add greatly to the program.

Livestock Masters seem to improve their own operations while teaching others. Sandi Beard began as an artificial inseminator of dairy cattle, but she also kept a few pigs. Inspired by her Livestock Master training in 1985, Beard persevered in learning to breed swine artificially. In 3 years, she improved the genetic potential of her herd and many others in western Washington. Now, at least 80 percent of the Washington State University swine research herd has incorporated many results of Beard's efforts. Beard was named the top pork producer in Washington State for both 1989 and 1990.

The Livestock Master Program and Small Farmers Prosper Together

The Livestock Master program grows stronger by the year. In seven western Washington counties since 1983, more than 120 people have been certified and have each returned at least 60 to 80 hours of volunteer time. More than half the volunteers have each returned hundreds of hours beyond their minimum 60- to 80-hour commitment.

The Livestock Master volunteer program works. Commercial livestock producers receive the more technical in-depth help from the livestock Extension agent, the 4-H youth program enjoys the benefits of the volunteers (more than one-third of the volunteers are 4-H livestock project and club leaders), and hundreds of small farmers get the crucial individual attention they need in spite of the reduced availability of county agents.

At least eight other States are taking a good look at the Livestock Master program. They hope to use its methods in counties that lack agent power and have many small farms.

In northwestern Washington, the county Extension agent and the Livestock Master volunteers have teamed up successfully to provide a higher quality educational program than the agent could ever hope to have done as the "Lone Agent."

Perry Rech/USDA 90BW1052-34

Marketing, a Window to Success

On an April day in the Imperial Valley of California, a farm laborer slices through stalks of broccoli and quickly places them in a well-lined box that will take them to supermarkets all over the country.

On the same day, a South Carolina farmer—who follows generations of farmers who produced only tobacco and row crops—walks his fields and tries to slice through a myriad of questions: "What vegetables should I plant, and when? How will I get the labor? Will the weather hold? How can I keep that lettuce cool? Is that buyer in New Jersey going to take it? And finally, will I hit that market window of opportunity following production in California, Arizona, Texas, Florida, and Georgia but just before farmers in North Carolina are getting their crops in for shipping?"

Jerry Dyer/Clemson University

Jim Rushing (center), Clemson University Extension specialist, discusses what, when, and how to plant for the best marketing window with vegetable producers in South Carolina. Coordinating these types of variables is a step toward getting an optimum price in the marketplace.

The Move to Vegetables

Because of the continued emphasis on the issue of smoking and health, many traditional South Carolina tobacco producers are taking steps to grow alternate crops, such as ready-to-market vegetables. Their steps are hesitant and more than a bit cautious, however, because they have seen the vagaries of the marketplace for such commodities. They have help, though, from Clemson University Extension agents, such as Bill Witherspoon, Powell Smith, and Tony Melton.

by Jerry Dyer, Clemson University Area News Editor, Pee Dee Research and Education Center, Florence, SC

"Vegetable production is not really new to us," explains Bill Witherspoon, director of Extension in Horry County, "but when it seemed that many farmers were going to go at it like grandpa did, we had to work with them in a hurry. Even so, we can't really push too fast on something like this. It takes time. These people have their ideas about things just like we do. Some of them are valid. Some are based on the old days when the railroad came through, bought their green beans off wagons pulled by mules, and the train steamed on up the tracks."

The Window

According to Witherspoon, "It's a different world now. It's got a catch called a market window." For a particular vegetable crop, the market window is the period between the end of shipments from farther south and the beginning of shipments from farther north. Farmers must harvest their vegetables and ship them to markets when the window is open. "They've got to have a labor force; proper harvesting, cleaning, cooling, and storage; and, most important, a viable market at the right time for their efforts. The word 'effort' doesn't really tell the story. They have to work day and night."

Jim Rushing is a Clemson Extension Service scientist who specializes in postproduction and packaging. He is based at Clemson's Coastal Research and Education Center near Charleston. According to Rushing, once growers make a firm commitment, they stand a good chance of making a profit.

"We have growers who bring in good crops, and several who make an investment in packaging coleslaw, shredded carrots, radishes, and some specialty oriental vegetables for supermarkets and restaurants," says Rushing. "They have clean, cold operations, good transportation, and a firm labor force for the field as well as for processing. If you don't have that multifaceted combination, you won't turn a dollar."

In several South Carolina counties, Extension Service agents have worked closely with elected officials for funding to create cooperatives and market associations. These organizations follow guidelines under which produce is cleaned, graded, packed, and shipped to market on time as ordered.

Planning for Profit

Extension Service agents continue to improve crop varieties, as well as production and harvest practices, and to assist in budget planning. Planning is the key to profiting from market windows.

"We just flat out had to tell some farmers who had financial problems that they'd be in worse difficulties if they thought vegetables were some sort of quick fix," Witherspoon adds. "It takes a healthy investment in capital and personal commitment.

"Many just don't understand the aspect of the market window and how vital it is. We've got good soils and good farmers who'll work their fingers off, but if they grow cabbage or lettuce, onions, and potatoes when the market is flooded from other States, then they've just lost a bundle of money that many may not have even had in the first place."

Powell Smith, Clemson Extension Service area agent in Horry, Georgetown, and Marion Counties, is troubled that the market window concept may not be understood by many growers.

"We monitor the markets nationwide and try to advise our farmers when it would be best to plant certain varieties of cabbage, for instance, to hit it right in Canada, New York City, Philadelphia, or Newark," he says. "Then we still see some folks going right along in a hit or miss manner."

"Many are receptive, though, and they turn out for our demonstrations and seminars. After each season shows them a profit, we pick up more and more credibility. That's the way it is in the world of the Extension Service trying to help our farmers. We've got to prove ourselves most every day."

Tony Melton, Smith's counterpart in Darlington and Florence Counties, agrees: "It's show time just about every day. We're excited about some grants which appear to be coming our way to get about 20 producers into the Pee Dee Packers and Produce Cooperative based at a State farmers' market. The growers buy in for $500 down and another $500 in a few months, so they are paying their part, too. We're working on well-timed market orders for bell peppers, cucumbers, squash, eggplants, and sweet potatoes."

"We have to be very, very careful," he adds, "because many of these crops have only a 2- to 3-week market window open between Georgia and North Carolina.

"We've met with the brokers up in the Northeast. They like our produce. They want our vegetables. But they all say the same thing: 'Hit that window.'"

Bill Brandvik:

North Dakota State Entomologist

During his 24 years with the North Dakota Department of Agriculture, 16 of them as the State entomologist, William J. Brandvik has had a constant goal: pest control. Bill will get the job done quietly and effectively, working where he is comfortable—behind the scenes, out of the spotlight.

Bill was born in Halliday, a small community in western North Dakota, in 1933, the fifth of six children. He is proud of the year he was born. "It means you came through the Depression," he says. "It means you survived hard times."

Bill's family ranched on the land his grandfather, Mike Brandvik, homesteaded north of Killdeer, ND, in 1916. Bill's father, Arthur, also homesteaded near Mike Brandvik's place at about the same time. However, the living quarters on Arthur's place later were abandoned, and the land was absorbed into another rancher's operation. In 1947, Bill's eldest brother took over the ranch, and the rest of the family moved into the town of Killdeer, where Bill's mother, Margaret, was a first-grade teacher and later the county superintendent of schools.

"Mom was the major breadwinner in the family," Brandvik says. "Lots of women supplemented the family income at that time. It was as necessary then as it is now."

In 1989, North Dakota's centennial year, Bill gathered up a 1916 photograph of his father's homestead and a map and went in search of the former homesite, which was located in the rugged badlands north of Killdeer.

by Ellen Crawford Delp, Public Information Specialist, North Dakota Department of Agriculture, Bismarck, ND

"I got out there on horseback. I spent a few days looking for it, but I found it. There sure wasn't much left of the old place, but I found some old stove parts where the house used to be," he recalls.

Bill had a camera with him, and he carefully took a picture from the same angle as the 1916 photograph. The two photographs now hang on a wall in Brandvik's home.

Perry Rech/USDA 90BW1056-28

North Dakota entomologist Bill Brandvik enjoys his work. For him, controlling pests is a job that one does working behind the scenes—quietly, effectively, and out of the spotlight.

An Interest in Agriculture

Bill's interest in agriculture was piqued after he graduated from high school, when he got a summer job working for USDA's Forest Service at a blister rust control camp near Missoula, MT. "I didn't know what I wanted to do then," he says. "I got to talking with the guys and just decided I'd go into agriculture."

Bill received a bachelor of science degree in agriculture education in 1958 and a master's degree in agricultural entomology in 1961, both from North Dakota State University. His master's thesis focused on livestock insects. "I like to work with animals," he says. "Livestock entomology is the way I wanted to go, but it didn't work out that way, which is okay, too. I like what I'm doing."

Bill believes that the title "State entomologist" is a misnomer. "I work with a variety of different things, not just insects; it also includes problems such as plant diseases. In some States, my position is called the State plant pathologist, which doesn't cover it all either," he says.

Nevertheless, as State entomologist Bill heads the North Dakota Agriculture Department's Plant Protection Division, which is responsible for nursery inspection, plant and plant product certification, and plant pest prevention, detection, evaluation, and suppression programs. He works with the USDA Animal and Plant Health Inspection Service on the plant and plant product certification program, as well as on the plant pest programs.

Avoiding the Spotlight

A high point of Bill's job was the grasshopper control effort of 1985 and 1986, which was conducted in cooperation with USDA's Animal and Plant Health Inspection Service.

"The McKenzie County Cooperative Control Program was a Federal rangeland control program," he says. "We went in there to take care of some grasshoppers that had taken over. We sprayed 600,000 acres during those 2 years. Each year we worked 3 weeks straight through, 16- to 17-hour days, weekends, too."

In the McKenzie County effort, Bill served as the contracting officer's representative, which is a Federal position, though he also served in his State government capacity. Keith Winks of the Bismarck Animal and Plant Health Inspection Service office says that Bill is "the most unselfish person I've ever worked with. He got out there and put in endless hours without complaining. He never tried to take credit for anything."

Bill prefers not to be highly visible, no matter how involved he is in a project. "I dread being out front. People start pecking at you. There are ways of getting your work done without being in the spotlight," he says, adding that more work gets done behind the scenes.

Bill was recognized for his efforts in McKenzie County in 1985 and 1986, but

Perry Rech/USDA 90BW1298

Grasshoppers pose the most consistent threat in the State. Due to several years of drought, their population and devastation to the land have been on the rise.

it was the type of recognition that he seems not to have minded. In appreciation for his efforts, the local grazing association made him an honorary member. "That had never been done before," he says. "I was particularly pleased by that."

More recently, Bill managed to attract the kind of public attention that makes him uncomfortable. During 1989, the North Dakota Legislature considered a bill that would have made the honeybee the State insect. Bill, who has had an unpleasant experience or two with honeybees, opposed the idea. He took personal leave from work and testified as a private citizen before senate and house committees in opposition to the legislation. The local media picked up on his opposition, and reported his testimony.

"I didn't like to do that," Bill says, "but I felt so strongly about it that I had to. I think we should have an insect that's a better symbol. I don't think it should be based on the insect's economic impact. It shouldn't be one that hurts people, and it shouldn't be an insect that's regulated, which honeybees are in North Dakota."

Pest Control in North Dakota

In his 24 years with the North Dakota Department of Agriculture, Bill has seen few changes in the State's pest control needs. "The only significant change has been brought by the growth of the sunflower industry," he says. "That brought on new pests and new needs. Otherwise, things have stayed pretty much the same over the last two and a half decades.

"In North Dakota, our insect problems are really minute compared with those of other States such as California or some of the Southern States. Our climate is so harsh up here that we don't have much of a problem."

The types of insects present in North Dakota also make the State a little different from others. Most pests in North Dakota are native to the State, Bill says, and therefore not subject to regulation. "Outbreaks just happen and there's no solution to it. There's nothing you can do except take care of them when they're a problem."

Grasshoppers pose the most consistent threat in the State. In recent years, grasshopper populations and devastation have been on the rise, due in part to several years of drought. In the spring of 1989, the grasshopper population began threatening areas in the State that previously had had few problems. "The grasshopper problem has moved from the rangelands in the west and the west-central part of the State into cropland area in the east. They're going where the high-value crops are," Bill says.

The shift in grasshopper concentration has brought problems for State officials and for farmers, and there are no "quick fixes" available. Bill believes that the only solution to grasshopper control in North Dakota will come in the form of a long-term plan. "I've seen enough to know that 'crash' programs don't work," he says.

"I'd like to see a long-range program involving integrated pest management implemented in the State. By 'integrated' I mean a program that involves biological, cultural, and chemical means to control grasshopper populations. The State should be divided into districts for the administration of a program like that."

Perry Rech/USDA 90BW1057-28

Bill says, "Surveying is the basic element to all other activity. Surveys help officials and agricultural producers pinpoint trouble spots."

Surveying Is the Key

Bill finds that the most satisfying and enjoyable part of his job is surveying pest populations. Surveys help officials and agricultural producers pinpoint trouble spots, and they alert the public about the problem. He says that North Dakota is one of the few States—if not the only one—that is still conducting cropland grasshopper surveys. "Surveying is the basic element to all other activities. You have to survey," Bill says. "It's basic to control, to regulation, and to inspection."

In addition to appreciating the necessity of pest surveys, Bill takes satisfaction in the actual process of conducting them. "You get out there by yourself and nobody bothers you," he says. "You're just out there with the land and the insects. I see maybe one or two people while I'm out. I like that."

Wide Open Spaces

Bill's love of solitude, the land, and wide open spaces carries over from his professional life into his private life. He lives in a house on a 40-acre lot 12 miles northwest of Bismarck. "I live out there by myself now, and I guess I'll continue to," he says. "I like the real quiet feeling that you get when you're out by yourself with nature. I have a hill on my place, and when I get on its top, I have a view of the Missouri River Valley. I can see about three counties."

Bill is not totally alone on his 40-acre place, however. He has plenty of animals around to keep him company. In addition to the two horses he owns, he has visits from the wildlife in the area.

"I have a pair of Hungarian partridges that I feed over the winter. If I'm outside when they come in, they'll start scolding me. They know I'm not supposed to be there when they come to eat," he laughs.

In recent years, more people have moved out of the city to the area where Bill lives. The area is zoned for 40-acre tracts, so it is not yet too crowded, but the increased human population has changed the wildlife population.

"I used to get up in the morning and see coyote tracks across my front yard," Bill says. "I still see them, but not as often. I still see plenty of deer tracks, though."

These animals have changed his perspective on a few things. "You get out there with them and they turn out to be your pets and neighbors. I used to hunt when I lived in town, but now that I'm out there, I've lost the urge. If I were hunting with someone now, I'd be really reluctant to shoot."

USDA Employees of the Future

The future holds great challenges for the USDA work force. Our society, including our national work force, is changing now and will change even more by the year 2000. Women, minorities, and people with disabilities are expected to make up a greater share of new entrants to the work force. The average age of workers is rising, and there are fewer young people in their teens and twenties who will be available for future employment.

These changes—along with the increasingly specialized training for information and service jobs and the decline in the number of students majoring in science, engineering, and agriculture—will have a major impact on the USDA work force.

U.S. employers, including USDA, will compete with employers in other industrialized countries for workers. USDA has diverse and rewarding career opportunities and is striving to achieve a multicultural work force of well-qualified and educated workers. This chapter shows who works at USDA and what USDA is doing to recruit a diverse work force of talented and capable employees for tomorrow.

Recruiting for Today and Tomorrow

USDA is striving to meet critical human resource needs today and toward the year 2000 by recruiting and retaining a competent work force. The Department is placing special emphasis on affirmative employment of women, minorities, veterans, and people with disabilities. We offer career opportunities at all grade levels and hire people based on their experience and education.

Richard Norwitz

Denise Decker, employee development specialist with the Soil Conservation Service, helps train other USDA employees. "My colleagues are very supportive," says Denise. "My influence reaches to every State, and I think my disability allows me to be of greater help to the people I counsel."

USDA recruitment and outreach programs to attract highly qualified candidates include recruitment brochures, videos, and participation at career and job fairs. USDA is becoming more visible on college campuses nationwide in order to alert educators and students to employment opportunities. In the future, USDA will participate in educational programs to explain USDA career opportunities to middle school and high school students.

Once employees are hired, USDA programs to retain them include providing job satisfaction, redesigning jobs to benefit both the employee and employer, training and retraining to provide necessary skills, and offering employee recognition and monetary rewards for outstanding job contributions.

Today's USDA Employees

USDA employment opportunities are almost unlimited. Over 30 different specialized USDA agencies employ people in over 300 different occupations in every State and in over 75 international locations.

Many employees choose USDA for its unique opportunities to combine education with practical job experience. USDA's responsibilities and programs are extremely diverse. The job matrix lists the most common occupations at USDA, grouped under three broad categories: Administration, Business and Industry, and Science and Technology.

---

by Terry Thir, Recruiting Specialist, Office of Personnel, USDA, Washington, DC

Careers at USDA

Agency Personnel Offices

Careers at USDA	Soil Conservation Service (SCS)	Rural Electrification Administration (REA)	Office of Personnel (OP)	Office of Finance & Management National Finance Center (NFC)	Office of International Cooperation & Development (OICD)	Forest Service (FS)	Foreign Agricultural Service (FAS)	Food Safety and Inspection Service (FSIS)	Food and Nutrition Service (FNS)	Federal Crop Insurance Corporation (FCIC)	Farmers Home Administration (FmHA)	Extension Service (ES)	Economics Management Staff (EMS)	Agricultural Stabilization and Conservation Service (ASCS)	Agricultural Research Service (ARS)	Animal and Plant Health Inspection Service (APHIS)	Agricultural Marketing Service (AMS)
Administration																	
Accounting/Auditing	●	●	●	●	●	●	●	●	●	●	●	●	●	●	●	●	●
Budget	●		●	●	●	●	●	●	●	●	●	●	●	●	●	●	●
Contracting/Procurement	●		●	●	●	●			●		●		●	●	●	●	●
Criminal Justice			●			●											
Equal Opportunity	●		●	●	●	●	●	●	●	●	●	●	●	●	●	●	●
Management/Program Analysis	●	●	●	●	●	●	●	●	●	●	●	●	●	●	●	●	●
Personnel Management	●		●	●	●	●	●	●	●	●	●	●	●	●	●	●	●
Public Affairs	●		●	●	●	●	●	●	●	●	●	●	●	●	●	●	●
Computer Sciences	●		●	●	●	●	●	●	●	●	●	●	●	●	●	●	●
Business and Industry																	
Agricultural Business					●					●	●			●			●
Agricultural Commodities					●											●	●
Agricultural Economics					●		●				●		●	●		●	●
Agricultural Extension												●					
Agricultural Management					●						●						●
Agricultural Marketing					●		●							●		●	●
Food Program Management									●								
International Trade Economist					●		●										
Loan Management/Finance		●									●						
Science and Technology																	
Agronomy	●				●					●					●	●	●
Animal Sciences					●						●	●			●	●	●
Archaeology						●											
Biological Sciences					●	●		●				●			●	●	●
Chemistry					●	●		●							●	●	
Engineering	●	●				●					●				●		
Food Technology					●			●	●						●		●
Forestry					●	●											
Geology/Hydrology						●									●		
Landscape Architecture						●											
Mathematics/Statistics						●							●				
Plant Pathology/Physiology					●	●						●			●	●	
Soil Sciences/Conservation	●				●	●						●			●		
Veterinary Medicine					●			●							●	●	
Wildlife Biology					●	●										●	

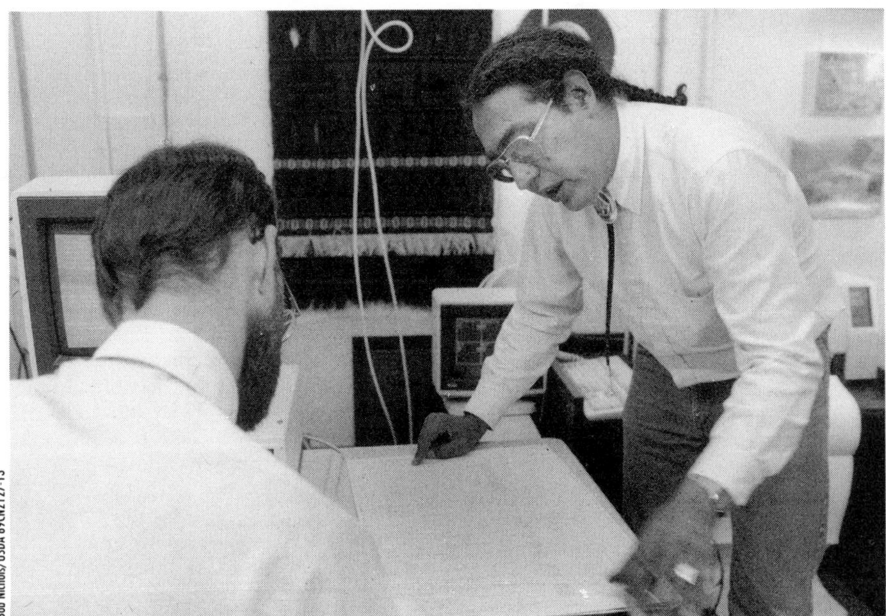

Bob Nichols/USDA 89CN2127-13

A computer specialist with the Agricultural Marketing Service, Wayne Brewer says, "Anyone looking for a career in computers will find exceptional opportunities at USDA."

Administration

Administrative employees at USDA have diverse careers in such areas as personnel management, financial management, computer science, information resources, public affairs, procurement, and contracting.

Denise Decker, an employee development specialist with the Soil Conservation Service, helps train other USDA employees, helping employees build their own careers.

"My colleagues are very supportive," she says. "They see the possibilities, not the limitations. Up-to-date technology helps. At USDA, I have a braille computer and an optical scanner that converts print to braille. My influence reaches to every State, and I think my disability allows me to be of greater help to the people I counsel."

Wayne Brewer is a computer specialist with the Agricultural Marketing Service. He came to work for USDA after completing military service and wanted a job where he could be creative. "I have tremendous creative freedom here: I've used personal computers, micros, minis, mainframes, and networks every day I've worked. Because we have unique applications at USDA, there's lots to explore. That's exciting. The people are all top notch. Anyone looking for a career in computers will find exceptional opportunities here."

Business and Industry

Diverse careers in business and industry specialties allow employees to combine their business skills with expertise in food production, processing, and distribution. These careers, so vital to our advanced industrial nation, include agricultural marketing, economics, food technology, import and export of commodities, inspection services, and financial and loan management.

Kelly Yee became a USDA intern after graduating from college and is now a food program analyst with the Food and Nutrition Service. Today, she leads project review teams and negotiates with education professionals in five States for a program that feeds over 24 million American school children daily. "I am proud that I help school children get what, in many cases, is their only nutritious meal all day," she says.

Science and Technology

A wide variety of exciting careers is available in science and technology. USDA has career opportunities for solving today's problems and for staying in the forefront in solving the problems of tomorrow. Positions are available in many scientific fields: animal science, wildlife biology, microbiology, veterinary medicine, chemistry, genetics, and plant science. Technical and natural resource positions are available in forestry, range management, hydrology, and soil and water conservation.

Linda Rivero, a civil engineer in the Soil Conservation Service with a degree in biological and agricultural engineering, is committed to soil and water conservation in her home State of New Jersey. In just 5 years she has risen to be supervisor of 13 counties. She says,

"Water conservation is one of the key factors in preventing future droughts. We provide farmers with irrigation system designs and concepts they can't get from the private sector, either because they are too expensive or too advanced. I think the Government is looking out for the public good more than anyone else."

Henry Affeldt, an agricultural engineer with the Agricultural Research Service, is one of the youngest people ever to run a major USDA research lab. He worked part-time in a trainee program while he earned his Ph.D.

"I was attracted to USDA because of the chance to train under one of USDA's world famous scientists," says Henry. "Environmental pollution is a growing concern. I've had great freedom to study ways to improve the durability of fruits without chemicals. Here I can use cutting edge technology and stay current on the latest research developments. USDA's chief advantage includes research autonomy, access to state-of-the-art technology, and a chance to work with world famous scientists in biochemistry, physics, and engineering. We're encouraged to stay current, to pursue advanced degrees, and to participate in international conferences. For college graduates looking for wide opportunity, I'd certainly recommend USDA."

John Kucharski/USDA 89CN2125-11

Linda Rivero, civil engineer with the Soil Conservation Service, is committed to soil and water conservation in her home State, New Jersey.

USDA Student Employment Programs

Today's students are tomorrow's workers, and USDA employs students at various levels. If you are a student in high school, you are probably thinking about your future. Studying math and science can help you develop the analytical tools you will need for research positions. Agricultural scientists specialize in many fields of study, such as dairy, poultry, fruits, vegetables, greenhouse, nursery crops, insects, soil, and water. Students can get involved in agricultural activities that will help prepare them for their future. There are many ways to learn about agriculture, and organizations such as 4-H and FFA provide excellent activities in agriculture (see Chapters 48 and 50).

Our future hinges on having an ample supply of well-educated people who achieve in mathematics and science, are science-literate, and can perform technical jobs with world-class competence. USDA provides those challenges.

At USDA, students have the opportunity to learn about their chosen careers through work-related experiences. Under the USDA **student volunteer program,** students work without compensation, but they obtain exposure to the working world and can explore career possibilities. Some colleges and universities have included volunteer service internships in their public administration curricula.

USDA employs students who need to earn money to continue their education, and many **summer positions** are available.

The popular **stay-in-school program** provides job opportunities for students meeting financial need criteria who are enrolled or accepted in any high school, technical or vocational school, or associate or baccalaureate degree program. While employed under this program, students work part-time when school is in session and full-time during vacations. Students with disabilities are eligible to participate in the program regardless of financial need.

Another USDA program is the **Federal junior fellowship program,** which is available to students who are pursuing either an associate or baccalaureate degree or an undergraduate certificate or diploma. Students must be nominated by their schools and meet the financial need criteria. Severely physically handicapped students are eligible to participate in this program regardless of financial need.

Student intern programs seek bright and innovative students who want to try out the occupation they are considering and get hands-on training with seasoned experts in that field. Students may be employed in positions

Bob Jones/USDA 90BW1172

Henry Affeldt, an agricultural engineer with the Agricultural Research Service, is one of the youngest people ever to run a major USDA research lab.

to help in scientific, professional, or technical work. Positions in this program are available primarily in the summer.

The **cooperative education program** is available to students at all levels—high school, technical or vocational school, associate degree, baccalaureate degree, and graduate degree—who wish to work in a job-related field. This program combines classroom learning with practical on-the-job experience. It lets students apply the theory and skills learned in the classroom to job situations and thus get a head start on their careers. In some instances, financial assistance may be available. Employment in this program usually leads to a permanent job upon graduation.

The **Presidential management intern program** is open to students completing graduate degrees who show an interest in management or analysis of public policies and programs. All professional and administrative occupations are available for internships at USDA.

USDA is transforming the challenges of the future into career opportunities for a diverse work force. Its goal is to use all the skills and talents of American citizens regardless of race, color, gender, marital status, religion, age, physical or mental disability, national origin, political affiliation, or any other nonmerit consideration.